Differential and Combinatorial Topology
A SYMPOSIUM IN HONOR OF MARSTON MORSE

DIFFERENTIAL AND COMBINATORIAL TOPOLOGY

*A Symposium in Honor of
Marston Morse*

STEWART S. CAIRNS

GENERAL EDITOR

PRINCETON, NEW JERSEY
PRINCETON UNIVERSITY PRESS
1965

The symposium on which this volume is based was held at the Institute for Advanced Study, Princeton, N.J., and was supported by the Mathematics Division of the U.S. Air Force Office of Scientific Research.

Printed in the United States of America

Foreword

The mathematical research of Marston Morse, extending over most of the past half-century, has exercised a deep and ever widening influence. In the tradition of great mathematicians, he initiated and extensively developed new and bold theories, affecting the main currents of modern mathematics. His investigations of critical points and his theory of the calculus of variations in the large involved a combination of analysis and topology in the spirit of Poincaré. These parts of Morse's research are basic to some of the major recent developments in differential and combinatorial topology. Of all the mathematical areas influenced by the broad spectrum of his research, this is the one in which the most vigorous and dramatic progress is now being made. Thus it was natural to select it as central theme of a symposium in observance of his having retired in 1961 and become Professor Emeritus of the Institute for Advanced Study.

The choice of speakers posed a difficult problem. The number of eminent and active research workers in differential and combinatorial topology far exceeds the number that could be included in the program of a four-day symposium. Those selected, the authors of this book, are but a sample of the many whose research bears an identifiable relation to Morse's topological and analytic work on manifolds.

The idea of honoring Morse by a symposium originated among his former students and associates. The writer served as chairman of the organizing committee, whose other members were Professors Gustav A. Hedlund of Yale University, Walter Leighton of Western Reserve University, and Atle Selberg of the Institute for Advanced Study.

The support of the Air Force Office of Scientific Research and the cooperation of its liaison representative, Dr. Robert G. Pohrer, are gratefully acknowledged.

Administrators of the Institute for Advanced Study provided indispensable assistance in making arrangements for the symposium and the associated social events.

The Department of Mathematics of Princeton University hospitably welcomed the symposium to Fine Hall when attendance at lectures exceeded the seating capacity of the Institute.

Special thanks are due to the authors, whose prompt submission of manuscripts expedited the publication of this book, and to Dr. E. H. Connell for editorial services in connection with the manuscripts.

Stewart Scott Cairns
UNIVERSITY OF ILLINOIS

January 15, 1964

Contents

Differential and Combinatorial Topology

On the Smoothings of Triangulated and Combinatorial Manifolds

NICOLAAS H. KUIPER

0. Introduction

The set of compatible C^∞-differential structures or smoothings on a triangulated or combinatorial manifold X can be divided into equivalence classes according to several equivalence relations. The weakest and most important of these relations is *diffeomorphy*. Two smoothings $\mathscr{D}_0$ and $\mathscr{D}_1$ are diffeomorphic if the corresponding C^∞-manifolds are diffeomorphic. The strongest equivalence, after equality, is *homotopy*. Under our definition, homotopy is equivalent to the existence of an interval I of piecewise C^∞-imbeddings of X with fixed triangulation onto some C^∞-manifold Y, such that the initial and final imbedding carry (dually) the smoothing of Y onto $\mathscr{D}_0$ and $\mathscr{D}_1$ respectively.

Two other equivalence relations have been suggested by Munkres and Milnor. Two smoothings $\mathscr{D}_0$ and $\mathscr{D}_1$ of X are *concordant in the sense of Munkres*, in case one can modify the identity map of X slightly in a specifically restricted manner and obtain a homeomorphism which carries $\mathscr{D}_1$ onto $\mathscr{D}_0$ [12]. Munkres did not use a word for the relation.

Two smoothings of X are called *concordant in the sense of Milnor* (see Hirsch [7], Mazur [8]) if the combinatorial manifold $X \times I$ admits a smoothing such that its restriction to the boundary parts $X \times 0$ and $X \times 1$ yields the initial smoothings $\mathscr{D}_0$ and $\mathscr{D}_1$ of X. Homotopy implies concordance in either sense, and concordance implies diffeomorphy. As far as I know, it is an open problem whether the two kinds of concordance are the same equivalence relation.

In the theory of Cairns and Whitehead [2, 18], X^n is imbedded simplexwise affine and in general position in some high dimensional euclidean space E^N. They prove that if a transversal field of $(N - n)$-planes exists, then a smoothing can be found. Moreover homotopic fields give rise to diffeomorphic smoothings. Their theory is therefore concerned with homotopy of smoothings.

In this paper we also give a homotopic theory of smoothings, which in a way is an intrinsic analogue (no imbedding of X in E^N is used) to the theory of Cairns.

It can also be considered as an elaboration of ideas suggested in Thom's stimulating paper [16]. Among others we obtain the theorem (Coroll. 5.3.B) that the space of those simplexwise linear homeomorphisms of a subdivided simplex σ onto itself, that are identity on the boundary of σ, is in general not acyclic. This gives a negative answer to a conjecture suggested by Thom [16, Theorem 4].

It seems likely but hard to prove in all technical detail that from our theory follows that the theory of Munkres concerning the existence of a differential structure, compatible or not with a given combinatorial structure, can be improved to give a compatible differential structure, if any. The interest in this problem has decreased with the beautiful new theory of Mazur and Hirsch.

1. Smooth and semi-smooth structures

A topological (C^0) n-manifold X is a Hausdorff-space with countable base, such that some neighbourhood U of any point $x \in X$ is homeomorphic with an open set in $\mathbf{R}^n$. (Often it will be assumed also that X is connected.) Such a homeomorphism $\kappa\colon U \to \mathbf{R}^n$ is called a C^0-*chart* for U. The n component functions $U \to \mathbf{R}^n$ form a system of local C^0-coordinates.

A *triangulation* of the n-manifold X is a homeomorphism, $\tau\colon T \to X$, for some simplicial complex T. The pair (X, τ) is called a *triangulated n-manifold*. If σ is a simplex of T, then $\tau\sigma$ is called a simplex of (X, τ). The union of the k-simplices of T is a simplicial complex, called the k-*skeleton* T_k.

The triangulation τ of the n-manifold X is called a *Brouwer triangulation* if the star $\mathrm{St}(\sigma)$ of every simplex $\sigma \in T$ has a simplexwise linear imbedding in $\mathbf{R}^n$. Such an imbedding of $\mathrm{St}(\sigma)$, or its restriction to an open part of $\mathrm{St}(\sigma)$ is called a *Brouwer chart*. All triangulations in this paper will be assumed to be Brouwer triangulations.

A differential C^∞-structures or *smoothing* on a topological n-manifold X is a subsheaf $\mathcal{D}$ of the sheaf of germs of continuous functions, which is locally isomorphic to the sheaf of germs of C^∞-functions on $\mathbf{R}^n$, by virtue of C^0-charts which are then called C^∞-charts.

Two smoothings $(X_1, \mathcal{D}_1)$ and $(X_2, \mathcal{D}_2)$ are called *diffeomorphic* if there exists a homeomorphism (then called diffeomorphism)

$$h\colon X_1 \to X_2 \quad \text{such that} \quad h^*\colon \mathcal{D}_2 \to \mathcal{D}_1$$

is an induced isomorphism of sheaves. Also the smoothed manifolds are called diffeomorphic.

Any rectilinear k-simplex σ_k lies in a linear k-variety, which we may take to be $\mathbf{R}^k$. The *natural smoothing of the simplex* σ_k is by definition the sheaf $\mathscr{D}(\sigma_k)$ of germs of restrictions to σ_k of C^∞-functions in $\mathbf{R}^k$.

Let $\tau\colon T \to X$ be a triangulation of the manifold X. The *semi-smooth* structure $\mathscr{D}(\tau)$ on X is the sheaf of germs of those continuous functions on X, $\xi\colon X \to \mathbf{R}$, such that for any simplex $\sigma \in T$, the restricted composition $\xi\tau\colon \sigma \to \mathbf{R}$ is smooth. If τ is the identity map on T then we have the natural semi-smooth structure $\mathscr{D}(id)$ on T.

A *smoothing* $\mathscr{D}$ on the C^0-n-manifold X is said to be *compatible with the triangulation* $\tau\colon T \to X$ in the case where the restriction of τ to each n-simplex is a smooth imbedding in $(X, \mathscr{D})$. In that case

$$(1) \qquad\qquad \mathscr{D} \subset \mathscr{D}(\tau)$$

and for every smooth function $\xi\tau\colon \sigma \to \mathbf{R}$ on any simplex σ of T, the function ξ can be obtained by restriction from a function on X with germs in $\mathscr{D}$.

If T' is a rectilinear subdivision of T and τ' is the same map as τ, but considered as operating on T' instead of T, then $\tau'\colon T' \to X$ defines a *subtriangulation* of $\tau\colon T \to X$. From the definitions, it follows that for a proper subdivision we have a proper inclusion of semi-smooth structures:

$$(2) \qquad\qquad \mathscr{D}(\tau) \subset \mathscr{D}(\tau')$$

If two triangulations have a common subdivision then they are called compatible. The directed system of all triangulations compatible with a given triangulation is called a *combinatorial structure*. The direct limit of the semi-smoothings $\mathscr{D}(\tau')$,

$$\lim_{\tau'} \mathscr{D}(\tau')$$

is called the semi-smoothing of the given combinatorial structure[1] on X.

2. The spaces Diff, Imb, and D_0 with a given $\tau\colon T \to (X, \mathscr{D}_0)$

Diff. The set of all diffeomorphisms of $(X, \mathscr{D}_0)$ is made into a topological space by using the C^1-topology. This is the compactopen topology for the induced diffeomorphisms on the tangent bundle space $\mathscr{T}(X)$ of $(X, \mathscr{D}_0)$. The space is denoted by Diff or Diff$(X, \mathscr{D}_0)$.

---

[1] An interesting generalization of smoothing is as follows. A semi-smoothing of codimension p, $\mathscr{D}^{-p}$ on a topological n-manifold, is a subsheaf of the sheaf of continuous functions, such that in some neighbourhood U of every point, there are $n + p$ functions $\xi_1, \ldots, \xi_{n+p}$ defining a topological imbedding of U in $\mathbf{R}^{n+p}$, and such that the subsheaf consists locally at U of all germs of all C^∞-functions of ξ_1, $\ldots, \xi_{n+p}$. A piecewise C^∞-imbedding of a triangulated n-manifold X into some C^∞-$n + p$-manifold determines for example a semi-smoothing of codimension p on

The space Imb. Any functorially covariant (usually called contravariant) tangent vector at a point of T with respect to any simplex of T will be called a tangent vector of T. The tangent vectors of T form in a natural way a topological $2n$-manifold $\mathscr{T}(T)$, total space of a fibre bundle over T with fibres homoeomorphic to $\mathbf{R}^n$, which are, however, not vector spaces. Locally, the topology of $\mathscr{T}(T)$ is obtained with a Brouwer chart from the tangent bundle of $\mathbf{R}^n$. The derivative of any C^∞-map $\lambda: T \to Y$ into any differential manifold Y is a *continuous* map $d\lambda: \mathscr{T}(T) \to \mathscr{T}(Y)$. *If λ as well as $d\lambda$ is a topological map, then λ is called a (C^∞) imbedding.* The set of all imbeddings $\lambda: T \to (X, \mathscr{D}_0)$ *with the C^1-topology* (compact open on the derivatives) is the space Imb or Imb(T, X).

Every imbedding $\lambda: T \to (X, \mathscr{D}_0)$ determines a smoothing $\lambda^*\mathscr{D}_0$ of T and a smoothing of X defined by

$$\mathscr{D}_1 = (\tau^{-1})^*\lambda^*\mathscr{D}_0 = (\lambda\tau^{-1})^*\mathscr{D}_0$$

Clearly, only smoothings that are diffeomorphic with $\mathscr{D}_0$ are so obtained. Let $D_0 = D_0(\tau)$ be the set of those smoothings and let $D = D(\tau)$ be the set of all smoothings compatible with τ.

If h is a diffeomorphism of $(X, \mathscr{D}_0)$ and $\lambda: T \to (X, \mathscr{D}_0)$ is an imbedding, then

$$h\lambda: T \to (X, \mathscr{D}_0)$$

is another imbedding, which defines the same smoothing $\mathscr{D}_1$ as λ. Vice versa if λ and λ' define the same smoothing

$$(\lambda\tau^{-1})^*\mathscr{D}_0 = (\lambda'\tau^{-1})^*\mathscr{D}_0$$

then $\lambda'\lambda^{-1}$ is a diffeomorphism of $(X, \mathscr{D}_0)$. Hence there is a map

$$(3) \qquad\qquad\qquad \text{Imb} \xrightarrow{\ \ j\ \ } D_0$$

such that for any $\mathscr{D} \in D_0$, $j^{-1}(\mathscr{D})$ is in a natural way homeomorphic with Diff($X, \mathscr{D}_0$).

X. If $\mathscr{D}^{-p} \subset \mathscr{D}(\tau)$ it is called compatible with τ. Every triangulated n-manifold can be imbedded in $\mathbf{R}^{2n}$ and it has therefore a compatible semi-smoothing of codimension n.

Problem 1.   Given n, what is the smallest value $p(n)$ of p for which every combinatorial n-manifold has a semi-smoothing of codimension p? By Munkres, e.g., $p(n) = 0$ for $n \leq 7$, $p(n) \geq 1$ for $n \geq 8$.

Problem 2.   Given n and q, what is the smallest value $p(n, q)$ of p such that for any combinatorial n-manifold X with a semi-smoothing $\mathscr{D}^{-q}$ of codimension q, X has a compatible semi-smoothing of codimension p: $\mathscr{D}^{-p} \subset \mathscr{D}^{-q}$? If the differential Schoenflies problem for imbeddings of S^{n-1} in S^n has for all n always a differential solution, then $p(n, 1) = 0$ in view of the theorem of Cairns-Hirsch.

The spaces D and D_0. We introduce a topology in $D(\tau)$ and $D_0(\tau)$ by giving a subbase for the open sets. The subbase consists of sets $\mathscr{U} \subset D(\tau)$ of the following kind. $\mathscr{U}$ is a set of smoothings of X such that
(a) X can be covered by open sets U_i, at least one for each simplex of $\tau(T)$ in X.
(b) The restriction of $\mathscr{D}_{\mathrm{U}}$ to U_i is induced by the composition with τ of an open set of C^∞-imbeddings of $\tau^{-1}(U_i) \subset T$ into $\mathbf{R}^n$, open in the C^1-topology as defined above. $\mathbf{R}^n$ of course is assumed to have its natural C^∞-structure.

With these topologies the map j is continuous and we can formulate

THEOREM 1. *The mapping* j: Imb $\to D_0$ *has a covering homotopy property and the following sequence is defined and exact.*

$$(4) \qquad F_0(\tau, X): \pi_{k+1}(D_0) \xrightarrow{\ \partial\ } \pi_k(\mathrm{Diff}) \xrightarrow{\ \tau\ } \pi_k(\mathrm{Imb}) \xrightarrow{\ j\ } \pi_k(D_0)$$

In other words, j *defines a fibre space with total space Imb, base space D_0 and fibre Diff.*

The base points which we omitted from the notation in (4) are: $\mathscr{D}_0 \in D_0$, identity $\in$ Diff, and $\tau \in$ Imb.

The directed system of those triangulations τ' of X that have some subdivision τ'' in common with τ, is the *combinatorial structure* defined by τ on X. The direct limit (compare (2)) of $F_0(\tau', X)$ for τ' in this combinatorial structure is again an exact sequence $F_0(X)$. From Theorem 1 we obtain

COROLLARY 1.A. *For the manifold X with its fixed combinatorial structure we have the exact homotopy sequence*

$$(5) \qquad F_0(X): \pi_{k+1}(D_0) \to \pi_k(\mathrm{Diff}) \to \pi_k(\mathrm{Imb}) \to \pi_k(D_0)$$

3. Tools for the study of homotopies in D and indications on the proof of Theorem 1

3.1. Germs, jets, and 1-jets of C^∞-imbeddings in $\mathbf{R}^n$

Let $W \subset T$ be a subset of the simplicial complex T. Two C^∞-imbeddings $f_1: U_1 \to \mathbf{R}^n$ and $f_2: U_2 \to \mathbf{R}^n$ of (open) neighbourhoods of $W(U_1 \cap U_2 \supset W)$ are called germ equivalent at W, if their restrictions to some neighbourhood $U \supset W$ are identical: $f_1|U = f_2|U$. The germ equivalence class is called the *germ* or *jet of f at W*, and it is denoted as

$$\mathscr{J}_W(f)$$

The restriction $df|\mathscr{T}(W)$ of the derivative

$$df: \mathscr{T}(U) \to \mathscr{T}(\mathbf{R}^n)$$

is called the 1-*jet of f at W* :

$$\mathscr{J}^1_W(f)$$

f_1 and f_2 are called *tangential* at W, if they have the same 1-jet at W. Clearly $\mathscr{J}^1_W(f)$ is completely determined by $\mathscr{J}_W(f)$. In the applications we will be mainly interested in the case where W is a point, or a simplex $\sigma_p \subset T$, or the interior of a simplex or some k-ball in a k-simplex. If a jet is the jet of a Brouwer chart then it is called a Brouwer jet.

3.2. A preliminary lemma.

Let

$$\varphi(u) = \begin{cases} \exp{(-u^{-1})} \text{ for } u > 0 \\ \qquad 0 \qquad \text{ for } u = 0 \end{cases}$$

have the inverse φ^{-1} and let ψ be any C^∞-function with $\psi(0) = 0$ and $\psi'(0) = 1$ (e.g., $\psi(u) = u$). Then all right derivatives of the function

$$\varphi^{-1}\psi\varphi(u)$$

at $u = 0$ exist, and they do not depend on ψ:

$$\frac{d^k}{du^k}\varphi^{-1}\psi\varphi(u) = \begin{cases} 1 \text{ for } k = 1 \\ 0 \text{ for } k \neq 1 \end{cases}$$

PROOF. Define $\alpha(u)$ by $\psi(u) = u[1 + u \cdot \alpha(u)]$ for u in some (non-negative) neighbourhood of $u = 0$.
Then

$$\psi\varphi(u) = \varphi(u)[1 + \varphi(u) \cdot \alpha\varphi(u)]$$

Taking the logarithm yields:

$$\ln \psi\varphi(u) = \ln \varphi(u) + \ln [1 + \varphi(u) \cdot \alpha\varphi(u)]$$
$$= -u^{-1} + \ln [1 + \varphi(u) \cdot \alpha\varphi(u)]$$

Consequently

$$\varphi^{-1}\psi\varphi(u) = \frac{u}{1 - u \ln [1 + \varphi(u) \cdot \alpha\varphi(u)]}$$

The kth derivative of $u \ln[1 + \varphi(u) \cdot \alpha\varphi(u)]$ at $u = 0$ is equal to zero for every $k \geq 0$. because the same is true for the function φ, and all derivatives of the function $\alpha(u)$ at $u = 0$ are defined (and finite).[2] Then the lemma follows by calculus.

[2] J. Th. Runnenburg showed by a counter example that the same conclusion does not necessarily hold in case $\varphi(x)$ for $x \geq 0$ is monotone increasing, C^∞, and all derivatives vanish at $x = 0$.

CoROLLARY. If α is a C^∞-function not only of u but also of some other parameters, then any partial derivative of $\varphi^{-1}\psi\varphi(u) - u$ at $u = 0$ with respect to these parameters and u, vanishes, also by the same argument. In the sequel, we will apply the analogous conclusions for the function $\varphi(u - 1)$ at $u = 1$.

3.3. Straightening a jet at a vertex.

Let f be a C^∞-imbedding of some neighbourhood of a vertex $\sigma_0 \subset T$ into the vector space $\mathbf{R}^n$, and let $f(\sigma_0) = 0 \in \mathbf{R}^n$. The derivative at σ_0 of f, the Brouwer 1-jet df, is the derivative of a unique Brouwer chart, which we also designate by df. We want to modify f slightly and gradually, so that we obtain a new map which for some neighbourhood of σ_0 coincides with the Brouwer chart. For convenience we first assume that the star of σ_0 in T, $\mathrm{St}(\sigma_0)$, is rectilinearly imbedded by the identity map in $\mathbf{R}^n$, and that the imbedding f has at $\sigma_0 = 0$ the Brouwer 1-jet df equal to the identity.

Let λ be a real C^∞-function with the properties:

$$\lambda(u) = \begin{cases} 0 & \text{for } u = 1 \\ \exp -(u - 1)^{-1} & \text{for } 1 < u < 2 \\ u & \text{for } u > 4 \end{cases}$$

and

$$\frac{d\lambda(u)}{du} > 0 \qquad\qquad \text{for } u > 1$$

We define a *contraction* λ_a in $\mathbf{R}^n$ by

$$\lambda_a(x) = \lambda\left(\frac{|x|}{a}\right) \cdot \frac{|x|}{x} \quad \text{for } x \in \mathbf{R}^n, \quad |x| > a$$

$|x|$ is the length of the vector $x \in \mathbf{R}^n$. λ_a is a C^∞-diffeomorphism of the set $\{x : |x| > a\} \subset \mathbf{R}^n$ onto the set $\{x : x \neq 0\}$. The inverse of λ_a is called an *expansion*. Observe that λ_a and its inverse transport points in the radial direction with respect to the point $x = 0$. Let $\mathrm{St}(\sigma_0)$ contain $\{x : |x| < a_0\}$. Finally we define a continuous map f_a by the formulas

$$(6) \qquad \text{for } 0 < a < a_0, \quad f_a(x) = \begin{cases} f(x) & \text{for } |x| > 4a \\ \lambda_a^{-1} f \lambda_a(x) & \text{for } |x| > a \\ x & \text{for } |x| \leq a \end{cases}$$

$$f_0(x) = f(x)$$

For the restriction of f_a to $\mathrm{St}(\sigma_0)$, which we also denote by f_a, we have the following:

LEMMA 3.3. f_a *is a C^∞-imbedding of the Brouwer star* $St(\sigma_0)$ *into* $\mathbf{R}^n$ *for* $0 < a < a_0$. *All derivatives of f_a depend continuously on a for $a > 0$. For $a \geq 0$ the first derivatives of f_a depend continuously on a.*

Observe that the second derivatives already may make a jump for $a = 0$ at $x = 0$.

PROOF. We will only prove the first statement. The other parts can be proved by continuity arguments. Only at points x for which $|x| = a$, it is not immediately clear that f_a behaves well. From (6) we see that at these points all derivatives have to be those of the identity map (for $|x| \leq a$). So we have to prove that this is the case also with respect to the outside directions ($|x| \geq a$). For convenience we make the nonessential assumption that $a = 1$.

Tacitly we will consider instead of f or f_a their *restrictions to one of the n-simplices* of $St(\sigma_0)$. It is sufficient to prove that f_a is a C^∞-diffeomorphism for each such case. By the assumptions on f (all) the derivatives of f at $x = 0$ can be formally read from a formal infinite polynomial of the kind

$$x + \sum_{k=2}^{\infty} \alpha_k(x)$$

by taking its formal derivatives at $x = 0$. Here $\alpha_k(x) \in \mathbf{R}^n$ has n coordinates each of which is a homogeneous kth degree polynomial in the n coordinates of $x \in \mathbf{R}^n$. Recall that all these derivatives are also continuous at $x = 0$. We use the notation $\overset{0}{=}$:

(7)
$$f(x) \overset{0}{=} x + \sum_{k=2}^{\infty} \alpha_k(x)$$

Let r and w be the radial and angular polar coordinates with values in $\mathbf{R}$ and in the unit sphere of $\mathbf{R}^n$ respectively, defined by

$$r(x) = |x|, \qquad r(x) \cdot w(x) = x \quad \text{for } x \in \mathbf{R}^n$$

Observe that for $x = 0$, $w(x)$ is not uniquely defined, but every value in the range applies. We have

(7')
$$f(x) = r(x)w(x) + \sum_{k=2}^{\infty} [r(x)]^k \alpha_k(w(x)) \quad \text{at } x = 0$$

We first examine the radial coordinate r. From (7) we see that

$$r(f(x)) = r(x) + [r(x)]^2 [\cdot \cdot \cdot] = \psi(w(x), r(x)),$$

where ψ is a function of the second variable $u = r(x)$, that has the properties given in the corollary in 3.2. We have:

$$rf_1(x) = r\lambda_1^{-1}f\lambda_1(x) \qquad \text{for } |x| > 1$$
$$= \lambda^{-1}rf(\lambda_1 x)$$
$$= \lambda^{-1}\psi(w(\lambda_1 x), r(\lambda_1 x))$$
$$= \lambda^{-1}\psi(w(x), \lambda(rx)) \qquad \text{for } |x| \geq 1$$

Application of the corollary now yields that $rf_1(x) - r(x)$ is a real function of $r(x)$ and $w(x)$ (or of x) all whose partial derivatives at a point x_0 for which $|x_0| = a = 1$ exist, and they also vanish.

For the angular polar coordinate w we have

$$wf_1(x) = w\lambda_1^{-1}f\lambda_1(x) \qquad \text{for } |x| > 1$$
$$= wf\lambda_1(x)$$

But by (7)

$$f(\lambda_1 x) \overset{0}{=} r(\lambda_1 x) \cdot w(\lambda_1 x) + \sum_2^\infty [r(\lambda_1 x)]^k \alpha_k(w(\lambda_1 x))$$

$$= \lambda rx \cdot w(x) + \sum_2^\infty (\lambda rx)^k \alpha_k(wx)$$

The length of $f(\lambda_1 x)$ is roughly equal to λrx in the sense that the ratio tends to one and also all (kth) derivatives with respect to x tend to zero (for $k \geq 1$), in case x tends to a point x_0 for which $|x| = 1$. Hence

$$wf_1(x) = wf(\lambda_1 x) = f(\lambda_1(x)/|f\lambda_1 x|$$
$$\overset{0}{=} f(\lambda_1 x)/\lambda rx$$
$$\overset{0}{=} w(x) + \sum_{k=2}^\infty (\lambda rx)^{k-1} \cdot \alpha_k(wx)$$

and again because all derivatives of λrx with respect to x at a point x at which $|x| = 1$ vanish, at such a point all derivatives of $wf_1(x) - w(x)$ also vanish.

Combining our remarks on both polar coordinates we have that all derivatives of $f_1(x) - x$ at a point x with $|x| = 1$ exist and vanish, as required in the lemma.

3.4. Straightening jets at a vertex, general case.

In the general case, where df (at σ_0) is not the identity, the following analogous but more general formulas are applied. Here df *means the unique Brouwer chart which at σ_0 has the same derivative as f.* The formulas hold for

x in some neighbourhood of $\sigma_0 \in \mathrm{St}(\sigma_0) \subset T$, and for a sufficiently small, say $a < a_0$.

$$
(8) \qquad
\begin{cases}
a > 0, \quad f_a(x) = \begin{cases} f(x) & \text{for } |df(x)| > 4a \\ \lambda_a^{-1} f(df)^{-1} \lambda_a df(x) & |df(x)| > a \\ df(x) & |df(x)| < a \end{cases} \\[2ex]
a = 0, \quad f_0 \colon x \to f(x)
\end{cases}
$$

The same formulas can clearly also be applied for some $a_0 > 0$ to all members of a compact family of imbeddings f_V at the same time. Therefore we conclude the following:

LEMMA 3.4.   (*Straightening at a vertex* σ_0.) *If* f_V *is a compact family of* C^∞-*imbeddings of a neighbourhood* U *of a vertex* $\sigma_0 \in U \subset \mathrm{St}(\sigma_0) \subset T$, *into* $\mathbf{R}^n$, *then there is a homotopy of the family,* $f_{V \times I}$ *with* $I = \{t | 0 \leq t \leq 1\}$ *such that:*

(a) $f_{V \times 0} = f_V$

(b) *Outside some neighbourhood* U_1, *with* $\sigma_0 \subset U_1 \subset \bar{U}_1 \subset U$, *the homotopy is constant:*

$$f_{v \times t}(x) = f_{v \times 0}(x) \text{ for } x \in U - U_1, \quad v \in V$$

(c) *Inside some neighbourhood* U_2, *with* $\sigma_0 \subset U_2 \subset U_1$, *the final imbeddings are* (parts of) *Brouwer charts.*

$$f_{v \times 1}(x) = df_v(x) \text{ for } x \in U_2, \quad v \in V$$

Observe that for every value $v \in V$ the smoothings of $U \subset T$ which are defined by the charts of $f_{v \times t}$, *determine diffeomorphic manifolds in the pointset* U. Indeed, inside U we get the different smoothings all dually by homeomorphisms onto one and the same open set $f_v(U) = f_{v \times t}(U) \subset \mathbf{R}^n$.

REMARK.   The homotopy described above can be approximated so as to give a homotopy for which all derivatives depend C^∞ on the parameter a, also for $a = 0$, but with the same final result for $a = a_0 > 0$ say.

3.5. Lifting homotopies of 1-jets at a vertex σ_0.

In this section we prove the following lemma:

LEMMA 3.5.   *Let* f_V *be a compact family of* C^∞-*imbeddings of a Brouwer star* $\mathrm{St}(\sigma_0) \subset T$ *into* $\mathbf{R}^n$, *which coincide in some neighbourhood* U *of* σ_0 *with Brouwer charts of the family* $g_V = g_{V \times 0}$. *Let* $g_{V \times I}$ *be a homotopy of this compact family of Brouwer charts. Then there exists a family of* C^∞-*imbeddings of* $\mathrm{St}(\sigma_0)$ *in* $\mathbf{R}^n$, $t_{V \times I}$ *such that:*

(a) $f_{V \times 0} = f_V$

(b) *Outside some neighbourhood* U_1 *with* $\sigma_0 \subset U_1 \subset \bar{U}_1 \subset U$ *the homotopy is constant:*

$$f_{v \times t}(x) = f_{v \times 0}(x) \qquad \text{for } x \in U - U_1$$

(c) *Inside some neighbourhood* U_2, *with* $\sigma_0 \in U_2 \subset U_1$, *the families* $f_{V \times I}$ *and* $g_{V \times I}$ *coincide:*

$$f_{v \times t}(x) = g_{v \times t}(x) \qquad \text{for } x \in U_2,$$

or equivalently there is equality of jets:

$$\mathscr{J}_{\sigma_0}(f_{V \times I}) = \mathscr{J}_{\sigma_0}(g_{V \times I})$$

PROOF. It will be sufficient, by analogy and straightforward generalization, to describe the construction of $f_{V \times I}$ for each value $v \in V$. So we take for V one point and we omit V from the notation. We write f, g_1, etc. $\varepsilon > 0$ will be a small number, for which upper bounds will be given in the sequel. First of all $\varepsilon < 1$ will be so small that in the following construction the condition (b) of the lemma is fulfilled for some arbitrarily given but fixed U_1. Moreover ε is so small that $g_0(x) = f(x)$ in case $f(x) < \varepsilon$. It will also be so small, that all the following maps are well defined. We may further assume, without essential restriction, that

$$f(\sigma_0) = g_t(\sigma_0) = 0 \in \mathbf{R}^n$$

The construction:

Let $\alpha_1(u)$ be a monotone C^∞-function, with

$$\alpha_1(u) = \begin{cases} 0 & \text{for } u \geq \varepsilon \\ 1 & \text{for } u \leq \varepsilon^2 \end{cases}$$

and let

$$\alpha(x) = \alpha_1(|f(x)|)$$

Let ε be so small that

$$|g_t(x)| < \varepsilon^3 \text{ for every } x \text{ for which } |g_0(x)| < \varepsilon^4$$

Next we define $f_t(x)$ for $0 \leq t \leq 1$ as follows:

$$\begin{aligned} f_0(x) &= f(x) \\ f_t(x) &= f(x) \qquad \text{in case } |f(x)| \geq \varepsilon \\ f_t(x) &= |f(x)| \cdot w[g_{t \cdot \alpha(x)}(x)] \end{aligned}$$

in case $\varepsilon^2 \leq |f(x)| \leq \varepsilon$. (Here w is the same polar coordinate as in Section 3.3.)

Thus far we have only modified the polar coordinate w and left the radius coordinate invariant:

$$|f_t(x)| = |f(x)| \qquad \text{for } |f(x)| \geq \varepsilon^3$$

However, we have obtained the required final value for w now for $|f(x)| = \varepsilon^2$, because

$$f_t(x) = |f(x)| \cdot w[g_t(x)] \qquad \text{for } |f(x)| = \varepsilon^2$$

or

$$w(f_t(x)) = w(g_t(x)) \qquad\qquad |f(x)| = \varepsilon^2$$

We define the second polar coordinate $w(f_t(x))$ by this same formula for $|f(x)| \leq \varepsilon^2$, but we will modify the map suitably in the radial direction as follows. First of all, let

$$f_t(x) = g_t(x) \qquad \text{in case } |f(x)| = |g_0(x)| \leq \varepsilon^4$$

In this set of x-values the maximal length of $f_t(x) = g_t(x)$ is by assumption $<\varepsilon^3$ and so we can extend the map on this part radially and connect with the part for which $|f(x)| \geq \varepsilon^2$. This is done with a suitable C^∞-function and then $f_t(x)$ is defined.

Given ε, the method (not the result of course) can be assumed independent of f and g_I. It gives the result required in the lemma.

As in Section 3.4, it is seen that the maps f_t define smoothings of U, hence differentiable manifolds on the pointset U, which are diffeomorphic. For $t \in I$ we obtain a homotopy of diffeomorphic, but not necessarily identical, smoothings of U, which is constant outside U.

3.6. Conclusions concerning smoothings at a vertex σ_0 and at a simplex σ_p.

Suppose we have a compact family $\mathscr{D}_V$ of smoothings of T which can be defined in some neighbourhood U of the vertex $\sigma_0 \in T$, by a compact family of C^∞-imbeddings f_V into $\mathbf{R}^n$. By classical differential topology (Cerf [4], Munkres [14]) it may be assumed that the restriction of f_v to one n-simplex σ_n of $\mathrm{St}(\sigma_0) \subset T \subset \mathbf{R}^n$ is the identity for each $v \in V$. By Lemma 3.4, the family $f_V = f_{V \times 0}$ can be modified by a homotopy, $f_{V \times I}$ ending with a family $f_{V \times 1}$ for which all members $f_{v \times 1}$ are Brouwer charts in some neighbourhood of σ_0 in T. The restrictions to σ_n of all these imbeddings in the family $f_{V \times I}$ are identity.

Next, suppose the family of these Brouwer charts $df_{v \times 0} = df_{v \times 1}$ at σ_0 is contractible. Then this contraction can be lifted by Lemma 3.5, and we can obtain a further homotopy $1 \leq t \leq 2$ such that at the end of it all maps $f_{v \times 2}$ for $v \in V$ are identical in some neighbourhood of σ_0. During the homotopy every member $\mathscr{D}_v$ of $\mathscr{D}_V$ stays within its diffeomorphy class. We may conclude the following:

LEMMA 3.6. Let the smoothings $\mathscr{D}_v$ of a compact family $\mathscr{D}_V$, in a neighbourhood U of a vertex σ_0 with $\sigma_0 \subset U \subset \mathrm{St}(\sigma_0)$ be defined by a family of imbeddings f_v which are identical on one n-simplex of $\mathrm{St}(\sigma_0)$. There exists a homotopy $\mathscr{D}_{V \times I}$ starting with $\mathscr{D}_V = \mathscr{D}_{V \times 0}$ such that $\mathscr{D}_{v \times 1}$ is constant with *respect to v in some neighbourhood U_1 of σ_0 if and only if the family of Brouwer jets df_V at σ_0 is contractible.*

PROOF. The sufficiency was proved above. The necessity is obvious by the definition of family of smoothings.

Analogous but more complicated processes can be used in case a compact family $\mathscr{D}_V$ of smoothings is defined in some neighbourhood of a p-simplex σ_p and all smoothings $\mathscr{D}_V$ for $v \in V$ restrict to the same smoothing in some neighbourhood of the boundary $\partial\sigma_p$. We only indicate some important aspects of this case without going into details. The smoothings can be defined by a family f_V of C^∞-imbeddings of $\mathrm{St}(\sigma_p)$ in $\mathbf{R}^n$, which coincide on some neighbourhood of $\partial\sigma_p$ and on σ_n where σ_n is one n-simplex of $\mathrm{St}(\sigma_p)$, and which are the identity map on σ_n.

First we "straighten" f_v. This means that we obtain a new imbedding f_v with the same 1-jet $\mathscr{J}^1_{\sigma_p}(f_v)$ as before, but which is linear on every straight normal of $\sigma_p \subset \mathrm{St}(\sigma_p)$, in some neighbourhood in $\mathrm{St}(\sigma_p)$ of a sufficiently large closed set in the interior of σ_p.

Then we normalize, that is we apply another homotopy to obtain the property that the images of these normals are normal to $f(\sigma_p) = \sigma_p$.

If σ_p is a p-simplex of $T \subset \mathbf{R}^n$, then the projection of the star of σ_p onto an $(n-p)$-plane orthogonal to the p-plane of σ_p, determines a star of a point in a simplicial complex of dimension $n - p$. Let $\mathrm{Br}_f(\sigma_p, T)$ be the space of all Brouwer charts of this latter star in $\mathbf{R}^{n-p}$, which are the identity map on one $(n-p)$-simplex. The study of the case under consideration now further can be reduced to the study of homotopy classes of certain maps into $\mathrm{Br}_f(\sigma_p, T)$.

In particular, if $\mathscr{D}_V = \mathscr{D}_I$ $I = \{t | 0 \leq t \leq 1\}$ then there exists a homotopy which leaves some neighbourhood of $\partial\sigma_p$ unchanged but carries $\mathscr{D}_I$ homotopically into one and the same smoothing in some neighbourhood of σ_p. During this "elementary move" the diffeomorphy class of $\mathscr{D}_v$ for $v \in \mathscr{D}_I$ remains the same (as in Section 3.4). The same can be done for an interval of smoothings $\mathscr{D}_I$ on T, for the simplices of the k-skeleton for $k = 0, 1, 2, n - 1$ respectively.

We can now prove the following:

THEOREM 2. *Homotopic smoothings are diffeomorphic.*

PROOF. Any given homotopy of smoothings $\mathscr{D}_t = \mathscr{D}_{t,0}$ $(0 \leq t \leq 1)$, can be homotopically modified with parameter s, $0 \leq s \leq 1$, by a homotopy $\mathscr{D}_{t,s}$, consisting of elementary moves, and such that $\mathscr{D}_{t,1}$ is constant. Then the path $(t, s): (0, 0) \to (0, 1) \to (1, 1) \to (1, 0)$ consists of elementary moves each of which preserves diffeomorphy. Hence the theorem.

For $s = 1$, the smoothings of the family can all be defined by the same map of T into some differential manifold $(X, \mathscr{D}_0)$. Call this map $\lambda_{t,1} =$

$\lambda_{1,1}\colon T \to (X, \mathcal{D}_0)$. For *decreasing* s starting with $s = 1$ we can now again represent the inverse of the earlier moves *in the differential manifold* $(X, \mathcal{D}_0)$, instead of in $\mathbf{R}^n$. Doing so we obtain for $s = 0$ a family of imbeddings

$$\lambda_{t,0}\colon T \to (X, \mathcal{D}_0)$$

which defines the family of smoothings $\mathcal{D}_{t,0}$. The same method applies to any contractible parameter space. Consequently, we have:

LEMMA 3.8. *Every contractible family of smoothings* (for example a ball) *of* T, *can be obtained from some family of imbeddings*

$$f\colon T \to (X, \mathcal{D})$$

onto a differential manifold.

This lemma expresses a homotopy property, which is used to prove the exact sequence (4) in Theorem 1. In particular, the operator ∂ can be described as follows. Let $\gamma \in \pi_{k+1}(D_0)$ be represented by $\mathcal{D}_{S^{k+1}}$, a $(k+1)$-sphere of smoothings of the manifold X with triangulation $\tau\colon T \to X$ with fixed point the smoothing $(X, \mathcal{D}_0)$. Let $\mathcal{D}_{B^{k+1}}$ be the $(k+1)$-ball of smoothings which projects on the $(k+1)$-sphere of smoothings $\mathcal{D}_{S^{k+1}}$ by mapping the boundary family $\mathcal{D}_{\partial B^{k+1}}$ onto $\mathcal{D}_0$.

$\mathcal{D}_{B^{k+1}}$ can be lifted onto a $(k+1)$-ball of imbeddings by Lemma 3.8 which has a k-sphere of imbeddings as boundary. The imbeddings of this k-sphere all determine the same smoothing $\mathcal{D}_0$ in X, hence one can obtain a k-sphere of diffeomorphisms which represents $\partial\gamma \in \pi_k(\text{Diff})$. It can be shown that $\partial\gamma$ so obtained is completely determined by γ.

4. General and projective triangulations of S^{n-1}

4.1. The spaces $\text{Br}_f(\sigma_p, T)$ and $\text{Pr}_f(S^{n-p-1}, \sigma_p, T)$.

Let $T^n = T = \text{St}(\sigma) \subset \mathbf{R}^m$ be the star of a vertex $\sigma_0 = 0 \in \mathbf{R}^m$ of a simplicial complex T, rectilinearly imbedded in $\mathbf{R}^m$. Let $v_1, \ldots, v_N$ be unit vectors at σ_0, one tangent to each 1-simplex of T that contains σ_0. Let $v_1, \ldots, v_n$ belong to one given simplex σ_n. Any Brouwer chart $\kappa\colon T \to \mathbf{R}^n$ with $\kappa(\sigma_0) = \sigma_0 = 0$ is completely determined by its restriction to $v_1, \ldots, v_N$. We consider *the space* $\text{Br}(\sigma_0, T)$ of all Brouwer charts with fixed σ_0.

A sequence of simplices $\Sigma\colon \sigma_0 \subset \sigma_1 \subset \sigma_2 \cdots \subset \sigma_n \subset \mathbf{R}^n$ belonging to the standard triangulation of the simplex σ_n, is called a flag of simplices. Two flags of simplices Σ and Σ' are called flag equivalent in case dimension $(\sigma_i \cap \sigma_i') = i$ for $i = 0, 1, \ldots, n$. An equivalence class is called a *flag* at σ_0.

Every element $\kappa \in \text{Br}(\sigma_0, T)$ is the product of an imbedding which is the identity on σ_n, and the unique automorphism of $\mathbf{R}^n$ which carries v_i on $\kappa(v_i)$ for $i = 1, \ldots, n$. The homotopy type of $\mathrm{Br}(\sigma_0, T)$ is therefore equal to the homotopy type of

$$\mathrm{GL}(n, \mathbf{R}) \times \mathrm{Br}_f(\sigma_0, T) \qquad \text{or} \qquad O(n) \times \mathrm{Br}_f(\sigma_0, T)$$

where $\mathrm{Br}_f(\sigma_0, T)$ is the space of all Brouwer charts that are the identity on σ_n, or, what amounts to the same, are the identity on some flag. $\mathrm{Br}_f(\sigma_0, T)$ is *the space of Brouwer charts "with a fixed flag."*

Observe that $\mathrm{Br}(\sigma_0, T)$ and $\mathrm{Br}_f(\sigma_0, T)$ can be contracted (are homotopy equivalent) to their subsets consisting of those charts κ for which $|\kappa(v_i)| = 1$ for $i = 1, \ldots, N$. In the sequel we will only be interested in the homotopy type of $\mathrm{Br}_f(\sigma_0, T)$.

Two nonzero vectors u and $v \in \mathbf{R}^n$ are equivalent if $\lambda > 0$ exists such that $u = \lambda v$. The equivalence class of u is a half ray denoted by $[u]$. The half rays are points of S^{n-1}, the double covering of the real projective $(n - 1)$-space, which is a topological $(n - 1)$-sphere with a well defined flat locally projective structure. If $\sigma_p \supset \sigma_0$ is one of the p-simplices of T, then the nonzero vectors v in σ_p, represent a set $[\sigma_p]$ of points of S^{n-1}, which is a $(p - 1)$-simplex of a triangulation of S^{n-1}. This $(p - 1)$-simplex has a natural projective structure and is a projectively straight $(p - 1)$-simplex.

If a triangulation of S^{n-1} consists of projective images of simples, then it is called a *projective triangulation* of S^{n-1}.

It may be remarked that S^{n-1} admits the usual Riemannian structure, with respect to which the triangulation consists of geodesic simplices. Cairns [1] has considered such geodesic triangulations.

Let $\mathrm{Pr}\,\mathrm{Imb}(S^{n-1}, \sigma_0, T)$ be the space of all homeomorphisms of S^{n-1} onto S^{n-1}, which are projective on each simplex of the given projective triangulation. Analogously $\mathrm{Pr}\,\mathrm{Imb}_f(S^{n-1}, \sigma_0, T)$ is defined by restricting moreover, to those homeomorphisms that are the identity on a flag, by which we now mean an image of a flag at σ_0 in T under the projection.

If σ_p is a p-simplex of $T \subset \mathbf{R}^n$, then the projection of the star of σ_p, onto an $(m - p)$-plane transversal to the p-plane of σ_p, determines a star of a point in an $(n - p)$-simplicial complex. The corresponding spaces are denoted by $\mathrm{Br}(\sigma_{,p} T)$, $\mathrm{Br}_f(\sigma_p, T)$, $\mathrm{Pr}\,\mathrm{Imb}_f(S^{n-p-1}, \sigma_p, T)$, etc. Now it is not hard to prove the following homotopy equivalence:

LEMMA. 4. $\mathrm{Br}_f(\sigma_p, T) \overset{h}{\sim} \mathrm{Pr}\,\mathrm{Imb}_f(S^{n-p-1}, \sigma_p, T)$

4.2. Imb S^n and Pr Imb S^n.

Given a projective triangulation T of S^n one may compare the space of all C^∞-imbeddings $\mathrm{Imb}(T, S^n)$ and the space of those imbeddings that are projective for each simplex of T, $\mathrm{Pr}\,\mathrm{Imb}(T, S^n)$. Clearly, $\mathrm{Pr}\,\mathrm{Imb}(T, S^n) \subset$

Imb(T, S^n). For the direct limits under the directed system of compatible triangulations we obtain (and denote)

(7) $$\text{Pr Imb } S^n \subset \text{Imb } S^n$$

Moreover:

THEOREM 3. *The injection* (7) *is a weak homotopy equivalence:*

(8) $$\pi_k(\text{Pr Imb } S^n) \approx \pi_k \text{Imb } S^n$$

Also

(8_f) $$\pi_k(\text{Pr Imf}_f S^n) \approx \pi_k \text{Imb}_f S^n$$

This follows from the following:

LEMMA 4.2. *Let* $\tau: T \to S^n$ *be a projective triangulation of* S^n *with its natural locally projective structure. For every compact family* $\lambda(v)$, $v \in V$, *of* C^∞-*imbeddings of* T *onto* S^n, *there exists a subdivision* $\tau': T' \to S^n$ *of* $\tau: T \to S^n$ *and a homotopy* $\lambda(v, t)$, $(v, t) \in V \times I$, *of* C^∞-*imbeddings such that* $\lambda(v, 0) = \lambda(v)$ *and* $\lambda(v, 1)$ *is a projective imbedding.*

Proof of the Theorem 3 from the Lemma. If $V = S^k$ is the parameter space of a k-sphere of C^∞-imbeddings, then after subdivision it is homotopic to a k-sphere of projective imbeddings. Therefore the natural map

$$\pi_k(\text{Pr Imb } S^n) \to \pi_k(\text{Imb } S^n)$$

is surjective. On the other hand, it is injective for the following reason.

If $V = S^k$ is a k-sphere of projective imbeddings and it is after subdivision equal to the restriction to the boundary of a $(k + 1)$-ball B^{k+1} of C^∞-imbeddings, then after some subdivision this $(k + 1)$-ball is homotopic to a $(k + 1)$-ball of projective imbeddings.

If we let the $(k + 1)$-ball of C^∞-imbeddings be constant near to the bounding k-sphere on radial segments, then we can assume that the final $(k + 1)$-ball of projective imbeddings has the boundary in common with the subdivided given k-sphere of projective imbeddings. Hence the injectivity.

The lemma is proved with methods which are analogous to those of J. H. C. Whitehead [18]; in particular see Theorem 4, p. 818. Compare also Munkres [14] Theorem 8.8. We plan to return to this lemma later.

5. Obstructions to contracting $\mathcal{D}_{S^k}$, with applications

5.1.

Given a k-sphere of smoothings $\mathcal{D}_{S^k}$ of a triangulated manifold, which gives rise to one and the same smoothing of some neighbourhood of the $(p - 1)$-skeleton, we may examine the obstruction to the existence of a homotopy which begins with $\mathscr{D}_{S^k}$, leads to one and the same smoothing on some neighbourhood $U(\sigma_p)$ of some p-simplex σ_p, and is constant on some neighbourhood of the boundary $\partial\sigma_p$. With the tools of Section 3, one finds that the obstruction is an element of $\mathrm{Pr}\ \mathrm{Imp}_f(S^{n-p-1}, \sigma_p, T)$. By repetition and induction one then obtains:

THEOREM 4 (Tr). *A sufficient condition for the existence of a $(k + 1)$-ball of smoothing $\mathscr{D}_{B^{k+1}}$, of a triangulated n-manifold $\tau\colon T \to X$, with a given k-sphere of smoothings $\mathscr{D}_{S^k}$ $(k \geq -1)$ as boundary, is*

$$(9) \qquad \pi_{p+k}\ \mathrm{Pr}\ \mathrm{Imb}_f(S^{n-p-1}, \sigma_p, T) = 0$$

Allowing subdivisions, one obtains from this theorem the combinatorial analogue:

THEOREM 4 (Comb). *A sufficient condition for the existence of a $(k + 1)$-ball of smoothings $\mathscr{D}_{B^{k+1}}$, of a combinatorial n-manifold X with a given k-sphere of smoothings $(k \geq -1)$ as boundary, is*

$$(10) \qquad \pi_{p+k}\ \mathrm{Pr}\ \mathrm{Imb}_f(S^{n-p-1}) = 0$$

By a (-1)-sphere we mean the void set. By a 0-ball we mean a point.

5.2. Applications to triangulated manifolds.

In view of the trivial lemma $\pi_k\ \mathrm{Pr}_f(S^1, \sigma_{n-2}, T) = 0$ for $k \geq 0$, and the Theorem of Cairns [1], $\pi_0\ \mathrm{Pr}_f(S^2, \sigma_{n-3}, T) = 0$, we obtain the following from Theorem 4.

COROLLARY 4.A (Cairns). *Given a triangulated n-manifold (X, τ), for which $D(X^n, \tau)$ is the space of smoothings, one has*

$$\pi_k D(X^n, \tau) = 0 \qquad \text{for } n \leq 2$$
$$\pi_0 D(X^n, \tau) = 0 \qquad \text{for } n \leq 3$$
$$D(X^n, \tau) \neq \text{void}, \qquad n \leq 4$$

In words, for example: *every k-sphere of smoothings of a triangulated surface $(n = 2)$ is homotopic to one smoothing. Any two smoothings of a triangulated n-manifold are homotopic, hence diffeomorphic, for $n \leq 3$. Any triangulated n-manifold has a compatible smoothing for $n \leq 4$.*

COROLLARY 4.B. *Let $\tau\colon \partial\sigma_{n+1} \to S^n$ be a triangulation of S^n with $n + 1$ vertices, then*

$$\pi_k D(S^n, \tau) = 0 \qquad k \geq 0$$

In particular $(k = 0)$: *Any two smoothings of $\partial\sigma_{n+1}$ are homotopic hence diffeomorphic with the usual smoothing of S^n. Consequently: any triangulation of an unusual smoothing on S^n has more than $n + 1$ vertices.*

PROOF.   In this case the space $\mathrm{Pr}\,\mathrm{Imb}_f(S^{n-p-1}, \sigma_p, \tau)$ is contractible to one point for each simplex σ_p on $\partial\sigma_{n+1}$, because one $(n-p-1)$-simplex on S^{n-p-1} is kept pointwise fixed and the unique non-adjacent vertex has freedom in a convex set (interior of a simplex) of S^{n-p-1} with its projective structure again.

5.3. Applications to combinatorial manifolds.

From Theorems 1A and 3, we obtain an exact sequence concerning the n-sphere with its locally projective structure, and with some combinatorial structure compatible with this locally projective structure:

(11) $\pi_{k+1}(D_0, S^n) \to \pi_k(\mathrm{Diff}_f S^n) \to \pi_k(\mathrm{Pr}\,\mathrm{Imb}_f S^n) \to \pi_k(D_0, S^n)$

For $n = 1$ all terms are 0. As $\pi_k(\mathrm{Pr}\,\mathrm{Imb}_f S^1) = 0$ then in view of Theorem 4B, $\pi_k(D_0, X^2) = 0$ for any k and any combinatorial 2-manifold X^2. In view of the theorem of Smale [15], $\pi_k(\mathrm{Diff}_f S^2) = 0$, of which Munkres [11] had also the special case $\pi_0(\mathrm{Diff}_f S^2) = 0$, the sequence (11) for $n = 2$ now yields $\pi_k(\mathrm{Pr}\,\mathrm{Imb}_f S^2) = 0$.

Consequently, by Theorem 4B again, we obtain:

$$\pi_k(D, X^3) = 0 \qquad \text{for any } k$$

and

$$\pi_k(\mathrm{Diff}_f S^3) \approx \pi_k(\mathrm{Pr}\,\mathrm{Imb}_f S^3)$$

This holds also for $k = 0$ in which case by the theorem of Cerf [4], $\pi_0(\mathrm{Diff}_f S^3) = 0$, we may conclude $\pi_0(\mathrm{Pr}\,\mathrm{Imb}_f S^3) = 0$. This again give results on X^4. Summarizing we have:

COROLLARY 5.3.A

$$\pi_k(\mathrm{Pr}\,\mathrm{Imb}_f S^2) = 0$$
$$\pi_k(\mathrm{Diff}_f S^3) \approx \pi_k(\mathrm{Pr}\,\mathrm{Imb}_f S^3)$$
$$\pi_0(\mathrm{Pr}\,\mathrm{Imb}_f S^3) = 0$$
$$\pi_k(D, X^n) = 0 \text{ for } n \leq 3;\ (k, n) = (0, 4) \text{ and } (-1, 5)$$

In particular, every k-sphere of smoothings of a combinatorial n-manifold X is homotopic to one smoothing in case $n \leq 3$ or $(k, n) = (0, 4)$.

Next let us consider the exact sequence for S^6:

$$\pi_1(D_0, S^6) \to \pi_0(\mathrm{Diff}_f S^6) \to \pi_0(\mathrm{Pr}\,\mathrm{Imb}_f S^6)$$

Suppose $\pi_{p+1}(\mathrm{Pr}\,\mathrm{Imb}_f S^{6-p-1}) = 0$ for $p = 0$, 1, 2. (For $p = 3$, 4, the same is known to be the case.) Then by Theorem 4 (Comb), we obtain

$$\pi_1(D_0, S^6) = 0$$

By Milnor [9], the term $\pi_0(\text{Diff}_f S^6)$ is not trivial, and so by exactness also $\pi_0(\text{Pr Imb}_f S^6)$ is nontrivial. Hence:

COROLLARY 5.3.B. $\sum_{r=0}^{3} \pi_r(\text{Pr Imb}_f S^{6-r})$ *is nontrivial.*

The significance of this corollary can be clarified by an equivalent theorem as follows: Let $\tau: T \to \sigma_n$ be a triangulation of a simplex σ_n. Let $\text{Imb}(\tau, n)$ be the space of all homeomorphisms of σ_n onto itself which are affine on each simplex of T and identity on the boundary $\partial \sigma_n$ of σ_n. Let $\pi_{k,n}$ be the inductive limit with respect to (the directed system of all triangulations τ belonging to) the combinatorial structure given by τ, of the homotopy groups $\pi_k(\text{Imb}(\tau, n))$. Then.

COROLLARY 5.3.C. $\pi_{0.6} \oplus \pi_{1.5} \oplus \pi_{2.4} \oplus \pi_{3.3}$ *is not trivial.*

REMARK. Observe that in the category of combinatorial manifolds with combinatorial isotopy, the set of PL-homeomorphisms of σ_n onto σ_n with boundary points fixed, has another topology with respect to which it is contractible by the Alexander argument (compare Guggenheim [5]).

UNIVERSITY OF AMSTERDAM

REFERENCES

[1] S. S. CAIRNS, Isotopic deformations of geodesic complexes on the 2-sphere and plane, *Annals of Math.*, 45 (1944), p. 207–217.

[2] ———, Introduction of a Riemannian geometry on a triangulable 4-manifold, *Annals of Math.*, 45 (1944), p. 218–219.

[3] ———, The manifold smoothing problem, *Bulletin AMS*, 67 (1961), p. 237–238.

[4] J. CERF, Seminaire H. Cartan, 1962–1963.

[5] V. K. A. M. GUGGENHEIM, Piecewise linear isotopy and imbedding of elements and spheres, *Proc. London Math. Soc.*, 3 (1953), p. 29–53 and p. 129–152.

[6] M. W. HIRSCH, On combinatorial submanifolds of differentiable manifolds, *Comment. Math. Helv.*, 36, 2 (1961), p. 103–111.

[7] ———, Obstruction theories for smoothing manifolds and maps, Research announcement *Bulletin AMS.*, 69 (1963), p. 352–356.

[8] B. MAZUR, Séminaire de topologie combinatoire et differentielle de l'Institut des Hautes Etudes Scientifiques, 1962/1963.

[9] J. MILNOR, On manifolds homeomorphic to the 7 sphere, *Annals of Math.*, 64 (1956), p. 399–405.

[10] ———, Microbundles and differential structures. To appear.

[11] J. MUNKRES, Differentiable isotopies of the 2-sphere, *Michigan Math. J.*, 7, (1960), p. 193–197.

[12] ———, Obstructions to the smoothing of piecewise-differentiable homeomorphism. *Annals of Math.*, 72 (1960), p. 521–554.

[13] ———, Obstructions to imposing differentiable structures. To appear.

[14] ———, *Elementary Differential Topology*, Annals of Mathematics Studies, No. 54 (1963).

[15] S. SMALE, Diffeomorphisms of the 2-sphere, *Proc. Am. Math. Soc., 10* (1959), p. 621–625.

[16] R. THOM, Des variétés triangulées aux variétés différentiables, *Proc. Int. Congr. Math.*, Edinburgh, 1958, p. 248–255.

[17] ———, Les structures differentiables des Boules et des spheres, *Colloque de Géométrie differentielle globale*, CBRM 1959, p. 27–35.

[18] J. H. C. WHITEHEAD, On C^1-complexes, *Ann. of Math., 41* (1940), p. 809–824.

[19] ———, Manifolds with transverse fields in euclidean space, *Ann. of Math., 73* (1961), p. 154–212.

On the Action of $\Theta^n(\partial\pi)$

WILLIAM BROWDER

---

1. Introduction

Since the paper of Milnor [11] in 1956, one of the central questions in differential topology has been determining the possible different (up to diffeomorphism) differentiable structures on a given combinatorial or topological manifold. For the sphere, the question has been largely answered by [9] and [17]. A natural way to try to get a new differentiable structure on an arbitrary manifold M^n is the following: Let T be a differentiable manifold homeomorphic (or combinatorially equivalent) to the n-sphere S^n. Remove a differentiably embedded n-cell e from M to get $M_0 = M -$ (interior e), and from T, to get $T_0 = T -$ (interior e). Then ∂M_0 is diffeomorphic to S^{n-1}, as is ∂T_0. Thus, we may identify ∂M_0 and ∂T_0 to get a new differentiable manifold without boundary $M \# T$, called the connected sum of M and T. If M and T are oriented and if the cell e is embedded in an orientation preserving way in M, and in an orientation reversing way in T, then $M \# T$ is oriented in a natural way, so that the orientation coincides with the original ones on M_0 and $T_0 \subset M \# T$. The manifold $M \# T$ is homeomorphic (or combinatorially equivalent) to M but may not be diffeomorphic to M. Among differentiable manifolds homeomorphic to S^n, $\#$ induces a group structure for the diffeomorphism classes, with S^n as the unit element. This group is called Γ_n. It follows that if $T \# T'$ is diffeomorphic to T, with T, $T' \in \Gamma_n$, then T' is diffeomorphic to S^n. For any manifold M, we may think of Γ_n acting on the diffeomorphism classes of manifolds homeomorphic to M.

One may ask whether the same result is true for an arbitrary oriented manifold M, i.e., does $M \# T$ diffeomorphic to M imply T is diffeomorphic to S^n? Examples where this "cancellation law" does not hold have been given by S. P. Novikov [16], I. Tamura [18], and E. H. Brown and B. Steer. C. T. C. Wall [19] has proved a cancellation law for certain $(n-1)$-connected $2n$-manifolds.

In [9], the group Θ^n of h-cobordism classes of differentiable homotopy n-spheres is studied, and largely determined. Smale [17] showed that $\Theta^n = \Gamma_n$, if $n \geq 5$, (in fact in [17] he shows h-cobordism = diffeomorphism

23

for simply connected manifolds M^n, $n \geq 5$). Define $\Theta^n(\partial \pi)$ to be the subgroup of Θ^n consisting of homotopy spheres which bound parallelizable manifolds. In [9], it is shown that $\Theta^n(\partial \pi) = 0$ if n is even, $\Theta^{4k+1}(\partial \pi)$ is either 0 or $\mathbf{Z}_2$, $\Theta^{4k-1}(\partial \pi)$, $k > 1$, is cyclic and its order is determined. One may consider Θ^n as acting on the h-cobordism classes of manifolds of a given homotopy type and normal bundle. In view of a theorem of Novikov [15, Theorem 2], the action of $\Theta^n(\partial \pi)$ is particularly important. However, Tamura's example [18] shows that even this subgroup of Θ^n may act trivially. He gives an example of a 7-manifold M such that $M \# T$ is diffeomorphic to M for every $T \in \Theta^7 = \Theta^7(\partial \pi)$.

In this paper we give some conditions on M^n and on the tangent bundle of a closed, oriented manifold M^n, $n = 4k - 1$, $k > 1$, so that some "cancellation law" may be proved for the action of $\Theta^n(\partial \pi)$. These conditions involve the vanishing of the rational Pontrjagin classes of M, the Stiefel–Whitney class $w_2(M)$, and $H^1(M; \mathbf{Z}_2)$ (note that these are combinatorial invariants). With some or all of these conditions we get some "cancellation" theorems (e.g., Corollaries 2.8 and 2.11). In case M^n is stably parallelizable (i.e., M is a π-manifold), $n = 4k - 1$, $k > 1$, and $H^1(M; \mathbf{Z}_2) = 0$, we get the following theorem (2.13): If $T \in \Theta^n(\partial \pi)$ and $T \# M$ is diffeomorphic to M by an orientation preserving diffeomorphism then (i) if k is odd, T is diffeomorphic to S^n, (ii) if k is even, then $T \# T$ is diffeomorphic to S^n.

The proof uses the result of Adams [1] on the order j_k of the image of the J-homomorphism in dimensional $4k - 1$. It is conjectured that

$$j_k = \text{denominator}\left(\frac{B_k}{4k}\right) = d_k,$$ where B_k is the kth Bernoulli number, and

Adams has shown this for k odd, but has shown only that $j_k = \varepsilon d_k$, where $\varepsilon = 1$ or 2, if k is even. If it were known that $\varepsilon = 1$ then the conclusion of (ii) would become "T is diffeomorphic to S^n."

J. Eells and N. Kuiper [6] have studied this problem by means of an invariant μ which they defined. Their technique works in many cases of manifolds satisfying our conditions and sometimes give stronger results, as well as sometimes giving results for more general manifolds. Unfortunately their techniques require assumptions on the manifold which involve more than the homotopy type and tangent bundle of M.

In case $n = 4k + 1$, E. H. Brown and B. Steer have shown that $\Theta^n(\partial \pi)$ always acts trivially on $V_{2k+2,2}$ the tangent sphere bundle to the $(2k + 1)$-sphere.

We will use the following notation:

If M and M' are oriented manifolds, $M \equiv M'$ will mean M is diffeomorphic to M' by an orientation preserving diffeomorphism. If X and Y are spaces, $X \simeq Y$ will mean X is homotopy equivalent to Y. If ξ is a bundle over X, $i: A \to X$ the injection of a subspace we will denote $i^*(\xi)$ by $\xi | A$. $\tau(M)$ will denote the tangent bundle of a differentiable manifold M, $\sigma(M)$ will denote the index of M, i.e., the signature of the quadratic form given by cup product,

$$H^{2k}(M; \mathbf{Q}) \otimes H^{2k}(M; \mathbf{Q}) \to H^{4k}(M; \mathbf{Q}),$$

when dimension of $M = 4k$. If W is a manifold with boundary, $\sigma(W)$ will denote the signature of the intersection pairing,

$$H_{2k}(W; \mathbf{Q}) \otimes H_{2k}(W; \mathbf{Q}) \to H_0(W; \mathbf{Q}),$$

(which is the same as considering the pairing

$$H^{2k}(W, \partial W; \mathbf{Q}) \otimes H^{2k}(W, \partial W; \mathbf{Q}) \to H^{4k}(W, \partial W, \mathbf{Q}).)$$

Similar to the operation of "connected sum" of two manifolds, we have an operation "connected sum along the boundary" for two oriented n-manifolds W_1, W_2 with boundaries M_1 and M_2, (again denoted by $\#$). Let M_1^0 and M_2^0 be components of M_1 and M_2, and let e be a closed $(n-1)$ cell. Let $f_i: e \to M_i^0$ be differentiable embeddings such that f_1 is orientation preserving, f_2 is orientation reversing. Let $W_1 \# W_2$ (along M_1^0 and M_2^0) be the union of W_1, W_2, and $e \times I$ with $(x, 0)$ identified with $f_1(x) \in M_1^0$, $(x, 1)$ identified with $f_2(x) \in M_2^0$. This can be made into a differentiable oriented manifold with boundary $M_1 \# M_2$ by the process of "rounding the corners" (see [12]).

2. Action of $\Theta^n(\partial \pi)$, $n = 4k - 1$, $k > 1$

In this section, we prove theorems on the action of $\Theta^n(\partial \pi)$. Let M be a closed, oriented differentiable manifold of dimension n. Suppose we have $T \in \Theta^n(\partial \pi)$, $T = \partial W$, W parallelizable, and, $T \# M \equiv M$. From this we construct a closed manifold Q of dimension $(n + 1)$ such that the index $\sigma(Q) = \sigma(W)$. The element $T \in \Theta^n(\partial \pi)$ is determined by $\sigma(W)$, so we study $\sigma(Q)$ and try to prove that it is divisible by various numbers. According to [9], $T \equiv S^n$ if and only if $\sigma(W)$ is divisible by an integer σ_k which they define. We use the Index Theorem [8] and the integrality of the $\hat{A}$ genus [2], to study $\sigma(Q)$. In case M is a π-manifold we may also get extra information on $p_k[Q]$ directly, which we do in §3.

We consider a homotopy sphere T such that $T = \partial W$, where W is a parallelizable manifold. Take the connected sum along the boundary of W and $M \times I$ (using $M \times 0$) to get a differentiable manifold with boundary $M \cup (-(T \# M))$. If M and $T \# M$ are diffeomorphic, then we may identify them in $W \# (M \times I)$ under the diffeomorphism to get a closed oriented manifold Q. We denote by M_0 and T_0, M and T with a cell removed so that $M \# T = M_0 \cup T_0$.

LEMMA 2.1. *Q/W is homeomorphic to a fibre bundle over S^1 with fibre M. It is described by identifying the two ends $M \times 0$, $M \times 1$ of $M \times I$ by the homeomorphism $f : M \to M$ which is defined by $p \circ g$ where $g : M \to T \# M$ is the given diffeomorphism, and $p : T \# M \to M$ is the identity on M_0 and p is a homeomorphism of T_0 with e^n extending the diffeomorphism on the boundary.*

PROOF. What the lemma says is that collapsing W to a point in Q is the same thing as retracting W onto $e^n \subset T = \partial W$, which is clear, $(e^n = T - T_0)$.

Let M_f be the fibre bundle over S^1 with fibre M, a closed oriented manifold, obtained from $M \times I$ by identifying $M \times 0$ and $M \times 1$ by an orientation preserving homeomorphism $f : M \times 0 \to M \times 1$.

THEOREM 2.2. *The index $\sigma(M_f) = 0$.*

PROOF. Consider M_f as $(M_1 \times I) \cup (M_2 \times I)$ where M_1, M_2 are two copies of M, identified along the boundaries, $M_1 \times 0$ identified with $M_2 \times 1$ by the identity, $M_1 \times 1$ identified with $M_2 \times 0$ by f, $f(m, 1) = (fm, 0)$. Then $M_1 \times I$ and $M_2 \times I$ intersect in two copies of M, call them $_1M$ and $_2M$, $_1M = M_1 \times 0 = M_2 \times 1$, $_2M = M_1 \times 1 = M_2 \times 0$. The inclusion of $_1M \cup {}_2M$ into $M_1 \times I$ and $M_2 \times I$ are given by

$$i_1 : {}_1M \cup {}_2M \to M_1 \times I, \qquad i_2 : {}_1M \cup {}_2M \to M_2 \times 1$$

$$i_1(m) = \begin{cases} (m, 0) & \text{if } m \in {}_1M \\ \\ (m, 1) & \text{if } m \in {}_2M \end{cases}$$

$$i_2(m) = \begin{cases} (m, 1) & \text{if } m \in {}_1M \\ \\ (f(m), 0) & \text{if } m \in {}_2M \end{cases}$$

Then we may study the Mayer–Vietoris sequence in cohomology for $M_f = M_1 \times I \cup M_2 \times I$, in particular in dimension $2q$, where dim $M = 4q - 1$, dim $Q = 4q$.

$$(2.3) \quad \cdots \to H^{j-1}(M_1 \times I) + H^{j-1}(M_2 \times I) \xrightarrow{i_1{}^* - i_2{}^*} H^{j-1}({}_1M) + H^{j-1}({}_2M)$$

$$\xrightarrow{\Delta} H^j(M_f) \xrightarrow{j_1{}^* + j_2{}^*} H^j(M_1 \times I) + H^j(M_2 \times I) \xrightarrow{i_1{}^* - i_2{}^*} \cdots$$

Identifying $H^*(M_1 \times I)$, $H^*(M_2 \times I)$, $H^*({}_1M)$, and $H^*({}_2M)$ with $H^*(M)$ by the inclusions $M \to M_1 \times 0$, $M \to M_2 \times 1$, $_1M = M_1 \times 0$,

$_2M = M_1 \times 1$ which all induce cohomology isomorphisms, the sequence (2.3) becomes:

$$(2.4) \qquad \cdots \to H^{j-1}(M) + H^{j-1}(M) \xrightarrow{\ell} H^{j-1}(M) + H^{j-1}(M)$$

$$\xrightarrow{\Delta} H^j(M_f) \to H^j(M) + H^j(M) \xrightarrow{\ell} H^j(M) + H^j(M) \cdots$$

where

$$\ell(x, y) = (x + y, -x - f^*(y)) \in H^*(M) + H^*(M),$$

when

$$(x, y) \in H^*(M) + H^*(M), \qquad (\ell = i_1^* - i_2^*).$$

Since f is a diffeomorphism of degree $+1$, it follows that f^* in dimensions j and $n - j$ are adjoint maps, so that ℓ in dimension j is the adjoint of ℓ in dimension $n - j$. Hence, considering (2.4) with real coefficients, we have that rank (coker $\ell)^{j-1}$ = rank (ker $\ell)^{j-1}$ = rank (ker $\ell)^{n-j+1}$. From (2.4) we get

$$(2.5) \qquad 0 \to (\text{image } \Delta)^j \to H^j(M_f; \mathbf{R}) \to (\ker \ell)^j \to 0$$

and taking $j = 2q$, rank (image $\Delta)^{2q}$ = rank (coker $\ell)^{2q-1}$ = rank (ker $\ell)^{2q}$. Hence, rank (image $\Delta)^{2q} = \frac{1}{2}$ rank $H^{2q}(M_f; \mathbf{R})$.

Now Δ, being a Mayer–Vietoris coboundary, may be factored through $H^{2q}(M_f, M_1 \times I)$ or $H^{2q}(M_f, M_2 \times I)$. It follows that (image $\Delta)^{2q}$ annihilates itself under cup product, for if

$$x \in H^*(M_f, M_1 \times I), \qquad y \in H^*(M_f, M_2 \times I),$$
$$x \cup y \in H^*(M_f, M_1 \times I \cup M_2 \times I) = 0$$

since

$$M_f = M_1 \times I \cup M_2 \times I.$$

Hence (image $\Delta)^{2q}$ is a self-annihilating submodule of rank $= \frac{1}{2}$ rank $H^{2q}(M_f; \mathbf{R})$, which implies that the index (signature) of the cup product $H^{2q} \otimes H^{2q} \to H^{4q}$ is zero, i.e., $\sigma(M_f) = 0$.

LEMMA 2.6. $\sigma(Q) = \sigma(W)$.

PROOF. The collapsing map $\eta: Q \to Q/W = M_f$ is a map of degree $+1$, as is the map $\xi: Q \to Q/(Q - \text{int}(W)) = \hat{W} = W \cup (\text{cone on } \partial W)$. It follows from the fact that $W \cap (Q - \text{int } W) = T$, a homotopy $(4q - 1)$-sphere, that $H^{2q}(Q) = \eta^* H^{2q}(M_f) + \xi^* H^{2q}(\hat{W})$, η^* and ξ^* are monomorphisms, and clearly the two summands are orthogonal to each other under the cup product pairing. Hence, since by Theorem 2.2 $\sigma(M_f) = 0$, we get $\sigma(Q) = \sigma(\hat{W})$, and clearly $\sigma(\hat{W}) = \sigma(W)$.

Thus we may study $\sigma(Q)$ to try to study elements of $\Theta^n(\partial\pi)$ which act trivially on a manifold M. In particular if $T = \partial W$, W a π-manifold, then $\sigma(W)$ determines T as an element of $\Theta^n(\partial\pi)$.

THEOREM 2.7. *Suppose all the rational Pontrjagin classes* $p_i(M) \in H^{4i}(M; \mathbf{Q})$ *are zero. Then all decomposable Pontrjagin numbers of* Q *are zero,* $p_{i_1} \cdots p_{i_e}[Q] = 0$, $e > 1$.

PROOF. Consider $Q = W \# (M \times I) \cup M \times I$, where the boundaries of the two pieces are identified, so that

$$W \# (M \times I) \cap M \times I = M \cup M.$$

Consider the Mayer–Vietoris sequence in rational cohomology

$$\cdots \to H^i(M) + H^i(M) \xrightarrow{\Delta} H^{i+1}(Q) \xrightarrow{j_1{}^* + j_2{}^*} H^{i+1}(W \# (M \times I))$$
$$+ H^{i+1}(M \times I) \xrightarrow{i_1{}^* - i_2{}^*} H^{i+1}(M) + H^{i+1}(M) \to \cdots$$

where we have written $H^*(M \cup M) = H^*(M) + H^*(M)$, i_1, i_2, j_1, j_2 are inclusions of submanifolds. Now $j_1^*(p_\ell(Q)) = p_\ell(W \# (M \times I))$ and $j_2^*(p_\ell(Q)) = p_\ell(M \times I) = 0$ since $p_\ell(M) = 0$. Using the Mayer–Vietoris sequence for $W \# (M \times I) = W \cup M \times I$, where $W \cap M \times I = e^n$, an n-cell, we get that $H^*(W \# (M \times I)) = H^*(W) + H^*(M \times I)$. Also W is a π-manifold. Hence $p_\ell(W \# (M \times I))$ goes into zero under the inclusions of W and $M \times I$ into $W \# (M \times I)$, so that

$$j_*(p_\ell(Q)) = p_\ell(W \# (M \times I)) = 0.$$

Hence, $(j_1^* + j_2^*)(p_\ell(Q)) = 0$ so that $p_\ell(Q) = \Delta x_\ell$, where

$$x_\ell \in H^{4\ell - 1}(M \cup M).$$

Hence $p_\ell(Q) \cup p_k(Q) = \Delta x_\ell \cup \Delta x_k = 0$, since (image Δ) annihilate itself under cup product. Hence all products of rational Pontrjagin classes of Q are zero, so all decomposable Pontrjagin numbers $p_{i_1} \cdots p_{i_e}[Q] = 0$.

We may use Theorem 2.7 to get results on the action of $\Theta^n(\partial \pi)$. For example:

COROLLARY 2.8. *Let* M^7 *be an oriented closed manifold with* $p_1(M) = 0 \in H^4(M; \mathbf{Q})$. *If* $T \in \Theta^7$, $T \# M$ *diffeomorphic to* M, *then* T *is divisible by 7 in* Θ^7.

PROOF. Here $\Theta^7 = \Theta^7(\partial \pi) = \mathbf{Z}_{28}$. It suffices to show that if $T = \partial W$, W a π-manifold, then $\sigma(W)$ is divisible by 7. But $\sigma(W) = \sigma(Q) = \frac{7}{45} p_2[Q]$, by (2.6), (2.7), and the Index Theorem [8]. Hence $\sigma(W)$ is divisible by 7.

One may obtain similar results using slightly different hypotheses. For example if M^7 is such that $p_1(M^7)$ is divisible by 7 and $H^4(M^7)$ is free, then one may show that $p_1^2[Q]$ is divisible by 7, so that if $T \in \Theta^7$ and $T \# M \equiv M$, then T is divisible by 7 in Θ^7.

Thus the Index Theorem may be combined with the previous results to get information on $\sigma(W)$, in case the rational Pontrjagin classes of M are zero. We may strengthen these results by obtaining information on the highest Pontrjagin number $p_q[Q]$, the only non-zero one. One way to do this is by using the $\hat{A}$ genus of Borel-Hirzebruch [3]. For Spin-manifolds integrality theorems have been proved for the $\hat{A}$ genus, [2].

LEMMA 2.9. *If* $H^1(M; \mathbf{Z}_2) = 0$ *and* $w_2(M) = 0$, *then* $w_2(Q) = 0$, *so that Q is a Spin-manifold.*

PROOF. Using the Mayer–Vietoris sequence as in the proof of (2.7) we have that $w_2(M \times I) = 0$ and $w_2(W \# (M \times I)) = 0$, since W is a π-manifold and hence $(j_1^* + j_2^*)(w_2(Q)) = w_2(M \times I) + w_2(W \# (M \times I)) = 0$ so $w_2(Q) \in$ image Δ. But $H^1(M; \mathbf{Z}_2) = 0$ implies (image Δ)^2 $= 0$ so $w_2(Q) = 0$. It follows, as in [3, §26.5], that Q is a Spin-manifold.

We recall a theorem of Atiyah–Hirzebruch [2]:

THEOREM 2.10. (i) *If* Y *is a Spin-manifold with even dimension then* $\hat{A}[Y]$ *is an integer.* (ii) *If in addition,* dim $Y \equiv 4$ mod 8, *then* $\hat{A}[Y]$ *is an even integer.*

We may apply this to study Q. For example:

CORROLLARY 2.11. *Let* M^7 *be a closed oriented 7-manifold such that* $p_1(M) = 0 \in H^4(M; \mathbf{Q})$, $w_2(M) = 0$, *and* $H^1(M; \mathbf{Z}_2) = 0$. *If* T *is a seven dimensional homotopy sphere such that* $T \# M$ *is diffeomorphic to* M, *then* T *is diffeomorphic to* S^7.

Hence such a manifold M has at least 28 different differentiable structures on it.

PROOF. Since $\Theta^7 = \Theta^7(\partial\pi)$, (see [9]) we may assume $T = \partial W$, W parallelizable. From (2.8), we deduce that Q, constructed as usual, is a Spin-manifold, so by (2.9), $\hat{A}[Q]$ is an integer. By (2.6), all decomposable Pontrjagin numbers of Q are zero so that

$$\hat{A}[Q] = \frac{B_2}{2(4\,!)}\, p_2[Q] = \frac{1}{2(4\,!)30}\, p_2[Q]$$

is an integer, and thus $p_2[Q] = 2(4\,!)30 \cdot x$. Then index of Q

$$\sigma(Q) = \frac{7}{45}\, p_2[Q] = \frac{7}{45} \cdot 2(4\,!)30x = 8(28)x,$$

by the Index Theorem [8]. But according to [9], if 8(28) divides $\sigma(W)$ ($= \sigma(Q)$ by (2.6)), then $T = \partial W$ is diffeomorphic to S^7. Hence, in particular if $T \not\equiv S^7$, then $T \# M \not\equiv M$ and hence as T runs through the elements of Θ^7 we get 28 different differentiable manifolds, all combinatorially equivalent to M.

Note that examples of such manifolds M may be obtained by taking the orbit space of S^7 under a fixed point free differentiable action of a group of odd order. This manifold M will have only odd torsion in cohomology except for $H^7(M) = \mathbf{Z}$. Hence all the conditions of (2.10) are satisfied.

Other examples of such manifolds in dimension 7 are S^3 bundles E over S^4 such that the Pontrjagin class of the bundle is zero, or such that the Euler class of the bundle is non-zero (which implies $H^4(E)$ is a torsion group). These manifolds have been studied by Tamura and the Eells–Kuiper invariant μ [6] may also be used to study the action of Θ^7 on them.

Similar results may be derived in higher dimensions, but the conclusions will be weaker unless we make more assumptions on M. If we assume that M is a π-manifold we may obtain a strong result based on the following lemma:

LEMMA 2.12. *Let M^{4k-1} be a π-manifold, and suppose T is a homotopy sphere, $T = \partial W$, W parallelizable, and $T \mathbin{\#} M \equiv M$. Then the manifold Q (constructed as usual) has its Pontrjagin class $p_k(Q)$ divisible by $(2k-1)! a_k$, where $a_k = 2$ if k is odd, $a_k = 1$ if k is even.*

We shall prove this in §3.

Using (2.12) we may now prove the main theorem:

THEOREM 2.13. *Let M^{4k-1} be a closed π-manifold with $H^1(M; \mathbf{Z}_2) = 0$ $k > 1$. Let T be a homotopy $(4k-1)$ sphere which bonds a parallelizable manifold W. If $T \mathbin{\#} M \equiv M$, then (i) if k is odd, then $T \equiv S^{4k-1}$, (ii) if k is even, then $2T = T \mathbin{\#} T \equiv S^{4k-1}$.*

PROOF. By (2.6), $\sigma(W) = \sigma(Q)$, where Q is as constructed earlier, and since M is a π-manifold, $p_i(M) = 0$ for all i so we have by (2.7) that all decomposable Pontrjagin classes of Q are zero. Thus the polynomial L_k of the Index Theorem has only one non-zero term, the highest term involving $p_k[Q]$.

By (2.11), $p_k[Q] = (2k-1)! \, a_k y$. By (2.9), since $w_2(M) = 0$ (M being a π-manifold) and $H^1(M; \mathbf{Z}_2) = 0$, we have that Q is a Spin-manifold, so the Theorem of Atiyah–Hirzebruch (2.10) applies. Now

$$\hat{A}[Q] = \frac{B_k}{2(2k)!} \cdot p_k[Q] = \frac{B_k a_k}{4k} y$$

According to (2.10), if k is odd, $\hat{A}[y]$ is an even integer, a_k is then 2, so that $\dfrac{B_k}{4k} y$ is an integer. Hence in that case y is a multiple of denominator $\dfrac{B_k}{4k} = d_k$ which equals j_k, the order of the image of the J homomorphism, by a Theorem of Adams [1], ($J : \pi_{4k-1}(SO) \to \pi_{N+4k-1}(S^N)$ N large). If k is even, $a_k = 1$, and again we get y is a multiple of d_k and now j_k equals either d_k or $2d_k$, by results of Adams [1]. Then, by the Index Theorem,

$$\begin{aligned}
\sigma(Q) &= 2^{2k}(2^{2k-1} - 1)B_k p_k[Q]/(2k)\,! \\
&= 2^{2k}(2^{2k-1} - 1)B_k(2k - 1)\,!\ a_k y/(2k)\,! \\
&= 2^{2k-1}(2^{2k-1} - 1)B_k a_k y/k
\end{aligned}$$

If k is odd, y is a multiple of j_k, so that $\sigma(Q)$ is a multiple of the number σ_k determined by Kervaire–Milnor [10], $\sigma_k = 2^{2k-1}(2^{2k-1} - 1)B_k j_k a_k/k$. Kervaire and Milnor [9] have shown that if $\sigma(W)$ is divisible by σ_k, then $T \equiv S^{4k-1}$, so conclusion (i) follows. If k is even, then $2\sigma(W)$ is divisible by σ_k, so $2T \equiv S^{4k-1}$ and (ii) follows, which completes the proof.

3. Pontrjagin classes and suspension

In this section we prove Lemma 2.12. To do this we first study Pontrjagin classes of bundles over special kinds of spaces.

Let X be a space with base point x_0. We will denote by ΣX the reduced suspension of X, $\Sigma X = X \times I/X \times 0 \cup X \times 1 \cup x_0 \times I$, and by ΩX the loop space of X, $\Omega X = \{f\colon I \to X, f(0) = f(1) = x_0\}$, with compact open topology. We denote by Σ also the maps in homotopy or homology or cohomology,

$$\Sigma\colon \pi_k(X) \to \pi_{k+1}(\Sigma X), \quad \Sigma\colon H_k(X) \to H_{k+1}(\Sigma X), \quad \Sigma\colon H^{k+1}(\Sigma X) \to H^k(X),$$

the last two being isomorphisms.

If ξ is a vector bundle over a space X, $p_k(\xi)$ will usually denote the rational Pontrjagin class of ξ, $p_k(\xi) \in H^{4k}(X\,;\mathbf{Q})$.

THEOREM 3.1. *Let ξ be an oriented q-plane bundle over a complex L, $H^i(L\,;\mathbf{Q}) = 0$, $i \geq n = 4s$, $q > n + 1$, and let $f\colon S^{n-1} \to L$ represent an element $\alpha \in \pi_{n-1}(L)$ such that $\Sigma^k\alpha = 0 \in \pi_{n-1+k}(\Sigma^k L)$, and set $K = L \cup_f e^n$. Then there is a q-plane bundle η over K such that $\eta|L = \xi$ and $p_s(\eta)$ is a polynomial in $p_1(\eta), \ldots, p_{s-1}(\eta)$.*

PROOF. If we have a map $h\colon L \to \Omega X$ then there is a map: $h_1\colon \Sigma L \to X$ obtained by "shifting the parameter" (see [7] for example), such that the diagram (3.2) commutes:

$$\text{(3.2)} \qquad \begin{array}{ccc}
H^*(L) & \xleftarrow{\ h^*\ } & H^*(\Omega X) \\
{\scriptstyle \Sigma}\big\uparrow & & \big\uparrow{\scriptstyle \sigma^*} \\
H^*(\Sigma L) & \xleftarrow{\ h_1{}^*\ } & H^*(X)
\end{array}$$

where σ^* is the cohomology suspension associated with the contractible fibre space EX, the space of paths of X, (see [5, p. 169] for example).

Let $h': L \to BSO(q)$ be the classifying map of ξ, and let $h = i \circ h'$, where i is the inclusion of $BSO(q)$ into the stable orthogonal group BSO, $h: L \to BSO$. By the Bott Periodicity Theorem [4], BSO is the homotopy type of an iterated loop space, $BSO \cong \Omega^n X_n$, for any n, where $X_n = \Omega X_{n+1}$. Note that for any given n, we may assume we have $BSO = X_0, X_1, \ldots, X_n$ with above properties and X_i connected, $0 \le i \le n$. For letting Y_n be any space such that $\Omega^n Y_n = BSO$, the n-connected fibre space $(Y_n, n) = X_n$ over Y_n has $\Omega^n X_n \cong \Omega^n Y_n \cong BSO$, and $\Omega^i X_n$ is connected for $0 \le i \le n$. Then, there is a map $h_k \colon \Sigma^k L \to X_k$ corresponding to the classifying map $h \colon L \to BSO = \Omega^k X_k$ such that the diagram

(3.3)
$$
\begin{array}{ccc}
H^*(\Sigma^m L) & \xleftarrow{h_m{}^*} & H^*(X_m) \\
{\scriptstyle \Sigma}\big\uparrow & & \big\uparrow{\scriptstyle \sigma^*} \\
H^*(\Sigma^{m+1} L) & \xleftarrow{h_{m+1}{}^*} & H^*(X_{m+1})
\end{array}
$$

commutes, where $X_m = \Omega X_{m+1}$.

Now, since $\Sigma^k \alpha = 0$, $\beta = \Sigma^k f \colon S^{n+k-1} \to \Sigma^k L$ is homotopic to the constant map, $\Sigma^k K = \Sigma^k L \cup_\beta e^{n+k}$ so that $\Sigma^k K \cong \Sigma^k L \vee S^{n+k}$. Hence, there is a retraction $r \colon \Sigma^k K \to \Sigma^k L$, so define $g_k \colon \Sigma^k K \to X_k$ by $g_k = h_k \circ r$, so that $g_k | \Sigma^k L = h_k$. It follows that $g_{k-1} | \Sigma^{k-1} L = h_{k-1}$ etc., and $g \colon K \to BSO = X_0$ is such that $g | L = h$.

Now the inclusion of $BSO(q)$ in BSO is a homotopy equivalence in dimensions $< q$. Since $H^i(K, L) = H^i(K) = 0$ for $i > n$ and $q > n + 1$, there is no obstruction to compressing $g \colon K \to BSO$ into a map $g' \colon K \to BSO(q)$, such that $g' | L = h$. Then g' induces a q-plane bundle η over K, and since $g' | L = h$, it follows that $\eta | L = \xi$.

Let $p_s \in H^{4s}(BSO; \mathbf{Q})$ be the unique element such that

$$
i^*(p_s) = p_s(\gamma) \in H^{4s}(BSO(q); \mathbf{Q}),
$$

where $p_s(\gamma)$ is the sth Pontrjagin class of the canonical q-plane bundle γ over $BSO(q)$, $(q > 4s)$. $H^*(BSO; \mathbf{Q}) = \mathbf{Q}[p_1, p_2, \ldots]$ so that p_s is indecomposable in the algebra $H^*(BSO; \mathbf{Q})$, i.e., p_s is not a linear combination of products.

We digress momentarily to recall some results from the theory of Hopf algebras. A Hopf algebra over a field $\mathbf{K}$ is an algebra with unit A, together with a homomorphism of algebras (called the diagonal map) $\psi \colon A \to A \otimes A$ with "counit," i.e., such that $\psi^* \colon A^* \otimes A^* \to A^*$ is a multiplication with unit, where $A^* = \mathrm{Hom}(A, \mathbf{K})$ and A_i is assumed finitely generated in each dimension. The homology and cohomology of loop spaces (such as $BSO = X_0$, or X_k) with coefficients in a field are Hopf algebras. The module of decomposable elements of A, $D(A)$, is defined to be $\bar{A}\bar{A}$, where

$\bar{A}$ = positive dimensional elements of A. The module of primitive elements of A, $P(A)$, is defined to be the set of elements $x \in \bar{A}$ such that

$$\psi x = x \otimes 1 + 1 \otimes x$$

in $A \otimes A$.

THEOREM 3.4. (Milnor and Moore [13]) *Let A be a Hopf algebra over the rationals $\mathbf{Q}$ such that $A_0 = \mathbf{Q}$, A is associative and commutative (in the graded sense) as an algebra, and the diagonal ψ is associative and commutative (or in other words, A^* is an associative, commutative algebra). If $x \in \bar{A}$, there exists an element $b \in D(A)$ such that $x - b \in P(A)$.*

Note that if $x \notin D(A)$, then $x - b \neq 0$ in $P(A)$.

The loop space of a loop space has a homotopy associative, homotopy commutative multiplication, and it follows that its rational cohomology satisfies the conditions of the theorem (provided it is connected). In particular $H^*(BSO; \mathbf{Q})$ and $H^*(X_k; \mathbf{Q})$ for all k, satisfy these hypotheses.

The following may be deduced from the analog of [5, Theorem 5.14] with $p = 0$.

THEOREM 3.5. *Let $x \in P(H^t(X_k; \mathbf{Q}))$. Then there exists $y \in H^{t+1}(X_{k+1}; \mathbf{Q})$ such that $\sigma^* y = x$.*

Now it follows from (3.4) that there is a decomposable element $b \in H^{4s}(BSO; \mathbf{Q})$ such that $p_s - b = x_0 \in P(H^*(BSO; \mathbf{Q}))$. Hence by (3.5), there is an element $y_1 \in H^{4s+1}(X_1; \mathbf{Q})$ such that $\sigma^* y_1 = x_0$. By (3.4) again, there is an element $b_1 \in D(H^*(X_1; \mathbf{Q}))$ such that

$$x_1 = y_1 - b_1 \in P(H^*(X_1; \mathbf{Q})),$$

so that by (3.5), $x_1 = \sigma^* y_2$, $y_2 \in H^*(X_2; \mathbf{Q})$. Now σ^* annihilates decomposable elements, so that $\sigma^* x_1 = \sigma^* y_1 = x_0$, so that $(\sigma^*)^2 y_2 = x_0$. Continuing the argument, we finally obtain an element $y_k \in H^*(X_k; \mathbf{Q})$ such that $(\sigma^*)^k y_k = x_0 \in H^*(X_0; \mathbf{Q}) = H^*(BSO; \mathbf{Q})$. Using (3.3) repeatedly (with K in place of L and g in place of h) we have that $\Sigma^k g_k^* = g^*(\sigma^*)^k$ so that $g^*(p_s - b) = g^*(x_0) = g^*((\sigma^*)^k y_k) = \Sigma^k g_k^*(y_k) = \Sigma^k r^* h_k^*(y_k) = 0$ since $H^{4s}(L; \mathbf{Q}) = 0$. Hence $p_s(\eta) = g^*(p_s) = g^*(b)$, and since $b \in D(H^*(BSO; \mathbf{Q}))$, $g^*(b) = p_s(\eta)$ is the sum of products of $p_i(\eta)$, $i < s$, which proves (3.1).

Note that since $\eta | L = \xi$, and the inclusion map $i: L \to K$ is a homotopy equivalence in dimensions $< n - 1$, we have $p_j(\eta) = i^{*-1}(p_j(\xi))$ for $j < s$.

THEOREM 3.6. *Let L be a complex, $H^i(L) = 0$ for $i \geq 4s$, $f: S^{n-1} \to L$, $n = 4s$, such that $\Sigma^k \alpha = 0 \in \pi_{n+k-1}(\Sigma^k L)$, $\alpha = \{f\} \in \pi_{n-1}(L)$, and set $K = L \cup_f e^n$. If ξ is a q-plane bundle over K, then there is a bundle γ over S^n such that if $g: K \to S^n$ is the map which collapses L to a point, $K \to K/L =$*

S^n, then $p_s(\xi) = p_s(g^*\gamma) = g^*p_s(\gamma)$, *modulo sums of products of* $p_j(\xi)$ *for* $j < s$.

PROOF. Let $\eta = \xi|L$, $\bar{\eta}$ a bundle inverse to η, so that $\eta \oplus \bar{\eta}$ is trivial. Then the Pontrjagin classes of $\bar{\eta}$ are polynomials in those of η, from the Whitney sum formula. Apply Theorem 3.1 to $\bar{\eta}$, and let ζ be the bundle over K obtained, so that $\zeta|L = \bar{\eta}$, and $p_s(\zeta)$ is a sum of products of lower Pontrjagin classes of ξ, $p_i(\xi)$, $i < s$, and $p_i(\zeta) = p_i(\bar{\eta})$ for $i < s$ Note that $p_i(\eta) = i^*p_i(\xi)$ if $i < s$. Then $\xi \oplus \zeta|L = \eta \oplus \bar{\eta}$ is trivial, so that the classifying map of $\xi \oplus \zeta$ factors through $K/L = S^n$. But

$$p_s(\xi \oplus \zeta) = p_s(\xi) + p_s(\zeta) + \sum_{\substack{i+j=s \\ i,j>0}} p_i(\xi)p_j(\zeta),$$

so that $p_s(\xi \oplus \zeta) = p_s(\xi)$ modulo sums of products of $p_i(\xi)$'s for $i < s$.

COROLLARY 3.7. *Let* K, L, ξ, *be as in* (3.6) *and assume further that any product of* $p_i(\xi)$, $i < s$, *of dimension* $4s$ *is zero, i.e.,* $p_{i_1}(\xi) \ldots p_{i_l}(\xi) = 0$ *in* $H^{4s}(K; \mathbf{Q})$. *Then* $p_s(\xi)$ *is divisible by* $(2s - 1)!a_s$ *in* $H^{4s}(K; \mathbf{Z})$, *where* $a_s = 2$ *if* s *is odd,* $a_s = 1$ *if* s *is even.*

PROOF. For a bundle which is trivial over the $(n - 1)$ skeleton $(n = 4s)$, this was proved by Milnor and Kervaire [10]. Since all the products of $p_i(\xi)$ $i < s$, in dimension $4s$ are zero, it follows from (3.6) that $p_s(\xi) = p_s(\gamma')$ where $\gamma' = g^*(\gamma)$, $g: K \to S^n$, γ a bundle over S^n. Then $p_s(\gamma)$ is divisible by $(2s - 1)! \, a_s$, since γ is a bundle over S^n, so

$$p_s(\gamma') = g^*p_s(\gamma)$$

is divisible by $(2s - 1)!a_s$, (all in cohomology with $\mathbf{Z}$ coefficients now). Now $H^n(K; \mathbf{Z}) = \mathbf{Z}$, since $\Sigma^k f \sim 0$ where f is the attaching map $f: S^{n-1} \to L$ and $H^n(L; \mathbf{Z}) = 0$. Hence the map of $H^n(K; \mathbf{Z})$ into $H^n(K; \mathbf{Q})$ is a monomorphism. Since $p_s(\xi) = p_s(\gamma')$ in $H^n(K; \mathbf{Q})$ it follows that they are equal in $H^n(K; \mathbf{Z})$, so that $p_s(\xi)$ is divisible by $(2s - 1)!a_s$.

PROOF OF LEMMA 2.12. Recall that M is a closed π-manifold of dimension $4k - 1$, $T = \partial W$ is a homotopy sphere, W a parallelizable manifold of dimension $n = 4k$, $T \# M \equiv M$. We defined Q by taking connected sum along the boundary of $M \times I$ and W to get a manifold with boundary $M \cup (-(T \# M))$ and identifying M and $T \# M$ by the diffeomorphism. Hence W is a submanifold of Q and since W is parallelizable, the classifying map for $\tau(Q)$ factors through Q/W. Since M is a π-manifold and $\tau(Q)|M \times \frac{1}{2} = \tau(M) \oplus \varepsilon^1$, $\varepsilon^1 = $ trivial line bundle, it follows that $\tau(Q)|M \times \frac{1}{2}$ is trivial and the classifying map for $\tau(Q)$ factors through $Q/W \cup M \times \frac{1}{2} = (Q/W)/M \times \frac{1}{2}$. By (2.1) Q/W is a fibre bundle over S^1 with fibre M, and $M \times \frac{1}{2}$ is one of the fibres. It follows easily that $(Q/W)/M \times \frac{1}{2}$ is homeomorphic to $\Sigma(M^+)$, where $M^+ = M \cup $ (point).

Thus there is a bundle ξ over $\Sigma(M^+)$ such that $\tau(Q) = c^*(\xi)$ where $c\colon Q \to \Sigma(M^+)$ is the collapsing map.

Now Milnor and Spanier [14] showed that if M is a π-manifold, then the top dimensional homology of M (or M^+) is stably spherical. Let $M_0 = M^+ - \text{int}(e)$, e some $(n-1)$-cell in M, so that $M^+ = M_0 \cup_f e$, where $f\colon \dot{e} \to M_0$, the attaching map, is given by the inclusion. It follows that $\Sigma^k f \sim 0$ for some k. Further, $H^i(M_0) = 0$ for $i \geq n$. Let $K = \Sigma(M^+)$, $L = \Sigma(M_0) \subset K$, so that $K = L \cup_{f'} e'$, where $f' = $ suspension of f, e' is an n-cell. Since K is a suspension, all cup products are zero (which yields another proof of (2.7) for this case), so that all the hypotheses of (3.7) are satisfied for K, L, ξ etc. Hence $p_k(\xi)$, is divisible by $(2k-1)!a_k$ in $H^{4k}(\Sigma(M^+); \mathbf{Z})$ and thus $p_k(Q) = c^*p_k(\xi)$ is divisible by $(2k-1)!a_k$ in $H^{4k}(Q; \mathbf{Z})$.

CORNELL UNIVERSITY

REFERENCES

[1] J. F. ADAMS, On the groups J(X) I, *Topology 2* (1963), p. 181–195, and *II* to appear.

[2] M. F. ATIYAH and F. HIRZEBRUCH, Riemann-Roch theorems for differentiable manifolds, *Bull. of A.M.S.*, *65* ((1959), p. 276–281.

[3] A. BOREL and F. HIRZEBRUCH, Characteristic classes and homogeneous spaces, *Amer. J. Math.*, *80* (1958), p. 458–538; *81* (1959), p. 315–383) *82* (1960), p. 491–504.

[4] R. BOTT, The stable homotopy of the classical groups. *Ann. of Math.*, (2) *70* (1959), p. 313–337.

[5] W. BROWDER, On differential Hopf algebras, *Trans. A.M.S.*, *107* (1963), p. 153–176.

[6] J. EELLS and N. H. KUIPER, An invariant for certain smooth manifolds, *Annali di Math.*, *60* (1963), p. 93–110.

[7] P. J. HILTON, Homotopy theory and duality, mimeographed notes, Cornell University, 1959.

[8] F. HIRZEBRUCH, *Neue topologische Methoden in der algebraischen Geometrie*, Springer, 1956.

[9] M. KERVAIRE and J. MILNOR, Groups of homotopy spheres I, *Ann. of Math.*, (2) *77* (1963), p. 504–537, and II to appear.

[10] J. MILNOR and M. KERVAIRE, Bernoulli numbers, homotopy groups and a theorem of Rohlin, *Proc. Int. Congress of Math.*, Edinburgh, 1958.

[11] J. MILNOR, On manifolds homeomorphic to the 7-sphere, *Ann. of Math.*, *64* (1956), p. 399–405.

[12] ———, Differentiable manifolds which are homotopy spheres, mimeographed notes, Princeton, 1958.

[13] J. MILNOR and J. C. MOORE, On the structure of Hopf algebras, mimeographed notes, Princeton, 1958.

[14] J. MILNOR and E. SPANIER, Two remarks on fibre homotopy type, *Pacific J. Math.*, *10* (1960), p. 585–590.

[15] S. P. NOVIKOV, Diffeomorphisms of simply connected manifolds, *Soviet Math. (Doklady) A.M.S.*, *3* (1962), p. 540–543.

[16] ———, Homotopy equivalent smooth manifolds, I, *Izv. Akad. Nauk. S.S.S.R., Ser. Mat.*, *28* (1964), p. 365–474 (in Russian).

[17] S. SMALE, On the structure of manifolds, *Amer. J. Math.*, *84* (1962), p. 387–399.

[18] I. TAMURA, Sur les sommes connexes de certaines variétés differentiables, *Comptes Rendues Acad. des Sci. Paris*, *255* (1962), p. 3104–3106.

[19] C. T. C. WALL, The action of Γ_{2n} on $(n-1)$-connected $2n$-manifolds, *Proc. A.M.S.*, *13* (1962), p. 943–944.

Critical Submanifolds of the Classical Groups and Stiefel Manifolds[1]

THEODORE FRANKEL

---

1. Introduction

The Betti numbers of the classical groups, i.e., the rotation groups $SO(n) = R(n)$, the unitary groups $U(n)$, and the symplectic groups $Sp(n)$, were first determined by Pontrjagin in 1935 and many authors since have concerned themselves with the topology of these groups (see Samelson's expository article [3] for a detailed survey. We will also refer to this article rather than original papers written before 1952 in what follows). Bott, starting in 1953, has applied Morse theory and his own extension of this theory to the study of Lie groups and homogeneous spaces. He applies that part of Morse theory dealing with geodesics, i.e., he studies not a function on the group G but rather the "length function" on the loop space to G. It was our intention to see if Morse theory might not yield some other type of topological information when applied to the more elementary situation of a function defined directly on G.

In Part I we consider the trace function on a classical group, i.e., we take the usual matrix representation and consider the trace tr (or real part of the trace) of the representation.

We find (Lemma 3) that the critical manifolds are always Grassmannian (real $G_{n,k}$, complex $W_{n,k}$, or quaternionic $Q_{n,k}$) submanifolds of G. These submanifolds also arise in an independent fashion: the critical submanifolds are precisely the fixed points of the period 2 transformation sending $g \in G \to g^{-1}$ (Lemma 4). It is essentially this fact that allows us to apply P. A. Smith theory, in particular some results of E. E. Floyd, to show that no topologically "extraneous" critical manifolds have been introduced.

In Part II we generalize these results to obtain a similar picture for Stiefel manifolds. We wish to thank Bruno Harris for discussions of this Part.

[1] Work supported by the National Science Foundation.

PART I. THE CLASSICAL GROUPS

2. Gradient of the trace

Let $f(g) = Re\ tr(g)$. G is endowed with an essentially unique bi-invariant Riemannian metric. The differential df has as contravariant representative the tangent vector field grad f with respect to this metric.

Let T be any maximal torus in G (i.e., T is a maximal connected abelian subgroup of G). We claim

LEMMA 1.   *grad f is tangent to T at each point $h \in T$.*

PROOF. The proof to be given will also serve to introduce the principal concepts and notation to be used later.

We may assume grad $f \neq 0$ at h and therefore also in some neighbourhood of h in G. The intersection of this neighbourhood and the level set $f_h = \{g \in G | f(g) = f(h)\}$ is a submanifold of G of codimension 1 and grad f is orthogonal to this submanifold. Now the trace is a class function; $f(ghg^{-1}) = f(h)$ for all $g \in G$. Thus the set $M_h = \{ghg^{-1}\}$ is a subset of f_h. It is well known what the set M_h is: M_h is an imbedding of the manifold $G/C(h)$, where $C(h)$ is the centralizer of h, i.e., the subgroup of all elements of G commuting with h. To see this we note that we have an onto map $\bar{\rho}: G \to M_h$ defined by $\bar{\rho}(g) = ghg^{-1}$ and that for $c \in C(h)$ we have $\bar{\rho}(gc) = \bar{\rho}(g)$. Thus $\bar{\rho}$ defines a map $\rho: G/C(h) \to M_h$ which is easily seen to be $1 - 1$. Frequently we will write $G/C(h) = M_h$, identifying $G/C(h)$ with its image.

Now consider the case when h is a regular element of T, i.e., the identity component of $C(h)$ is exactly T. It is known that the regular elements are dense on T. The tangent space to M_h at h can be obtained as follows. Let m be that maximal subspace of the tangent space to G at the identity e that is orthogonal to T and let $X \in m$ be a vector. Let $g(t)$ be a 1-parameter subgroup of G tangent to X at e, i.e., $\dot{g}(0) = X$ where the dot denotes differentiation with respect to t. Finally let Adh be the adjoint action; $Adh(X) = hXh^{-1}$. Now $g(t)hg^{-1}(t)$ is a curve in M_h through h and its tangent vector there is

$$\dot{g}(0)h - h\dot{g}(0) = Xh - hX = [(1 - Adh)X]h.$$

Since $g \to hgh^{-1}$ is an isometry and leaves T pointwise fixed we have that $Adh: m \to m$. Since h is a regular element 1 is not a characteristic value of Adh on m and so $(1 - Adh): m \to m$ is a nonsingular linear transformation. Right translation by h is a nonsingular linear transformation: $m \to$ tangent subspace at h orthogonal to T at h. Thus the orthogonal complement to the tangent space to T at h is the tangent space to M_h

at h. Since grad f is orthogonal to M_h we have that grad f is tangent to T at each regular $h \in T$ and therefore at all $h \in T$.

We remark that the same proof shows that for any $h \in T$, the tangent space to $M_h = G/C(h)$ is the orthogonal complement to the tangent space to $C(h)$ at h.

A subgroup $H \subset G$ is of maximal rank if a maximal torus of H is also a maximal torus of G. We will need

LEMMA 2.   *If $H \subset G$ is connected and of maximal rank, then grad f is tangent to H.*

PROOF.   Let $x \in H$. Then x lies on a maximal torus T' of H which is then a maximal torus of G. By Lemma 1 grad f is then tangent to T'.

Lemma 2 will be applied to the special case $H =$ identity component of $C(h)$.

3. Critical points of the trace

Let T be a fixed maximal torus of G. Again since the trace is a class function we conclude that if grad $f = 0$ at some point $x \in G$ then grad $f = 0$ at gxg^{-1} for each $g \in G$. Thus if x is a critical point for f the submanifold M_x of conjugates of x is critical. Now it is well known that any $x \in G$ is conjugate to at least one $h \in T$; in the classical groups this is merely the principal axes theorem as we shall see below. Hence the critical set of f is the set of conjugates to the critical points on T. Since grad f is tangent to T *the critical points of f on T are the critical points of the restriction of f to the maximal torus.*

We use the following notation. $R(n)$ operates on euclidean n-space. We denote by $R(k) \times R(n - k)$ the subgroup of $R(n)$ consisting of all matrices.

$$\begin{pmatrix} R(k) & 0 \\ 0 & R(n - k) \end{pmatrix}$$

where $R(k)$ is the rotation group in k variables that leaves the last $(n - k)$ variables of n space fixed and where $R(n - k)$ is the rotation group in $(n - k)$ variables leaving the first k variables in n-space fixed. Further, we can consider $U(k) \times U(n - k)$ and $Sp(k) \times Sp(n - k)$, etc. Likewise we can consider more factors, for example $A_1(k_1) \times A_2(k_2) \times \cdots + A_s(k_s)$ where $k_1 + \cdots + k_s = n$. We let $I(r)$ be the identity $r \times r$ matrix, 1 is the 1×1 identity matrix, $e^{i\theta}$ is a 1×1 matrix and $R_2(\theta)$ is the 2×2 rotation matrix

$$R_2(\theta) = \begin{pmatrix} \cos\theta & -\sin\theta \\ \sin\theta & \cos\theta \end{pmatrix}$$

Then the maximal tori can be chosen as the following (recalling that $Sp(n) \subset U(2n)$, see Case IV below)

$$
\begin{cases}
R(2m+1): T = \{1 \times R_2(\theta_1) \times \cdots \times R_2(\theta_m)\} \\
\quad R(2m): T = \{R_2(\theta_1) \times \cdots \times R_2(\theta_m)\} \\
\quad U(n): T = \{e^{i\theta_1} \times e^{i\theta_2} \times \cdots \times e^{i\theta_n}\} \\
\quad Sp(n): T = \{e^{i\theta_1} \times e^{-i\theta_2} \times \cdots \times e^{i\theta_n} \times e^{-i\theta_n}\}
\end{cases}
$$

(the unitary and symplectic tori are thus diagonal matrix groups).

While all the groups are handled in the same manner we treat them separately for notational convenience. We do $R(2m+1)$ in detail and indicate any differences that arise in the other cases.

Case I; **$R(2m+1)$**. We need to consider first the function $f = $ trace restricted to the maximal torus $T = \{1 \times R_2(\theta_1) \times \cdots \times R_2(\theta_m)\}$. Then $f(\theta) = 1 + 2\sum_{i=1}^{m} \cos \theta_i$, $df = -2\sum_{i=1}^{m} \sin \theta_i \, d\theta_i$ and so $\theta = (\theta_1, \ldots, \theta_m)$ is critical if and only if $\theta_i = 0$ or π, all i. Let σ be such a critical point; then σ is of the form

$$
\sigma = \begin{pmatrix}
1 & & & & & \\
& \pm\begin{pmatrix} 1 & 0 \\ 0 & 1 \end{pmatrix} & & & 0 & \\
& & \cdot & & & \\
& & & \cdot & & \\
& 0 & & & \cdot & \\
& & & & & \pm\begin{pmatrix} 1 & 0 \\ 0 & 1 \end{pmatrix}
\end{pmatrix}
$$

Any two such σ with the same number of negative signs are conjugate. Since each M_σ is connected each M_σ will pass through all conjugates of σ. Thus to discuss the critical manifolds we need only take one σ from each conjugacy class, i.e., we may assume that σ is of the form

$$
\sigma = I(2k+1) \times -I(r)
$$

where $r = 2(m-k)$ and $-I(r)$ is the negative identity $r \times r$ matrix. The centralizer of such a σ consists of the subgroup $R(2k+1) \times R(r)$ and the disjoint homeomorphic copy $R^-(2k+1) \times R^-(r)$, where $R^-(N)$ is the set of *improper* orthogonal $N \times N$ matrices. Thus $C(\sigma)$ is $R(2m+1) \cap [O(2k+1) \times O(r)]$ and so topologically

$$
M_\sigma = G/C(\sigma) = \frac{R(2m+1)}{R(2m+1) \cap [O(2k+1) \times O(r)]} = G_{2m+1, 2k+1}
$$

the classical Grassmann manifold of unoriented $(2k + 1)$ planes in euclidean $(2m + 1)$ space (beware!, there is no standardized notation for these manifolds).

We next need to discuss the degeneracy and indices of the critical manifolds. The theory of degenerate critical points, as worked out in Morse [2], has been adapted by Bott to cover especially the case of what he calls nondegenerate critical manifolds. We refer the reader to [1] for a brief discussion of this case.

Let H_f be the Hessian quadratic form for f at a critical point σ of G; if X is a tangent vector at σ then $H_f(X) = D_X D_X(f)$ where D_X is the directional derivative operator for X. Thus in local coordinates

$$D_X = \Sigma_i X^i (\partial/\partial x^i) \quad \text{and} \quad H_f(X) = \Sigma_{i,j} (\partial^2 f/\partial x^i \partial x^j)_\sigma X^i X^j.$$

The *index* λ of σ is defined to be the dimension of the largest subspace of the tangent space at σ on which H_f is negative definite. The critical *submanifold* M_σ is said to be *nondegenerate* if the nullspace of H_f coincides with the tangent space to M_σ at each of its points σ (of course the nullspace always contains this tangent space). If the critical manifold is connected (as it is in our case) nondegeneracy implies that the index λ of σ is independent of σ on M_σ; in this case λ is also called the index of the critical manifold M_σ. Roughly speaking the index gives the number of directions at σ for which the function is decreasing.

As we have seen the identity component of $C(\sigma)$ consists of the subgroup $R(2k + 1) \times R(r)$, with $r = 2(m - k)$. Let $C^-(\sigma)$ be the subgroup $C^-(\sigma) = R(2k + 1) \times I(r)$ of $C(\sigma)$ and let $\sigma C^-(\sigma)$ be the left translate $\sigma C^-(\sigma) = R(2k + 1) \times -I(r)$. We have seen in Lemma 2 that grad f is tangent to $C(\sigma)$ and we now claim that grad f is also tangent to $\sigma C^-(\sigma)$. To see this we need only show that the directional derivative of f at each point of $\sigma C^-(\sigma)$ in each direction orthogonal to $\sigma C^-(\sigma)$ is zero. If $\bar{g}(t)$ is a 1-parameter subgroup of $C(\sigma)$ orthogonal to $C^-(\sigma)$ at e, then $\bar{g}(t)$ is of the form $I(2k + 1) \times g(t)$. By translation to the point $A(k + 1) \times -I(r)$, where $A(k + 1)$ is a constant in $R(k + 1)$, we get a curve

$$\mathscr{C}(t) = A(k + 1) \times -g(t)$$

orthogonal to $\sigma C^-(\sigma)$ at this point. Then we have

$$f(\mathscr{C}(t)) = \text{tr } A(k + 1) - \text{tr } g(t)$$

and so

$$\frac{df(\mathscr{C}(0))}{dt} = - \text{tr } \dot{g}(0) = 0$$

since $\dot{g}(0)$, the infinitesimal generator of $g(t)$, is a skew symmetric matrix. Hence grad f is tangent to $\sigma C^-(\sigma)$ as desired.

We next claim that f, when restricted to $\sigma C^-(\sigma)$ has a nondegenerate absolute maximum at σ. To see this let $c^-(t)$ be a 1-parameter subgroup of $C^-(\sigma)$; $c^-(t)$ is then of the form $c(t) \times I(r)$. Then $\sigma c^-(t)$ is a curve tangent to $\sigma C^-(\sigma)$ with $\sigma c^-(0) = \sigma$. If $h \in C^-(\sigma)$ then $h\sigma c^-(t)h^{-1} = \sigma hc^-(t)h^{-1}$. By a proper choice of h we can assume that

$$hc^-(t)h^{-1} = 1 \times R_2(t\alpha_1) \times \cdots \times R_2(t\alpha_k) \times I(r)$$

where of course not all of the α's are 0. Then

$$\sigma hc^-(t)h^{-1} = 1 + R_2(t\alpha_1) \times \cdots \times R_2(t\alpha_k) \times -I(r)$$

and

$$tr\ \sigma c^-(t) = 1 + 2\sum_{i=1}^{k} \cos(t\alpha_i) - r$$
$$\leq tr\ \sigma$$

with equality only at σ. Further

$$\frac{d^2}{dt^2}\ tr\ \sigma c^-(0) = -2\sum_{i=1}^{k}\alpha_i^2$$

which shows that f has a nondegenerate absolute maximum at σ on $\sigma C^-(\sigma)$. In the language of differential equations we have shown that $\sigma C^-(\sigma)$ is the *stable manifold* in $C(\sigma)$ of the critical point σ (i.e., $\sigma C^-(\sigma)$ is the submanifold of $C(\sigma)$ formed by all trajectories of grad f that end at σ).

Likewise f has at σ a nondegenerate absolute minimum on $I(2k+1) \times R(r)$, the unstable manifold in $C(\sigma)$ for the critical point σ.

M_σ is a manifold through σ, orthogonal to $C(\sigma)$ at σ and of complementary dimension to $C(\sigma)$ and of course f is constant on M_σ. Hence, in summary we have proved the following

LEMMA 3. *When* $\sigma = I(2k+1) \times -I(r)$, *with* $r = 2(m-k)$, $M_\sigma = G_{2m+1,2k+1}$ *is the nondegenerate critical manifold through* σ *for the trace function. The submanifold* $R(2k+1) \times -I(r)$ *is the stable manifold for* σ *and so the tangent space to* $R(2k+1) \times -I(r)$ *at* σ *is the maximal subspace on which the Hessian is negative definite. Thus the index of* M_σ *is*

$$\dim R(2k+1) \times -I(r) = k(2k+1).$$

Suppose now that we consider another point $\tau = g\sigma g^{-1}$ in M_σ. The stable manifold for τ is clearly $g\sigma C^-(\sigma)g^{-1}$. Of course the representation for τ is not unique, but if $\tau = \bar{g}\sigma\bar{g}^{-1}$ is another representation then $\bar{g} = gc$ for some $c \in C(\sigma)$. The two homeomorphisms $x \to gxg^{-1}$ and $x \to \bar{g}x\bar{g}^{-1}$ sending $\sigma C^-(\sigma)$ onto the stable manifold of τ each induce an orientation in this stable manifold by means of a fixed orientation in $\sigma C^-(\sigma)$. It is clear that these orientations would agree if $C(\sigma)$ were connected; however, we have seen in the first paragraph of Case I that if $\sigma \neq e$ then $C(\sigma)$ consists of two disjoint pieces. In the terminology of Bott the negative normal bundle to M_σ is not necessarily orientable. It is for this reason that in discussing homology we must use the integers mod 2, Z_2, for coefficient field in the case of the rotation groups.

We remark that the minimum manifold for the trace on $R(2m+1)$ is the Grassmann $G_{2m+1,1}$ of unoriented lines in $2m+1$ space, that is the real projective $2m$-space $P_{2m}(R)$.

As a concrete example consider the usual group $R(3)$ of rotations in 3-space, represented as the solid ball in 3-space of radius π, with boundary points of the ball identified antipodally ($R(3)$ is thus topologically the real projective space $P_3(R)$). For maximal abelian subgroup take the 1-parameter subgroup of rotations about the x-axis

$$T = \begin{pmatrix} 1 & 0 & 0 \\ 0 & \cos\theta & -\sin\theta \\ 0 & \sin\theta & \cos\theta \end{pmatrix}$$

The critical points of the trace on T are the identity e and the diagonal matrix σ with entries $(1, -1, -1)$. The conjugates of e reduce to e itself while the conjugates of σ form the surface of the ball of radius π, which is the real projective plane. The trace thus has an isolated maximum at the origin and a projective plane of minima at distance π. Since the index of the minimum set is 0 there are here no problems with the negative normal bundle. Problems would arise, however, in the next group $R(5)$.

Case II; $R(2m)$. The procedure here is exactly the same as in $R(2m+1)$. Now, however, the minimum manifold reduces to the point $-e$ rather than a projective space. If $\sigma = I(2k) \times -I(2r)$, then $M_\sigma = G_{2m,2k}$ and the index of M_σ is dim $R(2k) \times -I(2r) = k(2k-1)$.

Case III; $U(n)$. This is the simplest case. The torus consists of the diagonal matrices $\{e^{i\theta_1} \times \cdots \times e^{i\theta_n}\}$ and the critical σ are of the form $(\pm 1) \times (\pm 1) \times \cdots \times (\pm 1)$. Again two σ's with the same number of negative signs are conjugate. If we take a representative σ of the form $\sigma = I(k) \times -I(n-k)$ then $C(\sigma) = U(k) \times U(n-k)$ and so

$$M_\sigma = G/C(\sigma) = \frac{U(n)}{U(k) \times U(n-k)} = W_{n,k}$$

the classical Grassmann manifold of complex k-planes in complex n-space. The stable manifold of σ is $U(k) \times -I(n-k)$ whose dimension, the index of M_σ, is k^2. Since $C(\sigma)$ is connected the stable manifolds can be oriented coherently and hence the negative normal bundles are orientable.

Case IV; $Sp(n)$. The symplectic group $Sp(n)$ is the group of those unitary matrices acting on complex $2n$ space and leave the exterior form $z_1 \wedge z_2 + \cdots + z_{2n-1} \wedge z_{2n}$ invariant. As stated above the maximal torus consists of all diagonal matrices of the form $e^{i\theta_1} \times e^{-i\theta_1} \times \cdots \times e^{i\theta_n} \times e^{-i\theta_n}$. Again the critical points are given by $\theta_i = 0$ or π and the (-1)'s now occur in pairs. If σ is $I(2k) \times -I(2(n-k))$ then

$$C(\sigma) = Sp(k) \times Sp(n-k)$$

and

$$M_\sigma = G/C(\sigma) = \frac{Sp(n)}{Sp(k) \times Sp(n-k)} = Q_{n,k}$$

the Grassmann manifold of quaternionic k-planes in quaternionic n-space. Again $C(\sigma)$ is connected, the negative normal bundles are orientable and the index of $M_\sigma = \dim Sp(k) \times -I(2n-k)) = k(2k+1)$.

4. The Morse–Bott inequalities

The Morse inequalities for functions with nondegenerate critical *points* has been extended by Bott to the case of functions with non-degenerate critical *manifolds* as follows. Let M be a compact manifold and f a real valued smooth function on M having only nondegenerate critical manifolds, as defined in Case I. Let $\{M_\alpha\}$ be the set of critical manifolds and let $\lambda_\alpha = $ index of M_α. For any space N let $b_i(N; K) = \dim H_i(N; K)$ be the ith Betti number of N using coefficient field K (if K is not written we assume the field to be the real numbers $K = R$). Then if the negative normal bundles are orientable we have

$$b_i(M; K) \leq \Sigma_\alpha b_{i-\lambda_\alpha}(M_\alpha; K).$$

If, however, the bundles are not known to be orientable we may only use Z_2 for coefficients in the above.

From the above Morse–Bott inequalities and from Lemma 3 and its unitary and symplectic analogues we therefore get (where $G_{n,0} = W_{n,0} = Q_{n,0} = $ point)

$$b_i(R(2m+1); Z_2) \leq \sum_{k=0}^{m} b_{i-k(2k+1)}(G_{2m+1,2k+1}; Z_2)$$

(1)

$$b_i(R(2m); Z_2) \leq \sum_{k=0}^{m} b_{i-k(2k-1)}(G_{2m,2k}; Z_2)$$

$$b_i(U(n); K) \leq \sum_{k=0}^{n} b_{i-k^2}(W_{n,k}; K)$$

$$b_i(Sp(n); K) \leq \sum_{k=0}^{n} b_{i-k(2k+1)}(Q_{n,k}; K)$$

where K is any coefficient field.

5. Application of fixed point theory

In this concluding section we show that the Morse-Bott inequalities
(1) are in fact equalities. We will express this result in terms of Poincaré
polynomials $P_K(M;t) = \Sigma_i b_i(M;K)t^i$; again if K is omitted the coefficient field is the reals R.

THEOREM 1. $U(n)$ and $Sp(n)$ have no torsion. The Poincaré polynomials
of the classical groups are related to those of the Grassmannians as follows:

$$
\begin{cases}
P_{Z_2}(R(2m+1);t) = \sum_{k=0}^{m} t^{k(2k+1)} P_{Z_2}(G_{2m+1,2k+1};t) \\[2mm]
P_{Z_2}(R(2m);t) = \sum_{k=0}^{m} t^{k(2k-1)} P_{Z_2}(G_{2m,2k};t) \\[2mm]
P(U(n);t) = \sum_{k=0}^{n} t^{k^2} P(W_{n,k};t) \\[2mm]
P(Sp(n);t) = \sum_{k=0}^{n} t^{k(2k+1)} P(Q_{n,k};t)
\end{cases}
$$

PROOF.   The absence of torsion in $U(n)$ and $Sp(n)$ was shown by
Pontrjagin; it will follow as soon as we show equality in (1) for $K = Z_p$,
p prime, and for $K = R$.

For the proof we invoke the Smith theory of fixed points of periodic
transformations. In particular we will use the following theorems of
E. E. Floyd (the two results below are actually special cases of a result
of Floyd; we do not state the results in any more generality than we need
here and we refer the reader to the Princeton seminar [4] for details of
the theory of fixed points).

THEOREM A.   If a transformation of period 2 acts on a compact manifold
M, if F is the fixed set, then

$$\Sigma_i b_i(F;Z_2) \leq \Sigma_i b_i(M;Z_2).$$

THEOREM B.   If a toral group operates on a compact manifold M and
if F is the fixed set (i.e., points fixed under each transformation of the group),
then

$$\Sigma_i b_i(F;K) \leq \Sigma_i b_i(M;K)$$

where K either $= R$ or Z_p where p is prime.

We apply these results as follows. On G we consider the period 2 transformation: $g \to g^{-1}$. Then the fixed set F is the collection of all elements
$g \in G$ of order 2, i.e., $g^2 = e$. It is clear that $g^2 = e$ if and only if $(hgh^{-1})^2 = e$,
i.e., the fixed set elements occur in entire conjugacy classes. Now the
elements of order 2 on the maximal torus T are precisely the elements
where $\theta_i = 0$ or π. Hence

LEMMA 4. *The fixed points of the inverse map $g \to g^{-1}$ are precisely the critical points of the function $f(g) = \operatorname{Re} tr(g)$.*

The combination of the Floyd inequalities of Theorem A and the opposed Morse–Bott inequalities (1) shows that the inequalities (1) are in fact equalities for coefficient field Z_2. Thus we have proved our Theorem for the case of the rotation groups.

The remaining cases $U(n)$ and $Sp(n)$ seem to require the following variation of the above argument.

We let the maximal torus T act on G by the adjoint action; $t \in T : g \to tgt^{-1}$. A point g is fixed under T if and only if g commutes with each $t \in T$, i.e., if and only if $g \in T$.[2] Hence the fixed set of $AdT : G \to G$ is T itself. From Floyd's Theorem B

$$(2) \qquad 2^n = \Sigma_i b_i(T; K) \leq \Sigma_i b_i(G; K)$$

where $n = \dim T$ and $K = R$ or Z_p, p prime.

Now let $h(t)$ be a 1-parameter subgroup of T that lies dense on T. We let $h(t)$ act again on G via the adjoint action and it is clear that T again is the fixed set of this action. We note that

$$Adjoint\ h(t) \colon M_\sigma \to M_\sigma$$

and the fixed points on M_σ are the intersection points of M_σ with T. We thus have a 1-parameter group of motions of M_σ having as fixed points the finite set of conjugates of σ on T. A well-known theorem of Weil and Hopf-Samelson (see [3]) says then that $\chi(M_\sigma) =$ number of conjugates of σ on T, where $\chi(M_\sigma)$, the Euler characteristic of M_σ, is $\Sigma_i(-1)^i b_i(M_\sigma)$. We then have that

$$\chi(\Sigma_\sigma M_\sigma) = 2^n$$

where we sum over all critical $\sigma \in T$ and use the fact that there are precisely 2^n such critical σ on T.

For $G = U(n)$ or $Sp(n)$ and for σ critical each M_σ is either of the form $W_{n,k}$ or $Q_{n,k}$ and it is well known (see [5]) that both types of manifolds are free of torsion and have odd Betti numbers 0. Hence we have

$$2^n = \chi(\Sigma_\sigma M_\sigma) = \Sigma_i b_i(\Sigma_\sigma M_\sigma) :$$
$$= \Sigma_i b_i(\Sigma_\sigma M_\sigma; K)$$

where K is any coefficient field. Combining this with (2) we get

$$\Sigma_i b_i(\Sigma_\sigma M_\sigma; K) \leq \Sigma_i b_i(G; K)$$

[2] See H. Hopf, Uber den Rang geschlossener Lie'scher Gruppen, *Comm. Math. Helv.*, **13** (1941), pp. 119–143.

for $G = U(n)$ or $Sp(n)$ and $K = R$ or Z_p, p prime. This last inequality yields with the opposing inequalities (1) the proof of Theorem 1.

PART II. THE STIEFEL MANIFOLDS

In this second part we indicate briefly, without complete proofs, how an analogous procedure works for the real, complex and quaternionic Stiefel manifolds, $V_{n,k}$, $U_{n,k}$, and $S_{n,k}$, of orthonormal k-frames in n-space (R^n, C^n, or Q^n). As coset spaces

$$V_{n,k} = \frac{O(n)}{I(k) \times O(n-k)}, \quad U_{n,k} = \frac{U(n)}{I(k) \times U(n-k)},$$

$$S_{n,k} = \frac{Sp(n)}{I(k) \times Sp(n-k)}$$

we write these three cases uniformly as G/H.

We define a real valued function on G/H as follows. Fix once and for all a k-frame $e_1, \ldots, e_k$ in n-space and let $v_1, \ldots, v_k$ be a variable k-frame. Define $f: G/H \to R$ by

$$f(v_1 \cdots v_k) = Re \sum_{\alpha=1}^{k} \langle v_\alpha, e_\alpha \rangle$$

where $\langle , \rangle$ denotes the real, hermitian, or symplectic scalar product in n-space (we refer the reader to Chevalley's *Theory of Lie Groups*). In terms of matrices, if we complete $e_1, \ldots, e_k$ to a full basis $e_1, \ldots, e_n$ of n-space, and complete $v_1, \ldots, v_k$ to $v_1, \ldots, v_n$, then $v_i = \sum_{j=1}^{n} g_{ji} e_j$ and

$$f(v_1 \cdots v_k) = Re \sum_{\alpha=1}^{k} g_{\alpha\alpha}$$

LEMMA 5. *If the frame $v_1, \ldots, v_k$ is a critical point for f, then the $v_1, \ldots, v_k$ all lie in the k-plane spanned by $e_1, \ldots, e_k$.*

PROOF. For a critical $v_1, \ldots, v_k$ we have the following two possibilities[3] (we let $w_1 \wedge \cdots \wedge w_k$ denote the plane spanned by $w_1, \ldots, w_k$).

(i) $e_\alpha \in (v_1 \wedge v_2 \wedge \cdots \wedge \hat{v}_\alpha \wedge \cdots \wedge v_k)^\perp$. Since v_α is also in this plane, we may rotate v_α in the plane $v_\alpha \wedge e_\alpha$ without effecting $v_1, \ldots, \hat{v}_\alpha, \ldots, v_k$. It is clear that the only critical positions for v_α are $v_\alpha = \pm e_\alpha$ and thus $e_\alpha \in (v_1 \wedge \cdots \wedge v_k)$.

(ii) $e_\alpha \notin (v_1 \wedge v_2 \wedge \cdots \wedge \hat{v}_\alpha \wedge \cdots \wedge v_k)^\perp$. Then either $e_\alpha \in (v_1 \wedge$

---

[3] In the following, $\perp$ denotes the orthocomplement and the roof $\wedge$ denotes omission.

$\cdots \wedge \hat{v}_\alpha \wedge \cdots \wedge v_k$) or not. In the first instance $e_\alpha \in (v_1 \wedge \cdots \wedge v_k)$. In the second we have that e_α is not orthogonal to $(v_1 \wedge \cdots \wedge \hat{v}_\alpha \wedge \cdots \wedge v_k)^\perp$. By a rotation of v_α in $(v_1 \wedge \cdots \wedge \hat{v}_\alpha \wedge \cdots \wedge v_k)^\perp$ we see that in order for $v_1, \ldots, v_k$ to be critical, we must have that v_α lies along $\pm$ projection of e_α into $(v_1 \wedge \cdots \wedge \hat{v}_\alpha \wedge \cdots \wedge v_k).^\perp$ In other words, we must have

$$v_\alpha = \pm \kappa_\alpha^{-1}(e_\alpha - \sum_{\beta \neq \alpha}^k \langle e_\alpha, v_\beta \rangle v_\beta)$$

where

$$k_\alpha = \left\| e_\alpha - \sum_{\beta \neq \alpha}^k \langle e_\alpha, v_\beta \rangle v_\beta \right\| \neq 0.$$

Hence,

$$e_\alpha = \pm(\kappa_\alpha v_\alpha + \sum_{\beta \neq \alpha}^k \langle e_\alpha, v_\beta \rangle v_\beta)$$

Thus in both cases (i) and (ii) we have that $e_\alpha \in (v_1 \wedge \cdots \wedge v_k)$ for all $\alpha = 1, \ldots, k$, as was desired.

We conclude that the critical points of f on G/H are among the critical points of the function $f_{\mathscr{E}} = f_{|\mathscr{E}}$, where by

DEFINITION. $\mathscr{E}$ is the submanifold of G/H consisting of all frames $v_1, \ldots, v_k$ where $v_\alpha \in (e_1 \wedge \cdots \wedge e_k)$, $\alpha = 1, \ldots, k$.

We shall see in Lemma 6 below that f and $f_{\mathscr{E}}$ have precisely the same critical points.

6. Critical points of $f_{\mathscr{E}}$

When considering frames $v_1, \ldots, v_k$ that lie in the k-plane $e_1 \wedge \cdots \wedge e_k$, we have $v_\alpha = \sum_{\beta=1}^k P_{\beta\alpha} e_\beta$ where the matrix P is in $O(k)$ or $U(k)$ or $Sp(k)$. The function $f_{\mathscr{E}}$ is then

$$f_{\mathscr{E}}(v_1, \ldots, v_k) = Re\ tr\ P = Re \sum_{\alpha=1}^k P_{\alpha\alpha}$$

In Part I of this paper we discussed the critical points of this $f_{\mathscr{E}}$ in the cases $P \in R(k)$, $U(k)$, and $Sp(k)$. In each case the critical submanifolds were Grassmannians. Hence, we have already completely analysed the critical set of $f_{\mathscr{E}}$ in the cases $U(k)$ or $Sp(k)$ but we have only found the critical set for the case $O(k)$ when $f_{\mathscr{E}}$ is restricted to the proper orthogonal matrices $R(k)$. To find the critical points of $f_{\mathscr{E}}$ on $R^-(k)$, the set of improper orthogonal matrices, we use the fact that any matrix $g \in R^-(k)$ is conjugate in $O(k)$ to a matrix of the form

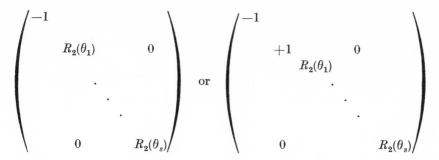

depending on whether $k = 2s + 1$ or $k = 2s + 2$. The set of all such matrices forms a submanifold of $R^-(k)$ and the critical points of $f_{\mathscr{E}}$ restricted to this submanifold are precisely the diagonal matrices with entries ± 1, the number of (-1)'s occurring being odd.

One then shows by an argument similar to Lemma 1 of Part I that such critical points of $f_{\mathscr{E}}$ restricted to the above submanifold are indeed critical points of $f_{\mathscr{E}}$ on $R^-(k)$ (i.e., one shows grad $f_{\mathscr{E}}$ is tangent to the above submanifold). Conjugation by $O(k)$ gives for the critical submanifolds of $R^-(k)$ the manifolds

$$\frac{O(k)}{O(\alpha) \times O(k - \alpha)} = G_{k,\alpha}$$

where α is always odd. Thus the critical manifolds of $f_{\mathscr{E}}$ in all of $O(k)$ are *all* of the Grassmannians $G_{k,\alpha}$, $\alpha = 0, 1, \ldots, k$.

For example, on $O(3)$ we have an isolated maximum at e, a projective plane of relative maxima, index 1, passing through diag. $(-1, +1, +1)$, a projective plane of relative minima passing through diag. $(-1, -1, +1)$, and an absolute minimum point diag. $(-1, -1, -1)$.

Since again the critical points on $O(k)$ are precisely the matrices of order 2, we again have that the Morse inequalities are equalities (coefficient field Z_2).

7. Critical points of f

In §6 we found all critical points of $f_{\mathscr{E}}$, the restriction of f to the submanifold $\mathscr{E}$ of all frames in $e_1 \wedge \cdots \wedge e_k$. Further, the critical points of f are among those of $f_{\mathscr{E}}$ (Lemma 5).

LEMMA 6. *The critical points of f are precisely those of $f_{\mathscr{E}}$.*

PROOF. We indicate briefly the proof for $V_{n,k}$.

$$O(k) = O(k) \times I(n - k) \subset O(n)$$

acts on $V_{n,k} = O_n/I_k \times O(n-k)$ as follows; if $\underline{v} = gO(n-k)$ is a left coset and if $\rho \in O(k) \times I(n-k)$, then define $\rho(\underline{v}) = (\rho g \rho^{-1})O(n-k)$. Thus if

$$g = \begin{pmatrix} A & B \\ C & D \end{pmatrix}, \qquad \rho = \begin{pmatrix} R_k & 0 \\ 0 & I_{n-k} \end{pmatrix},$$

then

$$\rho g \rho^{-1} = \begin{pmatrix} R_k A R_k^{-1} & R_k B \\ C R_k^{-1} & D \end{pmatrix}$$

One then sees that ρ defines a diffeomorphism $\rho : V_{n,k} \to V_{n,k}$ and that $f(\underline{v}) = \operatorname{tr} A = \operatorname{tr} R_k A R_k^{-1} = f(\rho(\underline{v}))$.

Now the critical frames $v_1 \cdots v_k$ of $f_{\mathscr{g}}$ are the frames $\pm e_1, \ldots, \pm e_k$ and their orbits under the above conjugation action of $O(k)$. This in essence was derived in Part I and §6 of Part II. It follows that if all the frames $\pm e_1, \ldots, \pm e_k$ are critical for f in $V_{n,k}$, then all the critical frames for $f_{\mathscr{g}}$ in $\mathscr{E}$ are critical for f.

If then $g = \operatorname{diag.}(\pm 1, \ldots, \pm 1)$ is a $n \times n$ matrix, i.e., $g_{ij} = \varepsilon_i \delta_{ij}$, $\varepsilon_i = \pm 1$, let $h(t)$ be an arbitrary 1-parameter subgroup of $R(n)$. Then for the function

$$f(t) = \sum_{\alpha=1}^{k} (h(t)g)_{\alpha\alpha} = \sum_{\alpha=1}^{k} \{ \sum_{j=1}^{n} h_{\alpha j}(t) g_{j\alpha} \}$$

we have

$$(0)\dot{f} = \sum_{\alpha=1}^{k} \sum_{j=1}^{n} \dot{h}_{\alpha j}(0) g_{j\alpha} = \sum_{\alpha=1}^{k} \sum_{j=1}^{n} \dot{h}_{\alpha j}(0) \varepsilon_j \delta_{j\alpha}$$

$$= \sum_{\alpha=1}^{k} \dot{h}_{\alpha\alpha}(0) \varepsilon_\alpha = 0$$

since $\dot{h}(0)$ is skew symmetric. Hence, $\pm e_1, \ldots, \pm e_k$ is indeed critical for f. Summarizing

COROLLARY. *The critical frames in $V_{n,k}$ (resp. $U_{n,k}$, $S_{n,k}$) are the conjugates under the action of $O(k)$ (resp. $U(k)$, $Sp(k)$) of the frames $v_\alpha = \pm e_\alpha$, $\alpha = 1, \ldots, k$. The critical submanifolds are thus precisely the Grassmannians $G_{k,r}$ (resp. $W_{k,r}$, $Q_{k,r}$) where $r \leq k$.*

8. The Morse structure of the Stiefel manifolds

From the previous corollary it follows that the index of a critical manifold can be determined at a frame of the form $v_\alpha = \pm e_\alpha$, $\alpha = 1$, ..., k.

Consider in $V_{n,k}$, for example, the critical frame $v_\alpha = -e_\alpha$, $\alpha \leq r$,

$v_\beta = +e_\beta$, $r < \beta \le k$. If we complete $e_1 \cdots e_k$ to a basis $e_1 \cdots e_n$ and if we look at the set of $(k-r)$-frames in the space spanned by e_{r+1}, $e_{r+2}, \ldots, e_n$, we see that the critical frame $v_{r+1} = e_{r+1}, \ldots, v_k = e_k$ gives a nondegenerate absolute maximum for the function

$$f' = \sum_{\beta=r+1}^{k} \langle v_\beta, e_\beta \rangle$$

This means that by keeping $v_1 = -e_1, \ldots, v_r = -e_r$ fixed and by varying the frame $v_{r+1} = e_r, \ldots, v_k = e_k$ in the space $V_{n-r,k-r}$ of all $(k-r)$-frames in $e_{r+1} \wedge \cdots \wedge e_n$, we get a variation of $v_1, \ldots, v_k$ on which the function f has a nondegenerate absolute maximum at $-e_1, \ldots, -e_r$, $+e_{r+1}, \ldots, +e_k$. Similarly, varying $v_1, \ldots, v_r$ in $e_1 \wedge \cdots \wedge e_r \wedge e_{k+1} \wedge \cdots \wedge e_n$, we get a variation space $V_{n-k+r,r}$ on which the function f has a nondegenerate absolute minimum at $-e_1, \ldots, -e_r, +e_{r+1}, \ldots, +e_k$. The critical manifold through $-e_1, \ldots, -e_r, e_{r+1}, \ldots, e_k$ is a $G_{k,r}$ and a computation shows

$$\dim G_{k,r} + \dim V_{n-r,k-r} + \dim V_{n-k+r,r} = \dim V_{n,k}$$

and so $G_{k,r}$ is a nondegenerate critical manifold of f with index $\lambda = \dim V_{n-r,k-r}$. Hence, we have proven

THEOREM 2.   *The critical set on $V_{n,k}$ (resp. $U_{n,k}$, $S_{n,k}$) for the function* $f(v_1, \ldots, v_k) = Re \sum_{\alpha=1}^{k} \langle v_\alpha, e_\alpha \rangle$ *consists of a single Grassmann manifold $G_{k,r}$ (resp. $W_{k,r}$, $Q_{k,r}$) for each r, $0 \le r \le k$. The index of $G_{k,r}$ (resp. $W_{k,r}$, $Q_{k,r}$) is precisely $\dim V_{n-r,k-r}$ (resp. $U_{n-r,k-r}$, $S_{n-r,k-r}$) and the critical set is nondegenerate.*

The negative normal bundle (see [1]) to $G_{k,r}$ at a point $v_1, \ldots, v_k$ of $G_{k,r}$ can be obtained from the negative normal bundle at $-e_1, \ldots, -e_r$, $+e_{r+1}, \ldots, e_k$ by conjugation with $O(k)$. Two conjugations giving the same frame differ by conjugation by an element in the centralizer of diag. $(-1, \ldots, -1, +1, \ldots, +1)$, i.e., by an element in $O(r) \times O(k-r)$. Since this last subgroup of $O(k)$ is not connected, we cannot claim that the negative normal bundle is orientable and Z_2 must be used in the resulting Morse inequalities. However, $U(r) \times U(k-r)$ and $Sp(r) \times Sp(k-r)$ are connected and so any field can be used as coefficient field in the $U_{n,k}$ and $S_{n,k}$ cases. Further,

THEOREM 3.   *The Morse inequalities that result from the situation of Theorem 2 (see §4 of Part I) are in fact equalities (using Z_2 coefficients for $V_{n,k}$ and Z for $U_{n,k}$ and $S_{n,k}$).*

PROOF.   Construct a reflection (in case $V_{n,k}$) or a suitable circle group of rotations (in cases $U_{n,k}$ and $S_{n,k}$) of n-space having $e_1 \wedge \cdots \wedge e_k$ as permanent fixed set. The induced action on frames has a fixed set of frames $\mathscr{E}$ in $e_1 \wedge \cdots \wedge e_k$. Hence, by Floyd's theorems (see §5, Part I) the total Betti number $\Sigma b_i(V_{n,k})$ of $V_{n,k}$ (or $U_{n,k}$ or $S_{n,k}$) is greater or equal to that of $\mathscr{E}$. One repeats then the argument of §5, Part I to show the total Betti number of $\mathscr{E}$ dominates that of the set of critical frames.

COROLLARY. $U_{n,k}$ and $S_{n,k}$ have no torsion.

PROOF. This follows since $W_{k,r}$ and $Q_{k,r}$ are torsion free.

9. Cells of low dimension

In each of the cases $V_{n,k}$, $U_{n,k}$, $S_{n,k}$ we have that the absolute minimum manifold reduces to a single point $v_\alpha = -e_\alpha$, $\alpha = 1, \ldots, k$ (this is $G_{k,k}$ or $W_{k,k}$ or $Q_{k,k}$). The next critical manifold of smallest index is a projective space $P_{k-1}(R) = G_{k,k-1}$, or $P_{k-1}(C) = W_{k,k-1}$ or $P_{k-1}(Q) = Q_{k,k-1}$ passing through the frame $v_1 = +e_1$, $v_\beta = -e_\beta$, $2 \leq \beta \leq k$ and the index is $(n-k)$ or $(2n - 2k + 1)$ or $(4n - 4k + 3)$ since (see Theorem 2) the corresponding stable manifolds through e_1, $-e_2$, $\ldots$, $-e_k$ are the spheres $V_{n-k+1,1} = S_{n-k}$ or $U_{n-k+1,1} = S_{2n-2k+1}$ or $S_{n-k+1,1} = S_{4n-4k+3}$.

Since each fiber of the negative normal bundle through the critical submanifold is completable by means of a single point $-e_1, -e_2, \ldots, -e_k$, we see that when the negative normal bundle to the critical submanifold is attached to $-e_1, \ldots, -e_k$ by means of the gradient lines of f, the resulting space is a realization of the Thom complex of the negative normal bundle.[4]

We note further that at the next level $G_{k,k-2}$ or $W_{k,k-2}$ or $S_{k,k-2}$ we have as index dim $V_{n-k+2,2}$ or dim $U_{n-k+2,2}$ or dim $S_{n-k+2,2}$ and these are respectively $2n - 2k + 1$ or $4n - 4k + 4$ or $8n - 8k + 10$. We conclude (see [1])

COROLLARY. (1) $V_{n,k}$ is of the same homotopy type as the Thom complex of an $(n - k)$-plane bundle over $P_{k-1}(R)$ with cells of dim. $\geq 2n - 2k + 1$ attached.

(2) $U_{n,k}$ is of the same homotopy type as the Thom complex of a $(2n - 2k + 1)$-plane bundle over $P_{k-1}(C)$ with cells of dim. $\geq 4n - 4k + 4$ attached.

(3) $S_{n,k}$ is of the same homotopy type as the Thom complex of a $(4n - 4k + 3)$-plane bundle over $P_{k-1}(Q)$ with cells of dim. $\geq 8n - 8k + 10$ attached.

BROWN UNIVERSITY

---

[4] For another treatment of the Thom complexes in this same context see M. F. Atiyah, "Thom complexes," *Proc. London Math. Soc.*, ser 3, *11* (1961), pp. 291–310.

References

[1] R. BOTT, The stable homotopy of the classical groups, *Ann. of Math.*, *70* (1959), p. 313–337.

[2] M. MORSE, *The Calculus of Variations in the Large*, Amer. Math. Soc. Colloquium Publications, vol. 18, New York, 1934.

[3] H. SAMELSON, Topology of Lie groups, *Bull. Amer. Math. Soc.*, *58* (1952), p. 2–37.

[4] A. BOREL, *Seminar on Transformation Groups*, Ann. of Math. Studies No. 46, Princeton University Press, 1960.

[5] W. WU, Sur les classes caractéristiques des structures fibrées sphériques, *Actualités Sci. Ind., no. 1183*, Hermann, Paris, 1952.

Remarks Concerning Spin Manifolds

JOHN W. MILNOR

This paper will consist of several unrelated remarks. In §2, as an application of the concept of "spin manifold," a non-standard involution of the 7-sphere is constructed. In §3 the spin cobordism ring is discussed.

1. Spin structures

Let ξ denote an oriented vector bundle with base space B. The concept of a "spin structure" on ξ can be defined in various ways. (See [4] §6.5, and [11].) The following definition is perhaps easiest to use. Let $P\xi$ denote the total space of the associated principal bundle. (One may use either the principal bundle with the rotation group $SO(n)$ as fibre, or with the linear group $GL^+(n, R)$ as fibre. It will not matter which is used, since the first is a deformation retract of the second.) First suppose that $n \geq 2$.

DEFINITION. A *spin structure* on ξ is a cohomology class $s \in H^1(P\xi, Z_2)$ whose restriction to each fibre is non-zero.

For the special case $n = 1$ we will allow s to be an arbitrary element of $H^1(P\xi, Z_2) \cong H^1(B; Z_2)$.

Such a class s determines a 2-fold covering of $P\xi$. This covering can be taken as the total space of a new principal bundle whose structural group is the 2-fold covering group of $SO(n)$ or $GL^+(n, R)$.

The following three lemmas give the basic properties of this concept.

LEMMA 1. *ξ admits a spin structure if and only if the Stiefel–Whitney class $w_2(\xi)$ is zero. This spin structure is unique if and only if $H^1(B; Z_2) = 0$.*

LEMMA 2. *Let U_1 and U_2 be open sets whose union is the base space B. Given spin structures s_1 on $\xi|U_1$ and s_2 on $\xi|U_2$ which coincide on $\xi|U_1 \cap U_2$, there exists a spin structure s on ξ which extends both s_1 and s_2.*

(Caution: In general s will not be uniquely determined by s_1 and s_2.)

LEMMA 3. *Given spin structures on two of the three bundles ξ, η, $\xi \oplus \eta$, there is a uniquely determined spin structure on the third.*

PROOFS. Lemma 1 follows (as in [11]) from the exact sequence

$$0 \to H^1(B) \to H^1(P\xi) \to H^1(\text{Fibre}) \to H^2(B),$$

55

where the coefficient group Z_2 is understood, and B is assumed to be connected. Lemma 2 follows from the Meyer–Vietoris sequence

$$\tilde{H}^0(P_1 \cap P_2) \to H^1(P\xi) \to H^1(P_1) \oplus H^1(P_2) \to H^1(P_1 \cap P_2),$$

where P_i stands for $P(\xi | U_i)$.

To prove Lemma 3, first consider the Cartesian product $\xi \times \eta$, and note that $P\xi \times P\eta \subset P(\xi \times \eta)$. Given spin structures $s \in H^1(P\xi)$ and $t \in H^1(P\eta)$, consider the class $s \times 1 + 1 \times t \in H^1(P\xi \times {}_d\eta)$.

ASSERTION. There exists one and only one cohomology class $u \in H^1(P(\xi \times \eta))$ which is a spin structure, and which extends the class $s \times 1 + 1 \times t$.

If B is connected then this fact is proved by chasing around the following diagram.

$$
\begin{array}{ccccccc}
H^1(B \times B) & \to & H^1 P(\xi \times \eta) & \to & H^1(\text{Fibre}) & \to & H^2(B \times B) \\
\downarrow & & \downarrow & & \downarrow & & \downarrow \\
0 \to H^1(B \times B) & \to & H^1(P\xi \times P\eta) & \to & H^1(\text{Fibre} \times \text{Fibre}) & \to & H^2(B \times B)
\end{array}
$$

The general case follows easily.

Now let $\Delta: P(\xi \oplus \eta) \to P(\xi \times \eta)$ denote the diagonal map. Then we can form the cohomology class $\Delta^* u \in H^1 P(\xi \oplus \eta)$.

DEFINITION. $\Delta^* u$ is the spin structure on $\xi \oplus \eta$ which is determined by s and t.

Finally we must verify that each of the cohomology classes $s, t, \Delta^* u$ is uniquely determined by the other two. The most general spin structure on ξ is $s + \pi_\xi^* a$, where $\pi_\xi: P\xi \to B$ denotes the projection map and a denotes an arbitrary element of $H^1 B$. If we replace s by $s + \pi_\xi^* a$ and similarly replace t by $t + \pi_\eta^* b$, then $\Delta^* u$ will be replaced by $\Delta^* u + \pi_{\xi \oplus \eta}^* (a + b)$. It is now clear that any two determine the third uniquely. This completes the proof of Lemma 3.

As an application of Lemma 3, consider a smoothly imbedded, oriented manifold $M^n \subset R^{n+k}$, with tangent bundle τ and normal bundle ν. Then $\tau \oplus \nu \cong \tau' | M^n$, where the tangent bundle τ' of R^{n+k} has a unique spin structure. Thus a spin structure on τ determines a spin structure on ν and conversely.

DEFINITION. The pair consisting of a manifold M^n together with a spin structure on its tangent bundle is called a *spin manifold*.

As another application of Lemma 3 one sees that the boundary of any spin manifold is again a spin manifold. Similarly the product of two spin manifolds is a spin manifold.

2. An exotic involution of S^7

In order to illustrate the utility of the concept of spin structure, we will use it to prove the following.

THEOREM 1.   *There exists a smooth involution* $f: S^7 \to S^7$ *without fixed points so that the orbit manifold* S^7/f *is not diffeomorphic to* P^7.

The proof will depend on an invariant which Eells and Kuiper [6] have defined for certain spin manifolds of dimension $4k - 1$. In order to simplify the exposition we will define this invariant only for 7-manifolds.

First consider a closed 8-dimensional spin manifold M with signature σ. According to Thom and Hirzebruch [7] one has the formula

$$\sigma = \tfrac{1}{45}(7p_2 - p_1^2)[M].$$

On the other hand Atiyah and Hirzebruch [3] define the $\hat{A}$-genus

$$\hat{A}[M] = \tfrac{1}{5760}(7p_1^2 - 4p_2)[M]$$

and prove that this is also an integer (for a spin manifold). Eliminating $p_2[M]$ between these two linear equations, we obtain the formula

$$\hat{A}[M] = (p_1^2[M] - 4\sigma)/896.$$

Now consider a compact 8-dimensional spin manifold (W, s') with boundary $(\partial W, s)$. Following Eells and Kuiper, one must assume:

HYPOTHESIS.   The natural homomorphism $H^4(W, \partial W; Q) \to H^4(W; Q)$ between rational cohomology groups is an isomorphism.

The signature σ of W is easily defined. Furthermore, after lifting the Pontrjagin class p_1 of W back to $H^4(W, \partial W; Q)$, the Pontrjagin number $p_1^2[W]$ is well defined. Now define $\mu(\partial W, s)$ to be the residue class, modulo 1, of the rational number $(p_1^2[W] - 4\sigma)/896$. It is not difficult to show that this is an invariant of the spin manifold $(\partial W, s)$: that is, it does not depend on the choice of (W, s').

Example 1.   Let M^7 be a homotopy sphere which bounds a parallelizable manifold W having signature $\sigma = +8$. (Compare Kervaire and Milnor [9].) Then

$$\mu(M^7) \equiv (0 - 4.8)/896 \equiv -\tfrac{1}{28} \pmod{1}.$$

But according to [9] the group Θ_7 consisting of all homotopy 7-spheres is cyclic of order 28, with generator (M^7). It follows easily that μ provides a complete invariant for homotopy 7-spheres.

Example 2.   The real projective space P^{2n+1} can be thought of as the total space of a circle bundle over the complex projective space $P_n(C)$. (An explicit projection map is given by the formula,

$$(x_0: y_0: x_1: y_1: \cdots : x_n: y_n) \to (x_0 + iy_0: x_1 + iy_1: \cdots : x_n + iy_n).)$$

Let ξ denote the associated 2-disk bundle, and let W denote its total space, so that $\partial W = P^{2n+1}$. If n is odd then $P_n(C)$ is a spin manifold; and it follows that W is a spin manifold. The Euler class $e(\xi)$ is equal to twice a generator:

$$e(\xi) = 2a \in H^2(P_n(C); Z),$$

hence the Pontrjagin class $p_1(\xi) = e^2$ is equal to $4a^2$. The first Pontrjagin class for the tangent bundle of $P_n(C)$ is equal to $(n+1)a^2$. Therefore the class

$$p_1(W) \in H^4(W; Z) \cong H^4(P_n(C); Z)$$

corresponds to $(n+5)a^2$.

Now let us specialize to the case $n = 3$, and compute $p_1^2[W]$. From the sequence

$$0 \to H^4(W, P^7; Z) \to H^4(W: Z) \to H^4(P^7; Z) \to 0,$$

where the first two groups are infinite cyclic and the third is Z_2, one sees that the class $p_1(W) = 8a^2$ lifts back to 4 times a generator. By Poincaré duality the groups $H^4(W, P^7; Z)$ and $H^4(W; Z)$ are dually paired to $H^8(W, P^7; Z)$ by the cup product. Therefore $p^2[W] = \pm 4.8$. Choosing the orientation of W correctly, and letting s_1 denote the induced spin structure on $\partial W = P^7$, this yields

$$\mu(P^7, s_1) \equiv (p_1^2[W] - 4\sigma)/896 \equiv (32 - 4)/896 \equiv \tfrac{1}{32} \ (\text{mod } 1).$$

Thus we have computed the invariant μ for P^7 with one of its two possible spin structures.

Now consider the manifold $-W$ with reversed orientation. Its boundary is a spin manifold $(-P^7, s')$ with $\mu(-P^7, s') \equiv -\tfrac{1}{32}$. But the projective space P^7 possesses an orientation reversing diffeomorphism. This proves that there exists a spin structure s_2 on P^7 so that $\mu(P^7, s_2) \equiv -\tfrac{1}{32}$. In other words:

LEMMA 4.   *The invariant μ of P^7 is equal to $\pm\tfrac{1}{32}$, where the sign depends on which of the two possible spin structures is chosen.*

Now consider connected sums of the form $P^7 \# M^7 \# \cdots \# M^7$; where M^7 is the homotopy sphere considered earlier. It can be shown that each such sum is homeomorphic to P^7. Clearly

$$\mu(P^7 \# M^7 \# \cdots \# M^7) \equiv \pm\tfrac{1}{32} - \tfrac{1}{28} - \cdots - \tfrac{1}{28}.$$

Since one can obtain 28 distinct invariants in this way, we have proved that the oriented manifold P^7 admits 28 distinct differentiable structures.

Let $r(M^7)$ denote the sum of r copies of M^7. Next note that the 2-fold covering space of $P^7 \# r(M^7)$ is diffeomorphic to $S^7 \# 2r(M^7)$. Taking

$r = 14$ it follows that the 2-fold covering space of $P^7 \# 14(M^7)$ is diffeomorphic to the standard sphere S^7. In other words there exists an involution of S^7 whose orbit space is diffeomorphic to $P^7 \# 14(M^7)$. Since $P^7 \# 14(M^7)$ is distinct from P^7; this proves Theorem 1.

3. Spin cobordism groups

Using Lemma 2 one sees that the relation of "spin cobordism" between closed n-dimensional spin manifolds is an equivalence relation. Let Ω_n^{spin} denote the resulting cobordism group. The cartesian product operation between spin manifolds (compare Lemma 3) gives rise to a product operation

$$\Omega_m^{\mathrm{spin}} \otimes \Omega_n^{\mathrm{spin}} \to \Omega_{m+n}^{\mathrm{spin}}.$$

Thus one obtains a graded ring.

Our ignorance concerning these groups is quite extensive. For example, to the best of my knowledge, it is not known whether any Ω_n^{spin} contains an element of order 4.

In studying spin cobordism it is natural to look at the homomorphism $\Omega_n^{\mathrm{spin}} \to \Omega_n$ into the ordinary (oriented) cobordism group. Here is a description of this homomorphism for three particular cases.

For $n = 8$ the group $\Omega_8^{\mathrm{spin}} \cong Z + Z$ maps monomorphically into Ω_8, which is also isomorphic to $Z + Z$. The quotient group $\Omega_8/\Omega_8^{\mathrm{spin}}$ is cyclic of order 2^7. (Compare [11].)

Now let $n = 9$. According to Adachi [1] an oriented 9-manifold bounds if and only if the Stiefel–Whitney numbers $w_2^3 w_3[M]$ and $w_2 w_7[M]$ are zero. (Compare Wall [12].) But these clearly vanish for a spin manifold. Therefore the homomorphism

$$\Omega_9^{\mathrm{spin}} \to \Omega_9 \cong Z_2 + Z_2$$

is zero. (Similarly this homomorphism is zero for $n = 5$, 11, and presumably for many higher dimensions.) On the other hand we will see presently that $\Omega_9^{\mathrm{spin}} \neq 0$.

Finally, let $n = 10$. Let $H_{2,4}$ denote a non-singular hypersurface of degree $(1, 1)$ in the product $P_2(C) \times P_4(C)$ of complex projective spaces. Then one can verify that

$$w_2(H_{2,4}) = 0, \qquad w_4 w_6[H_{2,4}] \neq 0.$$

Thus $H_{2,4}$ is a spin manifold, but is not an oriented boundary. It follows that the homomorphism

$$\Omega_{10}^{\mathrm{spin}} \to \Omega_{10} \cong Z_2$$

is non-zero.

An extremely interesting tool for studying the spin cobordism ring was suggested to the author by Atiyah. Namely there is a homomorphism

$$\alpha\colon \Omega_n^{\mathrm{spin}} \to \tilde{K}_O S^n$$

which is defined as follows. (Here $\tilde{K}_O S^n$ denotes the group of s-classes of vector bundles over S^n.) Consider a disk-bundle with spin structure, the fibre dimension being $8k$. Let E denote the total space, $\dot{E}$ the total space of the associated sphere bundle, and $E/\dot{E}$ the Thom space. The two half-spin representations of Spin $(8k)$ give rise to two vector bundles over E. Since these representations coincide over Spin $(8k-1)$, the two vector bundles coincide over $\dot{E}$. Thus their difference determines an element of $K_O(E, \dot{E}) \cong \tilde{K}_O(E/\dot{E})$.

Applying this construction to the universal Spin $(8k)$-bundle, with k large we obtain a canonical class $u \in \tilde{K}_O M$ (Spin $8k$). Now for any map $f\colon S^{n+8k} \to M(\mathrm{Spin}\ 8k)$ the class $f*u \in \tilde{K}_O S^{n+8k} \cong \tilde{K}_O S^n$ is defined. Thus we obtain a homomorphism from

$$\pi_{n+8k} M(\mathrm{Spin}\ 8k) \cong \Omega_n^{\mathrm{spin}}$$

to $\tilde{K}_O S^n$.

For $n \leq 7$ one can verify that this construction defines an isomorphism between Ω_n^{spin} and $\tilde{K}_O S^n$. (Compare [11].)

If $n \equiv 0 \pmod 4$ then the composition

$$\Omega_n^{\mathrm{spin}} \xrightarrow{\ \alpha\ } \tilde{K}_O S^n \subset \tilde{K}_U S^n \cong Z$$

turns out to be precisely the $\hat{A}$-genus. In fact this is essentially the method which Atiyah and Hirzebruch [3] used to prove that the $\hat{A}$-genus of a spin manifold is an integer (or an even integer for $n \equiv 4 \pmod 8$).

Now recall that the tensor product operation between vector bundles gives rise to a bilinear product operation $\tilde{K}_O S^m \otimes \tilde{K}_O S^n \to \tilde{K}_O S^{m+n}$. (See [5].) The following result will be proved in a forthcoming paper by Atiyah, Bott, and Shapiro [2].

THEOREM. *The function* $\alpha\colon \Omega_n^{\mathrm{spin}} \to \tilde{K}_O S^n$ *is a ring homomorphism: that is* $\alpha(M \times N) = \alpha(M)\alpha(N)$.

One interesting consequence of this theorem is the following. Let $n = 9, 10, 17$, or 18.

THEOREM 2. *For these n there exists a smooth manifold Σ^n which is a homotopy n-sphere, but is not a spin boundary.*

Thus the homomorphism $\Omega_n^{\mathrm{spin}} \to \Omega_n$ has a non-trivial kernel for $n = 9, 10, 17, 18$.

PROOF. First consider the case $n \equiv 1 \pmod 8$. Let $k = (n-1)/4$.

According to Kervaire and Milnor [8] there exists an almost parallelizable manifold M^{4k} with

$$\hat{A}[M^{4k}] = B_k a_k j_k / 4k,$$

where B_k is the kth Bernoulli number, $a_k = 1$ for k even, and where $j_2 = 240$, $j_4 = 480$. Thus for $k = 2, 4$ there exists such a manifold with $\hat{A}[M^{4k}] = 1$. We may assume that M^{4k} is $(2k - 1)$-connected, hence has a unique spin structure.

Let (S^1, s) denote the circle with the "bad" spin structure, so that $\alpha(S^1, s) \neq 0$. Since the product

$$\tilde{K}_O S^{4k} \otimes \tilde{K}_O S^1 \rightarrow \tilde{K}_O S^{4k+1}$$

is non-trivial for k even, it follows that $\alpha(M^{4k} \times (S^1, s)) \neq 0$. Now apply a surgery to $M^{4k} \times S^1$ so as to kill the infinite cyclic fundamental group. care must be taken that the surgery is compatible with the spin structure. (Compare [10, Theorem 2] or [9, §6].) The resulting manifold will be a $(2k - 1)$-connected spin manifold which is parallelizable except along an imbedded circle. Now apply a sequence of surgeries to kill the free abelian group π_{2k}. The resulting manifold Σ^{4k+1} will be a homotopy sphere which is spin-cobordant to $M^{4k} \times (S^1, s)$; so that $\alpha(\Sigma^{4k+1}) \neq 0$.

To obtain a corresponding example in dimension $4k + 2$ it is only necessary to apply a single surgery to $\Sigma^{4k+1} \times (S^1, s)$. Again the surgery must be compatible with the spin structure. This completes the proof of Theorem 2.

It may be conjectured that similar manifolds Σ^n exist whenever $n \equiv 1$ or 2 (mod 8). The above proof works for $n = 4k + 1$ whenever $B_k j_k / 4k \equiv 1$ (mod 2). An alternative attack would be based on the following.

CONJECTURE. *For $n \equiv 1$ (mod 8) there exists a map $f: S^{8r+n} \rightarrow S^{8r}$ so that the induced $f^*: \tilde{K}_O S^{8r} \rightarrow \tilde{K}_O S^{8r+n} \cong Z_2$ is non-zero.*

(The corresponding statement for $n \equiv 2$ (mod 8) would be a consequence.)

This is related to Theorem 2 as follows. Consider the composition

$$S^{8r} \subset M(\text{Spin } 8r) \xrightarrow{u'} BO$$

where u' corresponds to the Atiyah–Hirzebruch class $u \in K_O M(\text{Spin } 8r)$ which was described above. Thus any element of $\pi_{8r+n}(S^{8r})$ determines a spin cobordism class. If $n \not\equiv 2$ (mod 4) then it follows from [9] that this cobordism class has a representative which is a homotopy sphere. Now, assuming the Conjecture, it is not difficult to prove the generalized Theorem 2.

Conversely, using Theorem 2, it is easy to verify that the Conjecture is true for $n = 9, 17$.

PRINCETON UNIVERSITY

REFERENCES

[1] M. ADACHI, On the groups of cobordism Ω^k, *Nagoya Math. J.*, *13* (1958); p. 135–156.

[2] M. ATIYAH, R. BOTT and A. SHAPIRO, Clifford modules, *Topology, 3, Suppl. 1* (1964), p. 3–38.

[3] M. ATIYAH and F. HIRZEBRUCH, Riemann–Roch theorems for differentiable manifolds, *Bull. Amer. Math. Soc., 65* (1959), p. 276–281.

[4] A. BOREL and F. HIRZEBRUCH, Characteristic classes and homogeneous spaces, *Amer. J. Math., 80* (1958), p. 458–538 and *81* (1959), p. 315–382.

[5] R. BOTT, Some remarks on the periodicity theorems, *Bull. Soc. Math. France, 89* (1959), p. 293–310.

[6] J. EELLS and N. KUIPER, An invariant for certain smooth manifolds, *Annali di Mat., 60* (1962), p. 93–110.

[7] F. HIRZEBRUCH, *Neue topologische Methoden in der algebraischen Geometrie*, Springer, Berlin, 1956.

[8] M. KERVAIRE and J. MILNOR, Bernoulli numbers, homotopy groups and a theorem of Rohlin, *Proc. Int. Congress of Math.*, Edinburgh (1960), p. 454–458.

[9] M. KERVAIRE and J. MILNOR, Groups of homotopy spheres I, *Annals of Math., 77* (1963), p. 504–537. Part II is in preparation.

[10] J. MILNOR, A procedure for killing homotopy groups of differentiable manifolds, *A.M.S. Symposia in Pure Math.*, vol. III (1961), p. 39–55.

[11] J. MILNOR, Spin structures on manifolds, *L'Enseignement Math., 9* (1963), p. 198–203.

[12] C. T. C. WALL, Determination of the cobordism ring, *Annals of Math., 72* (1960), p. 292–311.

Diffeomorphisms with Many Periodic Points

STEPHEN SMALE

Introduction

Although this paper is motivated by problems in ordinary differential equations, we consider explicitly the topological conjugacy problem for diffeomorphisms. Recall that C^∞ diffeomorphisms T, T': $M \to M$ are topologically conjugate if there exists a homeomorphism h: $M \to M$ so that $Th = hT'$ where M is some differentiable manifold (see [10] and [11] for a background of this work here).

We consider here aspects of this problem which are related on one hand to the symbolic dynamics of Hadamard, Morse, and others (see Gottschalk and Hedlund [5]), and on the other hand to the homoclinic points of Poincaré and G. D. Birkoff.

The "shift automorphism" (on m symbols) of symbolic dynamics, described in section 1, is a homeomorphism of a Cantor set with a number of interesting properties which include periodic points of arbitrarily high period and a minimal set, itself homeomorphic to a Cantor set. We recall that $p \in X$ is a *periodic point* of a homeomorphism T: $X \to X$ if $T^\lambda(p) = p$ for some λ. The smallest positive λ is called the period of p. A *minimal set* of a homeomorphism is a compact invariant set with no proper compact invariant subsets except the empty set.

THEOREM A. *On every manifold M of dimension greater than one, there exists an open set U in the space of diffeomorphisms of M with the C' topology with the following property. If $T \in U$, then there is a Cantor set $\Omega \subset M$, invariant under T such that T restricted to Ω is topologically equivalent to the shift automorphism on 2 symbols.*

This means that if τ: $A \to A$ is the shift automorphism there is a homeomorphism h: $A \to \Omega$ with $Th = h\tau$.

COROLLARY. *On every manifold M of dimension greater than one, there is an open set of diffeomorphisms, C' topology, with each element possessing an infinite number of periodic points.*

63

This shows that the answer to problem A of [12] is negative, for every manifold of dimension greater than 1, in fact. That is, the diffeomorphisms (and dynamical systems also, via [11]) axiomatized there are not dense in all diffeomorphisms.

Previous to the research of this paper, N. Levinson had written me that his paper [6] would already yield this answer for problem A for 2-dimensional diffeomorphisms and 3-dimensional differential equations. His paper and those of Cartwright [3], and Littlewood [7], indicate strong relations between the theory developed in this paper and the theory of a 2nd order differential equation, time dependent, in particular that of van der Pol with a forcing term.

I presume that in view of G. D. Birkhoff's theorem on homoclinic points, see below in the Introduction, he would have known the answer to this problem A in dimension 2.

One last note on this problem is that by a different example, independently, R. Thom, unpublished, shows the answer to problem A to be negative. His example is an open set of diffeomorphisms of a 2-dimensional torus which have no "contracting" periodic points.

A point $x \in M$ is called a *homoclinic point* of a diffeomorphism $T: M \to M$ if

$$\lim_{n \to \infty} T_x^{nm} = \lim_{n \to \infty} T_x^{-nm} = y, \ x \neq y$$

(so in particular the limits exist), m a positive integer, for example 1. Homoclinic points were first found by Poincaré in the restricted three body problem and he was aware of the complexity that they contributed to the nature of dynamical systems. Birkhoff has pursued the study of homoclinic points (see [1], [2]).

THEOREM B. *If $D(M)$ denotes the space of diffeomorphisms of M with the C^r topology, $r > 0$, there is a subset D_0 which is the countable intersection of open dense sets of D with the following property. If $x \in M$ is a homoclinic point of $T \in D_0$, then there is a Cantor set $\Omega \subset M$, $x \in \Omega$, and p such that $T^p\Omega = \Omega$ and T^p restricted to Ω is equivalent to a shift automorphism of symbolic dynamics.*

One should note that the idea of Theorem B is excluding a few diffeomorphisms, the mild hypothesis, x is homoclinic point, leads to a rather strong conclusion.

COROLLARY. *If $T \in D_0$, then in every neighborhood of a homoclinic point of T there is an infinite number of periodic points of T.*

This follows from the well-known [5] and easily proved fact that the periodic points of a shift automorphism are dense in the Cantor set.

Birkhoff [1] proved the above corollary where the manifold was the plane using arguments which do not seem to generalize to higher dimensions.

The theorem that there exist diffeomorphisms of the n-sphere which are structurally stable and have an infinite number of periodic points was announced in [9], [10]. Our work here takes us a large part of the way toward this result, but we postpone the complete proof to another paper.

Everything is considered from the C^∞ point of view, e.g. diffeomorphisms and manifolds are always C^∞.

Some conversations with Dr. R. Abraham on the generalization of Birkhoff's theorem have been very helpful.

We take this opportunity to make some corrections to our paper "Morse Inequalities for dynamical systems" [12]. First, as we see in [11], as was first pointed out to us by Harold Rosenberg, the stable manifolds for a closed orbit may be twisted and hence non-orientable. Thus in the Morse inequalities one must either assume that the stable manifolds are orientable, or that the coefficients are Z_2. Also the axioms on page 49 should be augmented by the analogue of Axiom 5 for vector fields page 43.

§1

We discuss here some elements of symbolic dynamics. See Gottschalk–Hedlund [5] for more information with historical references.

Let S be a finite non-empty set with m elements. Let l, j be integers or ∞, $0 \leq l \leq \infty$, $-1 \leq j \leq \infty$, $[-l, j]$ the set of integers between $-l$ and j, inclusive when l, j are finite.

Let A_j^l be the set of functions from $[-l, j]$ to S, A_1^0 a set with one element.

Let each of S and Z (the integers) be provided with the discrete topology and A_j^l the Compact open topology.

Define a topological isomorphism $\tau : A_j^l \to A_{j+1}^{l-1}$, $0 \leq l - 1$, $-1 \leq j$, by $\tau[\alpha](i) = \alpha(i - 1)$. Then $\tau : A_\infty^\infty \to A_\infty^\infty$ is called the shift automorphism on m symbols.

We note the following properties of $\tau : A_\infty^\infty \to A_\infty^\infty$. For the proofs and further analysis of τ, see [5].

(1.1) (a) The periodic points form an invariant countable dense subset of A_∞^∞.

(b) There exists a minimal set, homeomorphic to a Cantor set.

If $l_0 \leq l$, $j_0 \leq j$, let $\rho - \rho(l, j, l_0, j_0)$ be the map $\rho : A_j^l \to A_{j_0}^{l_0}$ defined by restricting a function from $[l, j]$ to $[l_0, j_0]$.

For the proofs in Section 3, we include the following facts.

Let σ_j be the composition

$$A_j^0 \xrightarrow{\ \tau^{-1}\ } A_{j-1}^1 \xrightarrow{\ \rho\ } A_{j-1}^0$$

and $\rho_j\colon A_j^0 \to A_{j-1}^0$ be a special case of the above defined restriction.

The following is easily verified.

(1.2) LEMMA. *Let* $\beta_1, \beta_2 \in A_j^0$. *Then* $\rho_{j+1}^{-1}(\beta_1) \cap \sigma_{j+1}^{-1}(\beta_2)$ *has exactly one element if and only if* $\sigma_j(\beta_1) = \rho_j(\beta_2)$.

Define $\delta\colon A_{-1} \times A_j^0 \to A_j$ by taking $\delta(\alpha_1, \alpha_2)$ to be the function from $[-l, j]$ to S as that one whose restriction to $[-l, -1]$ is α_1 and whose restriction to $[0, j]$ is α_2. Then δ is an isomorphism and δ^{-1} is the product $\rho_1 \times \rho_2$ restricted to the diagonal, where $\rho_1\colon A_j \to A_{-1}$, $\rho_2\colon A_j \to A_j^0$ are restrictions.

§2

To obtain some geometric picture of what is going on in this section, we refer the reader to the remark at the end of Section 6.

Here we assume only that there is given a compact set R of a Hausdorff space M and a map $T\colon R \to M$, which is a homeomorphism onto its image. Define $B_{-1}^0 = R$ and inductively (on j), $B_j^0 = T(B_{j-1}^0) \cap R$, $j \geq 0$.

Similarly define $B_{-1}^l = T^{-1}(B_{-1}^{l-1} \cap B_0^0)$, $l \geq 1$, and $B_j^l = B_{-1}^l \cap B_j^0$, $j \geq -1, l \geq 0$.

Also let $B_j^\infty = \cap_{l \geq 0} B_j^l$, $B_\infty^l = \cap_{j \geq -1} B_j^l$, $B_\infty^\infty = \cap_{j \geq -1, l \geq 0} B_j^l$, so that B_j^l is a well defined closed subset of R for all l, j satisfying $-1 \leq j \leq \infty$, $0 \leq l \leq \infty$.

REMARK. Note that $B_j^0 = T(B_{j-1}^0 \cap B_{-1}^1)$.

(2.1) LEMMA. *If* $l_0 \leq l \leq \infty$, $j_0 \leq j \leq \infty$, *then* $B_j^l \subset B_{j_0}^{l_0}$.

PROOF. We show inductively that (a) $B_j^0 \subset B_{j-1}^0$ and (b) $B_{-1}^l \subset B_{-1}^{l-1}$. From this 2.1 follows immediately.

Note $B_0^0 = T(R) \cap R \subset R = B_{-1}^0$ so that (a) is true for $j = 0$. If $B_{j-1}^0 \subset B_{j-2}^0$, then $T(B_{j-1}^0) \subset (B_{j-2}^0)$ so $B_j^0 = T(B_{j-1}^0) \cap R \subset T(B_{j-2}^0) \cap R = B_{j-1}^0$ proving (a).

The proof of (b) is similar.

(2.2) LEMMA. *For* $0 \leq l \leq \infty$, $-1 \leq j \leq \infty$, T *restricted to* B_j^l *is a homeomorphism onto* B_{j+1}^{l-1}.

PROOF. First note that it is sufficient to consider the case $l, j < \infty$. Since T is a homeomorphism, it is sufficient for this to show that (a) $T(B_j^l) \subset B_{j+1}^{l-1}$ and (b) $T^{-1}(B_{j+1}^{l-1}) \subset B_j^l$.

For (a) recall $B_j^l = B_j^0 \cap B_{-1}^l$, $B_{j+1}^{l-1} = B_{j+1}^0 \cap B_{-1}^{l-1}$ and $T(B_j^0) \cap R = B_{j+1}^0$. So $T(B_j^l) \subset B_{j+1}^0$ if $T(B_{-1}^l) \subset R$. But this is true since $l > 0$, $B_{-1}^l = T^{-1}(B_{-1}^{l-1} \cap B_0^0)$ and $T(B_{-1}^l) \subset T(T^{-1}B_{-1}^{l-1}) = B_{-1}^{l-1} \subset R$.

Since $T(B_{-1}^l) \subset B_{-1}^{l-1}$, $T)B_j^l \subset B_{-1}^{l-1}$ and (a) is proved.

For (b) $T^{-1}(B_{j+1}^0) \subset T^{-1}(TB_j^0) = B_j^0$, so it remains to prove

$$T^{-1}(B_{j+1}^{l-1}) \subset B_{-1}^l.$$

But

$$T^{-1}(B_{-1}^{l+1} \cap B_0^0) = B_{-1}^l$$

so it is sufficient to show

$$T^{-1}(B_{j+1}^{l-1}) \subset B_0^0.$$

But this is clear. This finishes the proof of 2.2.

Let C_j^l be the set of components of B_j^l. From 2.1, let $r: C_j^l \to C_{j_0}^{l_0}$ be induced by inclusion. From 2.2, let $t: C_j^l \to C_{j+1}^{l-1}$ be induced by T; hence t is an isomorphism. The following is immediate.

(2.3) LEMMA. *The following diagram commutes*:

$$
\begin{array}{ccc}
C_j^l & \xrightarrow{\ t\ } & C_{j+1}^{l-1} \\
\downarrow{\scriptstyle r} & & \downarrow{\scriptstyle r} \\
C_{j_0}^{l_0} & \xrightarrow{\ t\ } & C_{j_0+1}^{l_0-1}
\end{array}
$$

If $\beta \in C_j^l$, we will write $x \in \beta$, $\beta \subset R$, etc. where β is considered to be a subset of R.

§3

We refer again the reader to the remark at the end of Section 6. Suppose as in Section 2, $T: R \to M$ is a homeomorphism onto its image where R is a compact subspace of a Hausdorff space M. We assume moreover that T satisfies the following axiom.

Axiom 1. R is connected, B_0^0 has a finite number of components, say m, $m > 1$. Furthermore if $\beta_1 \in C_{-1}^l$, $\beta_2 \in C_j^0$, l, $j < \infty$, then $\beta_1 \cap \beta_2$ has exactly one component.

Let A_j^l be as in Section 1, where the set S used in defining A_j^l is the set C_0^0.

The goal of Section 3 is to construct, under the assumption of Axiom 1, an isomorphism $\phi: A_j^l \to C_j^l$ with certain naturality properties.

More explicitly the goal of this section is to prove 3.1. Recall $r: C_j^l \to C_{j_0}^{l_0}$ is induced by inclusion, $t: C_j^l \to C_{j+1}^{l-1}$ by T.

(3.1) THEOREM. *There is an isomorphism* (1–1 *onto map*) $\phi: A_j^l \to C_j^l$, $0 \le l \le \infty$, $-1 \le j \le \infty$, *with commutativity in the following diagrams*:

$$
\begin{array}{ccc}
A_j^l & \xrightarrow{\ \phi\ } & C_j^l \\
\downarrow{\scriptstyle \rho} & & \downarrow{\scriptstyle r} \\
A_{j_0}^{l_0} & \xrightarrow{\ \phi\ } & C_{j_0}^{l_0}
\end{array}
\qquad\qquad
\begin{array}{ccc}
A_j^l & \xrightarrow{\ \phi\ } & C_j^l \\
\downarrow{\scriptstyle \tau} & & \downarrow{\scriptstyle t} \\
A_{j+1}^{l-1} & \xrightarrow{\ \phi\ } & C_{j+1}^{l-1}
\end{array}
$$

First observe that by considering A_∞^∞, as C_∞^∞ are inductive limits of A_l^l, C_l^l, respectively, (see also Section 4) it is sufficient to prove 3.1 for the case $l, j < \infty$.

Define first a map $d: C_{-1}^l \times C_j^0 \to C_j^l$ by taking for $d(\beta_1, \beta_2)$ the component $\beta_1 \cap \beta_2$ of B_j^l. By Axiom 1, d is a well-defined isomorphism. Furthermore d^{-1} is the restriction of $r_1 \times r_2$ to the diagonal where $r_1: C_j^l \to C_{-1}^l$, $r_2: C_j^l \to C_j^0$ are special cases of the r induced by inclusion. This is all quite analogous to the δ defined at the end of Section 1.

Let s_j be the following composition

$$C_j^0 \xrightarrow{\ t^{-1}\ } C_{j-1}^1 \xrightarrow{\ r\ } C_{j-1}^0$$

and $r_j: C_j^0 \to C_{j-1}^0$ the previously defined inclusion. We have the following analogue of 1.2.

(3.2) LEMMA. *Suppose* $\beta_1, \beta_2 \in C_j^0$. *Then* $s_{j+1}^{-1}(\beta_1) \cap r_{j+1}^{-1}(\beta_2)$ *has precisely one element if and only if* $r_j(\beta_1) = s_j(\beta_2)$.

PROOF. Consider the following (non-commutative) diagram.

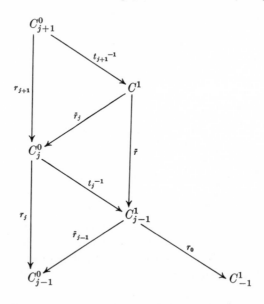

Here the various $\tilde{r}$, r_0, etc. are all induced by inclusion, t_j, t_{j+1} induced by T.

Let $\alpha = t_{j+1}(d(\beta_1, r_0 t_j^{-1} \beta_2))$, where $d: C_j^0 \times C_{-1}^1 \to C_j^1$ is as above, and $\alpha_1 = d(\beta_1, r_0 t_j^{-1} \beta_2)$.

Suppose now $r_j(\beta_1) = s_j(\beta_2)$. We will show first that $\alpha \in s_{j+1}^{-1}(\beta_1) \cap r_{j+1}^{-1}(\beta_2)$ This amounts to proving (a) $s_{j+1}(\alpha) = \beta_1$ and (b) $r_{j+1}(\alpha) = \beta_2$.

For (a), using definition of $s_{j\times 1}$, we need to show $\bar{r}_j(\alpha_1) = \beta_1$ or $\bar{r}_j(d(\beta_1, r_0 t_j^{-1})) = \beta_1$. But this is clear from the definition of $d, \bar{r}_j$.

For (b) first note that by 2.3 the following commutes

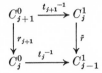

Hence it amounts to proving $t_j^{-1}\beta_2 = \bar{r}\alpha_1$. Since $\bar{r}_{j-1} \times r_0 \colon C_{j-1}^1 \to C_{j-1}^0 \times C_{-1}^1$ is an isomorphism, to prove (b) it is now sufficient to show (b_1) $\bar{r}_{j-1}\bar{r}\alpha_1 = \bar{r}_{j-1}t_j^{-1}\beta_2$ and (b_2) $r_0\bar{r}\alpha_1 = r_0 t_j^{-1}\beta_2$. For ($b_1$) we have $\bar{r}_{j-1}t_j^{-1}\beta_2 = s_j\beta_2 = r_j\beta_1$ by hypothesis. Then (b) is finished using the definition of α_1 and the various r's.

We leave for the reader the task of checking the uniqueness of α.

To finish the proof of 3.2 it must be shown that if $s_{j+1}^{-1}(\beta_1) \cap r_{j+1}^{-1}(\beta_2)$ consists of a single element α, then $r_j(\beta_1) = s_j(\beta_2)$. This follows from the commutativity of the previous diagram.

We proceed now to the proof of 3.1.

First define ϕ from A_{-1}^0 to C_{-1}^0, A_0^0 to C_0^0, to be the canonical isomorphisms. Now $\phi \colon A_j^0 \to C_j^0$ is defined inductively. Suppose ϕ has been defined up to A_{j-1}^0 so that the following diagrams commute:

We wish to complete the induction by defining $\phi \colon A_j^0 \to C_j^0$ with the corresponding diagrams commuting.

If $\alpha \in A_j^0$, let $\phi(\alpha) = r_j^{-1}(\phi\rho_j\alpha) \cap S_j^{-1}(\phi\sigma_j\alpha)$. By 3.2, this is well-defined. The hypothesis of 3.2. in this case follows from commutativity in the above diagrams and 1.2.

From 1.2, 3.2 and the inductive hypotheses, one can obtain an inverse of $\phi \colon A_j^0 \to C_j^0$, so ϕ is an isomorphism.

Next define ϕ from A_{-1}^1 to C_{-1}^1 in the unique way so that the following commutes:

By considerations similar to those used in the construction of $\phi \colon A_j^0 \to C_j^0$, and using analogues of 3.2 and 1.2, one obtains an isomorphism $\phi \colon A_{-1}^l \to C_{-1}^l$, each l, with commutativity in the following diagrams.

Here $\bar{\sigma}$, s are the compositions respectively,

$$A_{-1}^l \xrightarrow{\ \tau\ } A_0^{l-1} \xrightarrow{\ \rho\ } A_{-1}^{l-1},$$

$$C_{-1}^l \xrightarrow{\ t\ } C_0^{l-1} \xrightarrow{\ r\ } C_{-1}^{l-1}.$$

Let $\phi \colon A_j^l \to C_j^l$ be defined as the isomorphism which makes the following diagram commute:

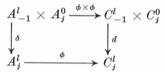

From previously discussed relations between the maps d and r, and similar relations between δ and ρ, it follows that the following diagram commutes.

It remains for the proof of 3.1 to prove commutativity in the 2nd diagram in its statement.

We first take care of the following special case

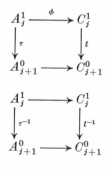

or equivalently that

commutes.

Now using δ and d it is sufficient for this to note that the following two diagrams commute.

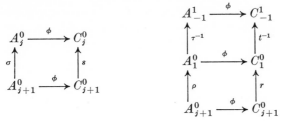

Next consider the following diagrams which define p_i, π_i, for $i = 1, 2$.

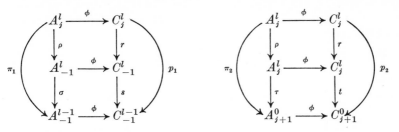

These commute by previous considerations, so that we have commutativity in

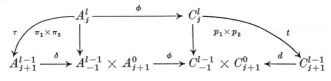

which finishes the proof of 3.1.

§4

To the structure $T: R \to M$ of Section 3 with Axiom 1, we add the following Axiom.

Axiom 2. Dim $B_\infty^\infty = 0$.

We will prove the following theorem.

(4.1) THEOREM. *Suppose R is a compact subspace of Hausdorff space M, $T: R \to M$ a homeomorphism satisfying Axioms 1 and 2. Then there exists a Cantor set $\Omega \subset R$, $T\Omega = \Omega$, and T restricted to Ω is topologically equivalent to the shift automorphism on m symbols, m of Axiom 1.*

Define $\Omega = B_\infty^\infty$; this is invariant under T by 2.2. By Axiom 2, B_∞^∞ can be identified with C_∞^∞, so that we can consider $\phi: A_\infty^\infty \to \Omega$. Then using 3.1, 4.1 is implied by the following lemma.

(4.2) LEMMA. $\phi: A_\infty^\infty \to \Omega$ is continuous.

PROOF. Both A_∞^∞, $C_\infty^\infty = B_\infty^\infty = \Omega$ are inverse limits of the systems $(A_{l'}^l, \rho)$, (C_l^l, r) respectively. Since $\phi: A_l^l \to C_l^l$ is map of these inverse systems, by 3.1, and continuous, its limit $\phi: A_\infty^\infty \to C_\infty^\infty$ is continuous (see [4]).

§5

To verify Axioms 1 and 2 in our applications, we need some linear theory.

Let E_1, E_2, $E_1 \times E_2 = E$ be Banach spaces (finite dimensional in our applications). For $0 < \mu < 1$, $0 < \varepsilon$, let $B(\mu, \varepsilon)$ be the set of bounded linear transformations of E, taking the following form in the product structure of E.

$$T = \begin{pmatrix} W & Z \\ Y & X \end{pmatrix}$$

where $\|X\| \leq \mu + \varepsilon$, $\|Y\| \leq \varepsilon$, and there exist bounded linear transformations $L: E_1 \to E_1$, $\|L^{-1}\| \leq \mu + \varepsilon$, $A: E_2 \to E_1$, $\|A\| \leq \varepsilon$, $B: E_1 \to E_1$, $\|B^{-1}\| \leq 1$ with $Z = BA$ and $W = BL$. For an important special case, B is the identity.

Furthermore let $B_l(\mu, \varepsilon)$ be all bounded linear transformations of E of the form $\pi_{i=1}^l T_i$, $T_i \in B(\mu, \varepsilon)$ and $B^*(\mu, \varepsilon) = \cup_{l>0} B_l(\mu, \varepsilon)$.

(5.1) LEMMA. Given $0 < \mu < 1$, $\eta > 0$, there exists an $\varepsilon > 0$ with the following property. If $T \in B^*(\mu, \varepsilon)$ is the form

$$T = \begin{pmatrix} a & b \\ c & d \end{pmatrix}$$

then for all $v \in E_1$, $\|cv\| \leq \eta\|av\|$.

PROOF. It can be assumed without loss of generality that $\mu + \eta < 1$. We use induction on the following hypothesis:

$\mathscr{H}_l(\varepsilon)$: for $T_l = T_0 T_{l-1}$, $T_0 \in B(\mu, \varepsilon)$, $T_{l-1} \in B_{l-1}(\mu, \varepsilon)$

$$T_i = \begin{pmatrix} a_i & b_i \\ c_i & d_i \end{pmatrix}, \text{ for } i = 0, l - 1, l,$$

(i) $\|c_l v\| \leq \eta\|a_l v\|$

(ii) $\|a_{l-1} v\| \geq (\mu + \eta)\|a_l v\|$ for all $v \in E_1$

Note that if we can find a fixed $\varepsilon > 0$ so that $\mathscr{H}_l(\varepsilon)$ is true for all l, then 5.1. is proved.

It is easily checked that there is an $\varepsilon > 0$ so small that (a) $(\mu + \varepsilon)\eta + \varepsilon < \eta$, (b) $(\mu + \varepsilon)^{-1} + \varepsilon\eta < (\mu + \eta)^{-1}$ and (c) $\mathscr{H}_1(\varepsilon)$ is true.

Also

$$\begin{pmatrix} a_l & b_l \\ c_l & d_l \end{pmatrix} = \begin{pmatrix} a_0 a_{l-1} + b_0 c_{l-1}, & a_0 b_{l-1} + b_0 d_{l-1} \\ c_0 a_{l-1} + d_0 c_{l-1}, & c_0 b_{l-1} + d_0 d_{l-1} \end{pmatrix}$$

If $\mathscr{H}_{l-1}(\varepsilon)$ is true then for any $v \in E_1$, we have for (ii)

$$a_l v = a_0 a_{l-1} v + b_0 c_{l-1} v = BL a_{l-1} v + BA c_{l-1} v$$

So

$$\|a_l v\| \geq \|B^{-1}\| \, \|a_l v\|$$

$$\geq \|B^{-1} a_l v\|$$

$$\geq \|L a_{l-1} v + A c_{l-1} v\|$$

$$\geq \|L a_{l-1} v\| - \|A c_{l-1} v\|$$

Also

$$\|L a_{l-1} v\| \geq (\mu + \varepsilon)^{-1} \|a_{l-1} v\|$$

So

$$\|a_l v\| \geq ((\mu + \varepsilon)^{-1} - \eta \varepsilon) \|a_{l-1} v\|$$

$$\geq (\mu + \eta)^{-1} \|a_{l-1} v\|$$

(i) $$\|c_l v\| \leq \|c_0\| \, \|a_{l-1} v\| + \|d_0\| \, \|c_{l-1} v\|$$

$$\leq \varepsilon \|a_{l-1} v\| + (\mu + \varepsilon) \eta \|a_{l-1} v\|$$

$$\leq ((\mu + \varepsilon)\eta + \varepsilon) \|a_{l-1} v\|$$

$$\leq \eta \|a_{l-1} v\|$$

$$\leq \eta \|a_l v\|$$

by (ii). This prove 5.1.

For any $t > 0$ define the *sector* S_t of $E_1 \times 0$ to be the set $\{x \in E \,|\, x = 0$ or $d(x/\|x\|, E_1 \times 0) \leq t\}$.

Then 5.1 has the following consequence.

(5.2) LEMMA. *Given* $0 < \mu < 1$, $\eta > 0$, *there exists* $\varepsilon > 0$ *such that if* $T \in B^*(\mu, \varepsilon)$ *then* $T(E \times 0) \subset S_\eta$.

Actually one has the following generalization of 5.2 which we do not use.

(5.3) LEMMA. *Given* $0 < \mu < 1$, $\eta > 0$ *there exists* $\varepsilon_1 > 0$ *with the property that if* $T \varepsilon B^*(\mu, \varepsilon_1)$ *then* $T(S_{\varepsilon_1}) \subset S_\eta$.

PROOF. Let $\varepsilon > 0$ be given by 5.2 so that if $v \in E_1 \times 0$, $T \in B^*(\mu, \varepsilon)$ then $Tv \in S\eta$. Let U be the set in E of all vectors of the form Tv, $T \in B^*(\mu, \varepsilon)$, $v \in E_1 \times 0$. Then it can be seen that U contains a sector S_{ε_1} of $E_1 \times 0$ for some $0 < \varepsilon_1 < \varepsilon$.

Now if $v \in S_{\varepsilon_1}$, $T \in B^*(\mu, \varepsilon_1)$, the following proves that $Tv \in S_\eta$. First $v = T_1 v_1$, $v_1 \in E_1 \times 0$, $T_1 \in B^*(\mu, \varepsilon_1)$. Then $Tv = TT_1 v_1$ and since $B^*(\mu, \varepsilon_1)$ is closed under products, this shows $Tv \in S\eta$, proving 5.3.

§6

Here we reduce the proof of Theorem A of the Introduction to 6.2 which is proved in Sections 7 and 8.

Let D^l be the solid ball of radius 1 in Euclidean space E^l, D_1^l that of radius 1/10.

Let $R = D^k \times D^{n-k} \subset E^k \times E^{n-k} = E^n$.

Let τ, σ be some translations of E^k, E^{n-k} respectively which move distances by $\frac{1}{2}$ unit.

Then let $R_1 = (\tau \times e)(D_1^k \times D^{n-k})$, $R_2 = (\tau^{-1} \times e)(D_1^k \times D^{n-k})$ so that R_1, R_2 are disjoint subsets of R. Here e denotes the identity map. Let $R_1' = (e \times \sigma)(D^k \times D_1^{n-k})$, $R_2' = (e \times \sigma^{-1})(D^k \times D_1^{n-k})$, be so that R_1', R_2' also are disjoint subsets of R.

Let $c: D^k \to D_1^k$, $d: D^{n-k} \to D_1^{n-k}$ be the natural contractions, shrinking the radius by $\frac{1}{10}$, and define

$$r_1: R_1 \to R_1', \quad r_1 = (e \times \sigma)(c^{-1} \times d)(\tau \times e)^{-1}$$
$$r_2: R_2 \to R_2', \quad r_2 = (e \times \sigma)^{-1}(c^{-1} \times d)(\tau \times e)$$

(6.1) We suppose that $T_0: R \to E^n$ is a C^∞ injection defined on a neighborhood U of R in E^n such that

(1) $T_0 R \cap R = R_1' \cup R_2'$
(2) $T(_0^{-1} T_0(R) \cap R) = R_1 \cup R_2$
(3) T_0 maps T_1 onto R_1' by r_1
   T_0 maps R_1 onto R_2 by r_2
(4) $T_0(U) \cap U$ is contained in a ball of radius 2 in E^n.

We leave to the reader the task of verifying that there exists such diffeomorphisms. (For Theorem A, the case $k = 1$ is sufficient.)

The following will be proved in Sections 7 and 8.

(6.2) THEOREM. *There exists an $\varepsilon > 0$ with the following property. If $T: U \to E^n$ is a diffeomorphism which satisfies*

(a) $\|T(x) - T_0(x)\| < \varepsilon$, $x \in U$,
(b) $\|T_{*x}\| - T_{0*x}\| < \varepsilon$, $x \in U$,

then T restricted to R satisfies Axioms 1 and 2 of sections 3 and 4. (Here T_{*x} is the derivative of T at x.)

The preceding theorem leads to Theorem A as follows. Extend $T_0: R \to E^n$ to a diffeomorphism $T_0: E^n \to E^n$ which is the identity outside of the ball in E^n of radius 3. From techniques of differential topology, it follows that such an extension exists (see, for example, [8]).

Now let M be any manifold of dimension greater than one and $E^n \subset M$

a coordinate system. Let $T_0: E^n \to E^n$ be as above (with $k = 1$, for example) and extend T_0 to a diffeomorphism of all of M by making it the identity outside of E^n. Then 6.2 and 4.1 apply to yield Theorem A of the Introduction.

Remark 1. We have constructed only the simplest examples in n dimensions which could be used for Theorem A. In these examples the corresponding m of Section 1 is 2. The reader will be able to construct further similar examples such that this m is an arbitrary positive integer. Also by changing the orientation in the definition of r_1 preceding 6.1, one obtains an example of this type where $T: R \to M$, $R \subset M$, and $R \cup TR$ is not imbeddable in E^n. The subsequent analysis covers all such cases.

Remark 2. To obtain some geometric feeling for what is going on here and the earlier sections, it may be helpful for the reader to verify that T_0 itself of 6.1 satisfies Axioms 1 and 2, and perhaps even to go through Sections 2 and 3 with this example in mind, for small k, n.

§7

We prove here that for ε small enough, the T of 6.2 restricted to R satisfies Axiom 1.

Let $\Pi_1: R \to D^k$, $\Pi_2: R \to D^{n-k}$ be the respective projections with R as in 6.1. The tangent space of R at any point is a direct sum $E^k \times E^{n-k}$. Let S_η be the sector of $E^k \times 0$ as defined in section 5.

(7.1) LEMMA. *Given $\eta > 0$, there is an $\varepsilon > 0$, so that if T satisfies 6.1 with respect to ε, then the following is true: Let $\beta \in C_j^0$, $x \in \beta$, $y \in R$ with $T^{j+1}y = x$. If $v \in E^k \times 0$ is a tangent vector to y, then $T_{*y}^{j+1}(v) \in S_\eta$.*

Here C_j^0 refers to that of Section 2 defined by the above T.

PROOF. This is a consequence of 5.2. Take $\mu = \frac{1}{10}$, $E_1 = E^k$, $E_2 = E^{n-k}$, $B =$ identity. The derivative of T_0 on $R_1 \cup R_2$ is

$$\begin{pmatrix} 1/\mu & 0 \\ 0 & \mu \end{pmatrix}.$$

Thus in a neighborhood of $R_1 \cup R_2$, the derivative of T will be in $B(\mu, \varepsilon)$ and that of T^{j+1} will be in $B^*(\mu, \varepsilon)$ (since $T^i(y) \in R_1 \cup R_2$, $0 \le i < j + 1$). Thus 7.1 follows.

(7.2) LEMMA. *Let $\beta = \beta_1 \cap \beta_2$, $\beta_1 \in C_j^0$, $\beta_2 \in C_{-1}^l$, j, $l < \infty$ (all with respect to T of 6.2). If ε of 6.2 is small enough, there exists a diffeomorphism $\psi_\beta: \beta \to D^k \times D^{n-k}$ which is given by $(\Pi_1 T^l \times \Pi_2 T^{-(j+1)})\Delta$ where $\Delta: \beta \to \beta \times \beta$ is the diagonal map and differentiability of ψ_β is with respect to the induced structure on β as a subset of R.*

Before we give the proof we note a consequence.

(7.3) COROLLARY. For $\varepsilon > 0$ small enough, T of 6.2 restricted to R satisfies Axiom 1.

PROOF OF 7.2. We take ε so small that in 7.1 for $v \in S_\eta$, the angle between η and $E^k \times 0$ is less than $\pi/8$. It must be shown that the composition ψ_β

$$\beta \xrightarrow{\;\Delta\;} \beta \times \beta \xrightarrow{\;\pi_1 T^l \times \pi_2 T^{-(j+1)}\;} D^k \times D^{n-k}$$

satisfies:

(a) well-defined
(b) differentiable
(c) of rank n
(d) onto
(e) $1 - 1$.

(a) It is sufficient to show that if $x \in \beta$, $T^l(x)$, $T^{-(j+1)}(x)$ are in R. In fact since $\beta_1 \subset B_j^0$, $\beta_2 \subset B_{-1}^l$, $x \in \beta$ if and only if $T^i(x) \in R$ for $-(j+1) \le i \le l$.

(b) This follows from the definition of ψ_β.

(c) Let $x \in \beta$. Then the kernels $(\Pi_1 T^l)_{*x}^{-1}(0)$ and $(\Pi_2 T^{-(j+1)})_{*x}^{-1}(0)$, say, L_1, L_2 respectively are linear subspaces of the tangent space R_x. If it can be shown that $L_1 \cap L_2$ is the zero vector, then ψ_β must have rank n.

Consider L_2. A vector $v \in R_x$ will belong to L_2 if and only if $(T^{-(j+1)})_{*x}(v)$ lies in $E^k \times 0$, or equivalently if $v \in (T^{j+1})_{*x}(E^k \times 0)$ where $y = T^{-(j+1)}(x)$. Thus $L_2 \subset S_\eta$ by 7.1 where S_η is the η sector of $E^k \times 0$ and any non-zero vector of S_η has angle with $E^k \times 0$ less than $\pi/8$.

A similar argument shows that if $v \in L_1$, then v has angle with $0 \times E^{n-k}$ less than $\pi/8$. Thus only the zero vector is in $L_1 \cap L_2$ and (c) is proved.

For (d) and (e) we show there exists an inverse to ψ_β. This is a consequence of

(7.4) LEMMA. Let $-1 \le j < \infty$, $0 \le l < \infty$, $x \in D^k$, $y \in D^{n-k}$, $\beta_1 \in C_j^0$, $\beta_2 \in C_{-1}^l$. Then

$$[\beta_2 \cap (\pi_2 T^l)^{-1}(x)] \cap [\beta_1 \cap (\pi_2 T^{-(j+1)})^{-1}(y)]$$

is a single point.

PROOF. Let $E_x = \Pi_1^{-1}(x) = x \times D^{n-k}$, $E_y = \Pi_2^{-1}(y) = D^k \times y$, $W_1 = T^{-l}(E_x) \cap \beta_2$, $W_2 = T^{(j+1)}(E_y) \cap \beta_1$. Then (7.3) says $W_1 \cap W_2$ is a single point.

Now inductivity define $B_j^0(y) = T(B_{j-1}^0(y) \cap B_{-1}^1)$ where $B_{-1}^0(y)$ is E_y; thus $B_j^0 = U_{y \in D^{n-k}} B_j^0(y)$. Then W_2 is a component of $B_j^0(y)$. Then by induction on j it is not difficult to see that Π_1 restricted to W_2 is a diffeomorphism $W_2 \to D^k$ and the tangent plane of W_2 is within η of $E^k \times 0$ with η as before.

Similar considerations apply to W_1. Putting this information together yields that $W_1 \cap {}_2$ is a single point. This finishes the proof of 7.4 and hence 7.2.

§8

The goal of this section is to verify that T of 6.2 satisfies Axiom 2 for ε small enough. This is done through complementing 7.2 with the case where l and j are allowed to become infinite.

We first prove (but not use here):

(8.1) LEMMA. *Let* $\beta \in C_\infty^0$. *Then* Π_1 *restricted to* β *is a homeomorphism* $\beta \to D^k$. *Similarly if* $\beta_1 \in C_\infty^0$, Π_2 *restricted to* β_1 *is a homeomorphism from* β_1 *to* D^{n-k}.

Here C_∞^0 refers of course to the T of 6.2 for sufficiently small ε.

PROOF. We claim that if $\beta \in C_\infty^0$, $x \in D^k$, then the diameter of $\beta \cap (x \times D^{n-k})$ is less than $(1/2)^j$. On one hand this statement clearly implies 8.1, and on the other hand it is consequence of the following lemma.

(8.2) LEMMA. *Let* α *be a compact subset of* R *with the property that for each* $x \in D^k$, $(x \times D^{n-k}) \cap \alpha$ *has diameter* $<K$. *Then if* α_1 *is a component of* $T\alpha$, $(x \times D^{n-k}) \cap \alpha_1$ *has diameter* $<K/2$ *for each* $x \in D^k$.

PROOF. If T were T_0 of 6.2, then 8.2 would be true. But since T is an approximation of T_0, it holds for T as well.

The following yields Axiom 2.

(8.3) LEMMA. *Let* $\beta_1 \in C_\infty^0$, $\beta_2 \in C_{-1}^\infty$. *Then* $\beta_1 \cap \beta_2$ *is a point*.

PROOF. We can write $\beta_1 = \cap_{i=1}^\infty \alpha_i, \alpha_i \in C_i^0, \alpha_i \supset \alpha_{i-1}$ and $\beta_2 = \cap_{i=1}^\infty \alpha^i$, $\alpha^i \in C_{-1}^i$, $\alpha^i \supset \alpha^{i-1}$ so that $\beta_1 \cap \beta_2 = \cap_{i=1}^\infty (\alpha_i \cap \alpha^i)$. Then $\alpha_i \cap \alpha^i \supset \alpha_{i-1} \cap \alpha^{i-1}$ and from 7.2 we get that $\beta_1 \cap \beta_2$ is non-empty. Then from 8.2 and the analogue of 8.2 for T^{-1}, the diameter of $\beta_1 \cap \beta_2$ must be zero, proving 8.3.

§9

The main goal of this section is to prove Theorem B of the Introduction. For this proof, we depend on the theory of stable manifolds [11]. We recall in fact from this paper, the following theorem (Theorem 6.1 of [11]).

Let $D(M)$ be the space of C^r diffeomorphism of M, C^r topology and D_0 the space of $T \in D$ satisfying the following condition: The periodic points of T are elementary and the stable manifolds have normal intersection with the unstable manifolds of T.

(9.1) THEOREM. D_0 *is the countable intersection of open dense subsets of* D.

Now note that we can assume that the periodic points of $T \in D_0$ can satisfy a slightly stronger condition without loss of generality, namely Sternberg's non-degeneracy condition of [13]. Thus by Sternberg's theorem [13] in the neighborhood of a point of M of period p, there will exist local coordinates in which T^p is linear. (I suspect that with a little effort, the use of this deep theorem could be bypassed.)

We can clearly assume without loss of generality in the proof of theorem B that the m in the definition of homoclinic point is 1.

Let now p be a homoclinic point of $T \in D_0$, and let

$$y = \lim_{n \to \infty} T^n p = \lim_{n \to \infty} T^{-n} p.$$

Then y is a fixed point of T with, say, stable manifold W^s, unstable manifold W^u and $p \in W^s \cap W^u$.

Now by the previous remarks, we can suppose that V is a neighborhood of y of the form

$$V = \{\|x_1\| \le r_0, \|x_2\| \le r_1\}, \ (x_1, x_2) \in E_1 \times E_2 = E$$

and that T restricted to V is linear and of the form

$$T|V = L_0 = \begin{pmatrix} A_1 & 0 \\ 0 & A_2 \end{pmatrix}$$

where $A_1 \colon E_1 \to E_1$, $A_2 \colon E_2 \to E_2$ are linear transformations, $\|A_1^{-1}\| < u < 1$, $\|A_2\| < u < 1$.

We can assume without loss of generality in the proof of Theorem B that $p \in V$.

(9.2) LEMMA.   *There exist compact domains with smooth boundary, K in W^s, J in W^u, $p \in K \cap J$, $\partial K \cap J = \emptyset$, $K \cap \partial J = \emptyset$, K, J diffeomorphic to disks, and $K \subset$ interior $T^{-1}K$, $J \subset$ interior TJ.*

PROOF.   Following Section 3 of [11], there exist K, J with all the above properties, except for perhaps the boundary properties. Then using transversality theorems (see e.g. Thom [14]) one can find suitable approximations of K, J satisfying 9.2.

The K and J of 9.2 will intersect in a finite number of points, $p_1, \ldots, p_r$, including the original homoclinic point p and y. Of course, the p_i are homoclinic points, except for y. We assume as before that the p_i and J lie in V.

Let m be large enough so that $T^{m_1}(p_i) \in V$ for each i and $m_1 \ge m$, and let L_i be the derivative of T^m at p_i, so that $L_i \colon E_1 \times E_2 \to E_1 \times E_2$. If we write

$$L_i = \begin{pmatrix} A & B \\ C & D \end{pmatrix}$$

according to this product decomposition then by the transversality of the homoclinic point p_i, $A: E_1 \to E_1$ is invertible. Choose $\varepsilon > 0$ so that for each i, if $\|S - L_i\| < \varepsilon$, and

$$S = \begin{pmatrix} S_1 & S_2 \\ S_3 & S_4 \end{pmatrix},$$

then S_1 is invertible.

Let U_i be a neighborhood of p_i such that $T^m(y) \in V$ and $\|T^m_*(y) - L_i\|$ $< \varepsilon$ if $y \in U_i$. (Here $T^m_*(y)$ is the derivative of T^m at y.)

(9.3) LEMMA. *There exists* $\lambda > 0$, k_0 *such that for all* $k \geq k_0$ *the derivative* $T^k T^m T^\lambda$ *satisfies the hypotheses of the linear transformation of 5.2 on the subset of* $T^{-\lambda}(U_i)$ *consisting of points* z *such that* $T^j(z) \in V$ *for* $m + \lambda \leq j$ $\leq m + \lambda + k$.

PROOF. This derivative is of the form $L_0^k S L_0^\lambda$ where L_0 is as before and S satisfies the condition of the S previously defined, i.e., S_1 below is invertible. Then

$$L_0^k S L_0^\lambda = \begin{pmatrix} A_1^k S_1 A_1^\lambda & A_1^k S_2 A_2^\lambda \\ A_2^k S_3 A_1^\lambda & A_2^k S_x A_2^\lambda \end{pmatrix}$$

$\|A_1^{-1}\|$, $\|A_2\| < 1$. Now 9.3 is clear.

Choose λ and k_0 of 9.3 valid for all the U_i at once and let $U = \cup_{i=1}^r T^{-\lambda} U_i$ and $D_r = \{x_2 \in E_2 : \|x_2\| \leq r \leq r_1\}$.

The following lemma can be proved without great difficulty.

(9.4) LEMMA. *There exists* $r > 0$ *and* $k \geq k_0$ *such that*

$$T^{-\lambda}(K \cap J) \subset T^{-(k+m+\lambda)}(T^{-\lambda}J \times D_r) \cap (T^{-\lambda}J \times D_r) \subset U.$$

Now consider $T^{k+m+\lambda}$ restricted to $T^{-(k+m+\lambda)}(T^{-\lambda}J \times D_r)$ By 9.3 and 9.4, and by the following sections 7 and 8, we obtain as before that this pair satisfies axioms one and two. Then by 4.1, Theorem B is proved.

REMARK. Of course the conclusion of Theorem B applies to homoclinic points of diffeomorphisms T satisfying weaker assumptions than $T_0 \in D_0$. For example, all of this is valid for the homoclinic points Poincaré originally found in the restricted 3-body problem, and thus one obtains information about the "motions" in this problem.

COLUMBIA UNIVERSITY

REFERENCES

[1] G. D. BIRKHOFF, Nouvelles recherches sur les systèmes dynamiques, "Pontifical Memoir," *Collected Works*, Vol. 2, Amer. Math. Soc., New York, 1950.

[2] ———, On the periodic motions of dynamical systems, *Collected Works*, Vol. 2, Amer. Math. Soc., New York, 1950.

[3] M. CARTRIGHT, Forced oscillations in nonlinear systems, *Contributions to the Theory of Non-linear Oscillations, I*, Princeton University Press, 1950.

[4] EILENBERG and STEENROD, *Foundations of Algebraic Topology*, Princeton University Press, 1952.

[5] GOTTSCHALK and HEDLUND, *Topological Dynamics*, Amer. Math. Soc., Colloquium Publications, Vol. 36, Providence, 1955.

[6] N. LEVINSON, A second order differential equation with singular solutions. *Ann. of Math., 50* (1949).

[7] J. E. LITTLEWOOD, On non-linear differential equations of the 2nd order, IV. The general equation $y'' + kf(y)y' + g(y) = bkp(\phi)$, $\phi = t + \alpha$, *Acta Math., 98* (1957), p. 1–110.

[8] R. PALAIS, Extending diffeomorphisms, *Proc. Amer. Math. Soc., 11* (1960), p. 274–277.

[9] S. SMALE, Report on the symposium on non-linear oscillations, Kiev Math. Institute, 1961.

[10] ———, Dynamical systems and the topological conjugacy problem for diffeomorphisms, International Congress of Mathematicians at Stockholm, 1962.

[11] ———, Stable manifolds for differential equations and diffeomorphisms to appear.

[12] ———, Morse inequalities for a dynamical system, *Bull. Amer. Math. Soc., 66* (1960), p. 43–49.

[13] S. STERNBERG, On the structure of local homeomorphisms of Euclidean space, II, *Amer. Jour. of Math., 80* (1958), p. 623–631.

[14] R. THOM, Quelques propriétés globales des variétés différentiables, *Comm. Math. Helv., 28* (1954), p. 17–86.

Bowls of a Non-Degenerate Function on a Compact Differentiable Manifold[1]

MARSTON MORSE

1. Introduction

Let $\mathbf{M}$ be a connected, compact, oriented, differentiable n-manifold of class C^∞, with $n > 2$. There exist non-degenerate functions f on $\mathbf{M}$ of class C^∞, as the author showed in his Colloquium Lectures in 1934 (see p. 243). The relevant theorem is that if $\mathbf{M}$ is in a euclidean m-space E_m the set of points in E_m which are not focal points of $\mathbf{M}$ in the distance problem are everywhere dense in E_m. If P is not on $\mathbf{M}$ nor a focal point the distance from P to a point on $\mathbf{M}$ defines a non-degenerate function on $\mathbf{M}$.

In [1] it is shown that by suitable elimination of pairs of critical points with indices n and $n - 1$ or indices 1 and 0, f is replaced by a non-degenerate function of *polar* type, that is a function having only one point of relative minimum and one point of relative maximum. It is one of the objects of this paper to present conditions under which critical points w, $\dot{w}$ with respective indices $k - 1$ and k, where $1 < k < n$, can be eliminated by a modification of f that does not introduce other critical points nor alter f in sufficiently small neighborhoods of the critical points of f other than w and $\dot{w}$. We suppose that f is of polar type and that the values of f at different critical points are different.

We have found that sufficient conditions for such an elimination of critical points can be given in terms of differentiable k and $(n - k)$-submanifolds of $\mathbf{M}$, associated with the respective critical points of f of index k, and termed *bowls* of f.

We use methods which combine the study of the critical points of f and of diffeomorphisms of level manifolds of f, with the study of bowls of f and of families of f-arcs, analogous to the orthogonal trajectories of the level manifolds of f. The first objective is to reveal in differential terms fundamental topological characteristics of $\mathbf{M}$. The ultimate, but presently

[1] This research was supported by the Air Force Office of Scientific Research.

more remote objective, is the determination of the classes of mutually diffeomorphic n-manifolds $\mathbf{M}$.

To define the bowls of f it is necessary to define *canonical* representations of neighborhood of the critical points of f together with *canonical* representations of f thereon.

All mappings and manifolds to which reference is made in this paper will be of class C^∞.

Notation. Let E_n be a euclidean n-space of points x with rectangular coordinates $(x^1, \ldots, x^n)$. We shall regard x as a vector with components $x^1, \ldots, x^n$ and length $\|x\|$. For each positive constant a set

(1.1) $$D_a^x = (x|\|x\| < a)$$

We shall make use of the following projections of E_n into E_n:

(1.2) $$x \to pr_k x = (x^1, \ldots, x^k, 0, \ldots, 0)$$

(1.3) $$x \to pr^k x = (0, \ldots, 0, x^{k+1}, \ldots, x^n)$$

(1.4) $$x \to pr_k^1 x = (0, x^2, \ldots, x^k, 0, \ldots, 0) \quad (k > 0)$$

DEFINITION 1.1. *Coordinate presentations* on $\mathbf{M}$. Let U be a nonempty open subset of E_n and

(1.5) $$x \to F(x): U \to X$$

a homeomorphism F of U onto an open subset X of $\mathbf{M}$. We say that F maps the coordinate *range* U onto the coordinate *domain* X of $\mathbf{M}$, and term $(F: U, X)$ a *coordinate presentation*, or more explicitly a *presentation of X on $\mathbf{M}$ with coordinates* $(x^1, \ldots, x^n)$.

DEFINITION 1.2. *An oriented differentiable structure ST on $\mathbf{M}$.* Such a structure is defined by a set W of presentations $(F: U, X)$ of open subsets X of $\mathbf{M}$ whose *union* is $\mathbf{M}$, and which are *compatible* in the following sense. If

$$(F_1: U_1, X_1) \qquad (F_2: U_2, X_2)$$

are two coordinate presentations of $\mathbf{M}$ such that $X_1 \cap X_2 = X \neq \emptyset$, the homeomorphism

(1.6) $$x \to F_2^{-1}(F_1(x)): F_1^{-1}(X) \to F_2^{-1}(X)$$

shall be of class C^∞ with a positive jacobian. An arbitrary presentation $(F': U', X')$ of an open subset X' of $\mathbf{M}$ will be termed *admissible* in the given differentiable structure ST, if it is compatible, in the above sense, with each presentation in W whose domain X intersects X'.

Let Ω be the set of critical points of f. Let $\mathbf{0}$ be the origin in E_n. Let R be the axis of reals.

The following lemma is a consequence of Lemma 6.1 of [1].

LEMMA 1.1. *There exists a Riemannian metric $\mathcal{R}^0$ on $\mathbf{M}$ and a positive constant σ so small that the following is true.*

Corresponding to each critical point $z \in \Omega$ there exists an admissible coordinate presentation

$$(1.7) \qquad (T_z : D_\sigma^x, X_z) \qquad (T_z(\mathbf{0}) = z)$$

of a domain X_z of $\mathbf{M}$ which contains z and has the following properties:

(i) *If z has the index k then*

$$(1.8) \qquad f(T_z(x)) - fT_z(\mathbf{0}) = -\|pr_k x\|^2 + \|pr^k x\|^2$$

(ii) T_z *maps D_σ^x isometrically into $\mathbf{M}$.*

(iii) *The sets X_z, $z \in \Omega$ have disjoint closures in $\mathbf{M}$, and the sets $f(X_z)$ have disjoint closures in R.*

Reference to §6 of [1] discloses the following freedom in choosing the metric $\mathcal{R}^0$ in Lemma 1.1. Let $\mathcal{R}$ be an arbitrary Riemannian metric on $\mathbf{M}$, and Y an arbitrary open subset of $\mathbf{M}$ whose closure does not meet Ω. Then in Lemma 1.1, the metric $\mathcal{R}^0$, the constant σ and the coordinate presentations (1.7) can be chosen so that $\mathcal{R} | Y = \mathcal{R}^0 | Y$.

DEFINITION 1.3. *A family $\mathbf{H}$ of f-arcs.* In terms of the Riemannian metric $\mathcal{R}^0$ of Lemma 1.1 the trajectories orthogonal to the level manifolds of f are well-defined on $\mathbf{M} - \Omega$. We term these trajectories *ortho-f-arcs.* The family of ortho-f-arcs on $\mathbf{M} - \Omega$ is a special case of a family $\mathbf{H}$ of f-arcs on $\mathbf{M} - \Omega$ satisfying the following three conditions:

I. *In each coordinate domain X on $\mathbf{M} - \Omega$ with admissible coordinates $(x^1, \ldots, x^n)$, the f-arcs of $\mathbf{H}$ shall be represented by solutions of differential equations*

$$(1.9) \qquad \frac{dx^i}{dt} = Z^i(x) \qquad (i = 1, \ldots, n)$$

of class C^∞, where $Z(x)$ is a contravariant vector on $\mathbf{M}$ whose orthogonal projection into the gradient g of f at the point $p \in \mathbf{M}$ represented by x, is a non-null vector with the sense of g.

II. *The vectors Z are such that $df|dt = 1$ along each f-arc of $\mathbf{H}$. Each f-arc k of $\mathbf{H}$ is so parameterized as a solution of (1.9) that a point $p \in k$ is represented by the point $t = f(p)$ in R.*

III. *The subarcs of an f-arc in the canonical domains X_z of Lemma 1.1 are ortho-f-arcs.*

H-arcs. The maximal connected arcs of the family $\mathbf{H}$ will be called H-arcs. In terms of these H-arcs we now define the bowls of f.

With each critical point z with index $k > 0$, we shall associate a descending k-bowl $B_-(z, k)$, and with each critical point z of index $k < n$, an ascending $(n - k)$-bowl $B_+(z, n - k)$.

DEFINITION 1.4. *If $k > 0$, $B_-(z, k)$ shall be the differentiable k-submanifold of* **M** *formed by the union of z and the H-arcs which have z as "upper" limiting end point.*

If $k < n$, $B_+(z, n - k)$ shall be the $(n - k)$-submanifold of **M** *formed by the union of z and the H-arcs which have z as a "lower" limiting end point.*

We term z the *pole* of the bowls just defined, and observe that in case $0 < k < n$

$$(1.10) \qquad B_+(z, n - k) \cap B_-(z, k) = z$$

By definition a bowl contains no critical points other than its pole. The differential properties of a bowl in a neighborhood of its pole follow from Lemma 1.1.

We state the following theorem.

THEOREM 1.1 (α). *A descending k-bowl $B_-(z, k)$ is the C^∞-diffeomorph of an open euclidean k-ball.*

(β). *An ascending $(n - k)$-bowl $B_+(z, n - k)$ is the C^∞-diffeomorph of an open euclidean $(n - k)$-ball.*

We shall sketch the proof of (α). For full details of the proof see [2].

Without loss of generality in proving (α) we can suppose that $f(z) = 0$.

We introduce a $(k - 1)$-sphere S_{k-1} in $pr_k E_n$ by setting

$$(1.11) \qquad S_{k-1} = (x \in pr_k E_n | \|x\| = \sigma)$$

A point $u \in S_{k-1}$ determines an open ray ρ_u in $pr_k E_n$, with one end at the origin and the other at the point $u \in S_{k-1}$. Moreover $T_z(\rho_u)$ is a subarc of a unique H-arc λ_u in $B_-(z, k)$. Let $(0, a(u))$ be the open interval of values of $|f(p)|^{\frac{1}{2}}$ on λ_u. Let ρ'_u be an extension of ρ_u in $pr_k E_n$ as an open ray which has one end point at the origin and the other at a distance $a(u)$ from the origin. We introduce the open subset

$$(1.12) \qquad Z_z = (\rho'_u | u \in S_{k-1}) \cup z$$

of $pr_k E_n$ and affirm the following.

LEMMA 1.2 (a). *The k-bowl $B_-(z, k)$ is the C^∞-diffeomorph of Z_z under a mapping in which a point in ρ'_u at a distance $t < a(u)$ from the origin corresponds to the point p on the H-arc λ_u at which $|f(p)|^{\frac{1}{2}} = t$, while the origin in Z_z corresponds to z.*

(b) *The set Z_z is the real analytic diffeomorph of an open k-ball.*

Statement (a) follows from the definition of $B_-(z, k)$, and from the classical properties of trajectories of the system (1.9). The proof of (b) can be readily given with the aid of Corollary 9.1 of [3], as will be shown in detail in [2].

Statement (α) of Theorem 1.1 follows from Lemma 1.2. The proof of (β) in Theorem 1.1 is similar.

2. The choice of the family **H** of f-arcs

As indicated in §1 one can start with an arbitrary Riemannian metric $\mathscr{R}$ on **M**, and by suitable modifications of $\mathscr{R}$ near the respective critical points of f, arrive at the Riemannian metric $\mathscr{R}^0$ affirmed to exist in Lemma 1.1. Let the family of ortho-f-arcs on **M** $- \Omega$, determined by $\mathscr{R}^0$, be denoted by $\mathbf{H}^0$. The family $\mathbf{H}^0$ satisfies the conditions I, II, III of §1 on an admissible family of f-arcs.

Our purposes will be served if the ultimate family **H** of f-arcs on **M** $- \Omega$ is obtained by a finite number of special modifications of $\mathbf{H}^0$, the character of which we shall presently define. We begin with notation.

If α is an arbitrary value of f set

$$(2.1) \qquad f^\alpha = (p \in \mathbf{M} | f(p) = \alpha)$$

If $[\alpha, \beta]$ is a closed interval of ordinary values of f set

$$(2.2) \qquad f_{\alpha\beta} = (p \in \mathbf{M} | \alpha \le f(p) \le \beta)$$

DEFINITION 2.1. *An isotopy on f^a.* Cf. [8]. Let a be an ordinary value of f, and h and k two diffeomorphisms of f^a onto f^a. A C^∞-mapping,

$$(2.3) \qquad (x, t) \to F(x, t) \colon f^a \times R \to f^a$$

is called an isotopy F of h into k, if each partial mapping

$$(2.4) \qquad x \to F(x, t) = F^t(x) \qquad\qquad (x \in f^a)$$

is a diffeomorphism of f^a onto f^a, if $h = F^t$ for $t \le 0$ and if $k = F^t$ for $t \ge 1$. We say that such an isotopy is *determined* by the diffeomorphisms F^t, $0 \le t \le 1$.

DEFINITION 2.2. Let Y be a subset of **M** $- \Omega$. Two admissible families $\mathbf{H}'$ and $\mathbf{H}''$ of f-arcs will be said to *differ at most on Y* if the ensemble of subarcs on **M** $- \Omega - \bar{Y}$ of H'-arcs is identical with the ensemble of subarcs on **M** $- \Omega - \bar{Y}$ of H''-arcs.

DEFINITION 2.3. *H-related points.* Corresponding to an admissible family **H** of f-arcs, two points of **M** $- \Omega$ will be said to be *H-related* if they lie on the same H-arc.

The diffeomorphisms $H_{c,e}$. Let c and e be ordinary values of f between which there are no critical values of f. We admit the possibility that $c < e$, $c = e$, or $c > e$. Let $H_{c,e}$ denote the diffeomorphism of f^e onto f^c in which a point $p \in f^e$ is mapped into the H-related point of f^c. Note that $H_{e,c}$ is the inverse of $H_{c,e}$.

DEFINITION 2.4.   *An* [a, b]-*replacement of* **H**. Let [a, b] be a closed interval of ordinary values of f assumed at no point of the subsets $X_z|(z \in \Omega)$ given in Lemma 1.1. By an [a, b]-*replacement of* **H** is meant an admissible family **H*** of f-arcs whose subarcs differ from those of **H** at most on f_{ab}. We say that this replacement *belongs* to the pair of consecutive critical values between which a and b lie.

By virtue of the following lemma such a replacement of H by H* may properly be called *isotopic*. In Lemma 2.1 we refer to values

$$(2.5) \qquad\qquad c(t) = ta + (1 - t)b \qquad\qquad (0 \leq t \leq 1)$$

interpolating between a and b.

LEMMA 2.1.   *If* **H*** *is an* [a, b]-*replacement of* **H**, *the composite diffeomorphisms*

$$(2.6) \qquad\qquad \Gamma^t = H_{a,c(t)} H^*_{c(t),a} \qquad\qquad (0 \leq t \leq 1)$$

of f^a *onto* f^a *"determine" an isotopy* Γ *on* f^a *of the diffeomorphism* $\Gamma^0 = H_{ab} H^*_{ba}$ *into the identity* Γ^1.

Conversely if γ *is an arbitrary diffeomorphism of* f^a *onto* f^a, *admitting an isotopy* Γ *on* f^a *of* γ *into the identity, there exists a unique* [a, b]-*replacement* **H*** *of* **H** *such that* (2.6) *holds. Cf.* [2] *for proof.*

DEFINITION 2.5.   *General isotopic replacements of* **H**⁰. Given the family **H**⁰ of ortho-f-arcs determined by the Riemannian metric $\mathscr{R}^0$ of Lemma 1.1, let **H** be an admissible family of f-arcs obtained from **H**⁰ by a finite sequence of [a, b]-replacements, including at most one [a, b]-replacement belonging to each pair of successive critical values of f. We term such a family **H** an *isotopic replacement* of **H**⁰.

We shall presently condition **H** in terms of the bowls of f defined with the aid of **H**.

The intersections of bowls of f. Note first that no descending (ascending) bowl meets another descending (ascending) bowl. Apart from the special case of an ascending and descending bowl which have the same pole, two bowls intersect, if at all, in an ensemble of H-arcs. That is, if two bowls intersect in a point p, not a common pole, they intersect in the maximal H-arc g containing p. Such an H-arc has as upper limiting end point the pole of the descending bowl, and as lower limiting end point the pole of the ascending bowl.

DEFINITION 2.6.   *The trace of a bowl on level manifold*. If α is a value of f, not the minimum or maximum value of f, the intersection with f^α of a k-bowl B will be called the *trace* B^α *of* B *on* f^α. If this trace is not empty, or the pole, it is a differentiable $(k - 1)$-submanifold of f^α.

The special bowls B_- *and* B_+. Let B_- be a descending k-bowl with the pole $\dot{w}$, and B_+ an ascending $(n - k + 1)$-bowl with the pole w. The point $\dot{w}$ has the index k, the point w the index $k - 1$. These are the bowls with which the principal theorem is concerned.

DEFINITION 2.7. *Regular intersections of B_- and B_+.* If the intersection of B_- and B_+ contains a point p, set $f(p) = \alpha$. The intersection of B_- and B_+ will be termed *regular* at p if the $(k - 1)$- and $(n - k)$-dimensional traces of B_- and B_+ on f^α intersect in p on f^α without tangent in common at p. It is shown in [2] that if B_- and B_+ interesect regularly at p, they intersect regularly at each point p' of the f-arc ω meeting p. In such a case we say that B_- and B_+ *intersect regularly along ω.*

Lemma 2.1 prepares the way for the main theorem, Theorem 2.1.

LEMMA 2.1. *There exists an isotopic replacement* **H** *of the family* **H⁰** *of ortho-f-arcs such that the bowls of f, defined in terms of H-arcs, have the following properties.*

(i) *A descending k-bowl and an ascending r-bowl for which $r + k \leq n$ intersect at most in a common pole.*

(ii) *A descending k-bowl, with $1 < k < n$, and an ascending $(n - k + 1)$-bowl do not intersect, or intersect regularly in a finite ensemble of maximal f-arcs of* **H**. *See* [4] *and* [11].

To state Theorem 2.1 a definition is needed.

DEFINITION 2.8. *The k-dome $\mathscr{B}_-$ (z, k) of $B_-(z, k)$.* Each H-arc of $B_-(z, k)$ has a critical point $z' \in \Omega$ as lower limiting end point. The corresponding values $f(z')$ are finite in number, and so have a maximum at some critical point z^0. The restriction of $B_-(z, k)$ on which $f(z) \geq f(p) > f(z^0)$ will be called the *k-dome $\mathscr{B}_-(z, k)$ of $B_-(z, k)$*. We note the following.

The k-dome of a descending k-bowl is the diffeomorph of an open k-ball.

Inverted domes of ascending bowls can be similarly defined and treated. The principal theorem follows. See [2].

THEOREM 2.1. *Let B_- be a descending k-bowl with pole $\dot{w}$ and B_+ an ascending $(n - k + 1)$-bowl with pole w, such that B_- and B_+ intersect regularly in a single H-arc ω, and such that the closure of B_- meets no critical point between the f-levels of w and $\dot{w}$.*

Let N be a prescribed open neighborhood of the closure of the dome of B_- such that N contains w and $\dot{w}$ and $\bar{N}$ no other critical points of f.

There then exists a non-degenerate function $\hat{f}$ on **M** *without critical points on $\bar{N}$ and such that $\hat{f}(p) = f(p)$ for $p \in$* **M** $- N$.

DEFINITION 2.9. *Admissible changes of coordinates* in Lemma 1.1. We shall admit changes in rectangular coordinates $(x^1, \ldots, x^n)$ in Lemma 1.1 of the following types.

The coordinates can be arbitrarily permuted, the coordinates whose squares are summed can be orthogonally transformed, the remaining coordinates orthogonally transformed, and such changes can be made any finite number of times in any order, provided the resultant transformation has the determinant 1.

Choice of $T_{\dot{w}}$. After a suitable admissible change of coordinates an isometric presentation of $X_{\dot{w}}$ in Lemma 1.1 will become an isometric presentation

$$(T_{\dot{w}} \colon D_\sigma^x, X_{\dot{w}})$$

of $X_{\dot{w}}$ such that the interval $-\sigma < x^1 < 0$ of the x^1-axis has the terminal arc of ω of length σ as its image under $T_{\dot{w}}$, while

(2.7) $$f(T_{\dot{w}}(x)) - f(\dot{w}) = -\|pr_k x\|^2 + \|pr^k x\|^2 \qquad (x \in D_\sigma^x)$$

Choice of T_w. After a suitable admissible change of coordinates an isometric presentation on X_w in Lemma 1.1 will become an isometric presentation (T_w, D_σ^y, X_w) of X_w such that conditions (a) and (b) are satisfied.

(a) *The interval $0 < y^1 < \sigma$ of the y^1-axis has the initial arc of ω of length σ as its image under T_w.*

(b) $$f(T_w(y)) - f(w) = (y^1)^2 - \|pr_k^1 y\|^2 + \|pr^k y\|^2 \qquad (y \in D_\sigma^y)$$

An isometric presentation T_w of X_w satisfying conditions (a) and (b) is not necessarily an adequate final choice of T_w. In particular suppose that T_w^* is such a presentation of X_w in terms of coordinates $(u^1, \ldots, u^n)$. To satisfy (i) below it may be necessary to change from coordinates $(u^1, \ldots, u^n)$ to coordinates $(y^1, \ldots, y^n)$ identical with $(u^1, \ldots, u^n)$, except that $y^2 = -u^2$ and $y^n = -u^n$. We are thus led to *two* final choices of an isometric presentation T_w of X_w satisfying (a) and (b).

DEFINITION 2.10.   Let $\mathbf{H}^*$ be an admissible family of f-arcs on $M - \Omega$ such that the corresponding bowls B_-^* and B_+^* intersect regularly in $\omega = B_- \cap B_+$. We say that such a family $\mathbf{H}^*$ is ω-*canonical* if for one of the two choices of T_w indicated in the preceding paragraph the following is true.

(i) *Each point $T_{\dot{w}}(x)$ for which $x^1 = -\sigma/2$ and for which x is sufficiently near the x^1-axis, is $\mathbf{H}^*$-related to the point $T_w(y)$ for which $y = \sigma/2$ and $(y^2, \ldots, y^n) = (x^2, \ldots, x^n)$.*

With ω-canonical families $\mathbf{H}$ so defined we state the following lemma.

LEMMA 2.2.   *Under the conditions of Theorem 2.1 on $\mathbf{H}$, B_- and B_+, there exists an isotopic replacement $\mathbf{H}^*$ of $\mathbf{H}$ satisfying the following three conditions.*

(α) *The family $\mathbf{H}^*$ contains $\omega = B_- \cap B_+$ as an f-arc and differs from $\mathbf{H}$ at most on a prescribed open neighborhood N^* of ω.*

(β) *The new bowls* B^*_- *and* B^*_+ *satisfy the conditions on* B_- *and* B_+ *of Theorem 2.1.*

(γ) *The family* $\mathbf{H}^*$ *is* ω-*canonical.*

In §3 we make use of a family $\mathbf{H}^*$ satisfying Lemma 2.2. The presentation T_w in §3 will mean one for which (i) in Definition 2.10 is satisfied.

3. The replacement $\hat{f}$ of f

Without loss of generality in proving Theorem 2.1 we can suppose that $f(w) = 0$ and that $f(\dot{w}) = 1$. Let the dome of the k-bowl B^*_- of Lemma 2.2 be denoted by $\mathscr{B}^*_-$. The subset

$$(3.1) \qquad T_w(pr_k D^y_\sigma)$$

of $\mathbf{M}$ is a k-dimensional, differentiable submanifold of $\mathbf{M}$ whose intersection with $\mathscr{B}^*_-$, includes an open subset of $\mathscr{B}^*_-$, in accord with Lemma 2.2.

A k-manifold β_e extending the dome $\mathscr{B}^*_-$. If $e < \sigma/2$, the open subset,

$$(3.2) \qquad \beta'_e = (p = T_w(pr_k y)||y^1| < e, \quad f(p) > -e^2)$$

of the k-manifold (3.1) is well-defined. Moreover

$$(3.3) \qquad \beta''_e = (p \in B^*_- |1 \geq f(p) > -e^2)$$

is an open subset of B_-^* and so is a k-dimensional differentiable submanifold of $\mathbf{M}$. If e is sufficiently small

$$(3.4) \qquad \beta'_e \cap \beta''_e = (p = T_w(pr_k y)|0 < y^1 < e, f(p) > -e^2)$$

as a consequence of Lemma 2.2.

Thus if e is sufficiently small, β'_e and β''_e intersect in a k-dimensional, differential manifold, namely the right member of (3.4), *so that the union*

$$\beta_e = \beta'_e \cup \beta''_e \supset Cl\,\mathscr{B}^*_-$$

is a k-dimensional, differentiable submanifold of $\mathbf{M}$. *We suppose e so conditioned.*

In Theorem 2.1 there is given a neighborhood N of the closure of the dome of B_-. If the neighborhood N^* of ω, prescribed in Lemma 2.2, is taken sufficiently small, and if the constant e conditioning β_e, is sufficiently small, then

$$(3.5) \qquad Cl\,\mathscr{B}^*_- \subset N \qquad Cl\,\beta_e \subset N$$

We suppose that N^* and e are chosen so that (3.5) *holds.*

Let Δ_r be an open $(n-k)$-ball in a euclidean space E_{n-k}, where Δ_r has the radius r and a center at the origin $\mathbf{0}$ in E_{n-k}.

The domain of redefinition of f. This domain of redefinition will be taken as the carrier $|W|$ of a differentiable f-fibre-bundle W with the following properties.

I. The *base* of W shall be β_e and $|W|$ a neighborhood of β_e, open relative to **M** and included in the neighborhood N of $Cl\,\mathscr{B}_-$ given in Theorem 2.1. Cf. (3.5).

II. The *fibre* of W shall be the $(n-k)$-ball Δ_2 of radius 2.

III. For $p \in \beta_e$ the fibre Y_p of W over p shall be a differentiable $(n-k)$-manifold in **M**, orthogonal to β_e at p, and meeting β_e only in p.

IV. The *fibre-bundle* W shall be defined by a diffeomorphism

$$(3.6) \qquad (p, v) \to \Lambda(p, v)\colon \beta_e \times \Delta_2 \to \mathbf{M}$$

onto $|W|$, and such that $\Lambda(p, \mathbf{0}) = p$ for $p \in \beta_e$.

V. For each $p \in \beta_e$ the partial map

$$(3.7) \qquad v \to \Lambda(p, v) = \Lambda(v) \qquad [v = (v^1, \ldots, v^{n-k}) \in \Delta_2]$$

shall be a diffeomorphism of Δ_2 onto the fibre Y_p over p.

VI. W shall be an f-fibre-bundle in the following sense. For each $p \in \beta_e$ and for v restricted to an arbitrary ray λ emanating from the origin and of length 2, the partial mapping

$$(3.8) \qquad v \to f(\Lambda(p, v))\colon \Delta_2 \to R$$

defines a mapping of λ into R in which f is non-decreasing as the arc length s, measured along λ from the origin, increases.

The principal difficulty is in defining the fibre-bundle W so that property VI is realized. For the terms involved in I to V, see [6]. The term *f-fibre-bundle* is introduced here for the first time. That such an f-fibre-bundle exists follows from [5].

Redefinition of f on β_e. We state the following essential lemma.

LEMMA 3.1. *There exists a relatively compact open subset V of β_e such that w and $\dot{w}$ are in V and $\bar{V} \subset \beta_e$, and a real-valued differentiable function f^0 of class C^∞ on β_e, without critical points on β_e, and such that*

$$(3.9)' \qquad f^0(p) = f(p) \qquad\qquad (p \in \beta_e - V)$$

$$(3.9)'' \qquad f^0(p) < f(p) \qquad\qquad (p \in V)$$

Method of proof of Lemma 3.1. We turn to the euclidean k-space E_k of points $(u_1, \ldots, u_k)$ and introduce a model function,

$$(3.10) \qquad u \to \zeta(u) = 3u_1^2 - 2u_1^3 - (u_2^2 + \cdots + u_k^2)$$

The function ζ has a critical point at the origin and at the point on the u_1-axis at which $u_1 = 1$. Other points of E_k are ordinary points of ζ. The critical values of ζ are 0 and 1, respectively. These are the critical values of f on β_e, that is, the values of f at w and $\dot{w}$.

One shows in [2] that if e_0 is a sufficiently small positive constant, and if $0 < e < e_0$, the open subset

$$(3.11) \qquad b_e = (u \in E_k | \zeta(u) > -e^2, u_1(3 - 2u_1)^{\frac{1}{2}} > -e)$$

of E_k is the diffeomorph of β_e under a mapping $p \to \theta(p) = u$ in which

$$(3.12) \qquad \zeta(\theta(p)) = f(p)$$

The problem of redefining f on β_e so that Lemma 3.1 is satisfied, is thereby reduced to an equivalent problem of redefining ζ on b_e. The latter problem is solved in relatively explicit manner in [7].

Definition of $\hat{f}$ on **M.** We shall need an auxiliary C^∞-mapping $t \to \mu(t)$ of R onto $[0, 1]$ such that

$$(3.13)' \qquad\qquad \mu(t) = 1 \qquad\qquad (t \leq 0)$$

$$(3.13)'' \qquad\qquad \mu(t) = 0 \qquad\qquad (t \geq 1)$$

$$(3.13)''' \qquad\qquad \mu'(t) < 0 \qquad\qquad (0 < t < 1)$$

We shall refer to the $n - k$-ball Δ_1 of radius 1 and to the set

$$(3.14) \qquad \Pi = (q = \Lambda(p, v) | p \in V, v \in \Delta_1)$$

observing that $\overline{\Pi} \subset |W|$.

The function $\hat{f}$ will be defined on **M** as an extension of the function f^0 defined on β_e in Lemma 3.1. For this purpose recall the representation

$$(3.15) \qquad\qquad q = \Lambda(p, v) \qquad\qquad (p \in \beta_e, v \in \Delta_2)$$

of points $q \in |W|$. Let $\hat{f}$ be defined on **M** by setting

$$(3.16) \qquad\qquad \hat{f}(q) = f(q) \qquad\qquad (q \in \mathbf{M} - \overline{\Pi})$$

and, subject to (3.15), by setting

$$(3.17) \qquad \hat{f}(q) = f(q) - \mu(\|v\|^2)[f(p) - f^0(p)] \qquad (p \in \beta_e, v \in \Delta_2)$$

The function $\hat{f}$ is thereby over defined on $|W| - \overline{\Pi}$, but consistently, as one readily verifies. The mapping $\hat{f}$ is of class C^∞ on **M**, since the domains of definition of $\hat{f}$ in (3.16) and (3.17) are open subsets of **M** and the restrictions of $\hat{f}$ to these sets are of class C^∞. Finally one shows that $\hat{f}$ has no critical points on $|W|$. For details see [2].

Since $\hat{f}(q)$ differs from $f(q)$ at most on $|W|$ and since $|W| \subset N$, the non-degenerate function $\hat{f}$ satisfies Theorem 2.1.

4. Composite manifolds

The theory of bowls of a non-degenerate function f on **M** is naturally associated with the theory of composite manifolds. Cf. [9].

Let a be an ordinary value of f. We are assuming that **M** is orientable. It follows that the level manifold f^a is orientable. Let λ then be an orientation-preserving diffeomorphism of f^a onto f^a. We could cut **M** along f^a and join a point p on the lower side of the cut to the point $\lambda(p)$ on the upper side, thereby forming a composite manifold. However, this intuitive approach is not adequate for our purposes.

We wish to form a composite manifold which, like **M**, possesses an oriented differentiable structure, a Riemannian metric $\mathscr{R}^*$, a non-degenerate function f^*, and a family **H*** of f^*-arcs, not arbitrarily defined on the new manifold, but related respectively to the oriented differentiable structure, Riemannian metric, non-degenerate function f and family **H** of f-arcs on **M**. For this reason we review a general formal approach to the composition of manifolds as presented in [9].

General compositions. Let M and $\mathscr{M}$ be two abstractly given, oriented, differentiable n-manifolds, without points in common. Let W and $\mathscr{W}$ be fixed, open, non-empty subsets of M and $\mathscr{M}$ respectively. We presuppose the existence of an orientation-preserving diffeomorphism

$$(4.0) \qquad\qquad \mu : W \to \mathscr{W} \qquad\qquad (\text{onto } \mathscr{W})$$

Let each point $p \in W$ be identified with its image $\mu(p) \in \mathscr{W}$ to form a "point" $[p : \mu(p)]$. Subject to this identification let Σ be the ensemble of all points of M and $\mathscr{M}$.

The mappings Π, Π_1, Π_2. To each point $p \in M$ corresponds a "point" $\Pi(p) \in \Sigma$, represented by p if $p \notin W$ and by $[p : \mu(p)]$ if $p \in W$. To each point $q \in \mathscr{M}$ corresponds a point $\Pi(q) \in \Sigma$ represented by q if $q \notin \mathscr{W}$, and by $[\mu^{-1}(q) : q]$ if $q \in \mathscr{W}$. Thus Π maps $M \cup \mathscr{M}$ onto Σ. Set

$$(4.1) \qquad\qquad \Pi_1 = \Pi | M, \quad \Pi_2 = \Pi | \mathscr{M}$$

The mappings $\Pi_1 : M \to \Sigma$ and $\Pi_2 : \mathscr{M} \to \Sigma$ are biunique, but not in general onto Σ. The mapping $\Pi : M \cup \mathscr{M} \to \Sigma$ is onto Σ but not biunique. For $p \in W$ or $q \in \mathscr{W}$

$$(4.2) \qquad\qquad \Pi_1(p) = \Pi_2(\mu(p)), \quad \Pi_2(q) = \Pi_1(\mu^{-1}(q))$$

Observe that

$$\Pi_1(M) \cap \Pi_2(\mathscr{M}) = \Pi_1(W) = \Pi_2(\mathscr{W})$$
$$\Pi(M \cup \mathscr{M}) = \Pi_1(M) \cup \Pi_2(\mathscr{M}) = \Sigma$$

Σ *topologized.* Let X and $\mathscr{X}$ be arbitrary open subsets of M and $\mathscr{M}$ respectively. The ensemble of subsets $\Pi_1(X)$ and $\Pi_2(\mathscr{X})$ of Σ will be taken as a base for the open sets of Σ. So topologized Σ is not necessarily a Hausdorff space. Cf. [9]. In the application which we shall make Σ will be a Hausdorff space, so that we here assume that Σ is a Hausdorff space.

We note that Π_1 and Π_2 are homeomorphisms of M and $\mathscr{M}$ respectively onto open subsets $\Pi_1(M)$ and $\Pi_2(\mathscr{M})$ of Σ.

Let maximal bases for the oriented C^∞-structures of M and $\mathscr{M}$ respectively be given by coordinate presentations of the form

$$(4.3) \qquad\qquad (F_i\colon U_i, X_i)_{i\in\alpha} \qquad\qquad (F_j\colon U_j)_{j\in\beta}$$

It follows from Lemma 2.1 of [9] that the ensemble of coordinate presentations

$$(4.4) \qquad (\Pi_1 F_i\colon U_i, \Pi_1(X_i))_{i\in\alpha}, \quad (\Pi_2 F_j\colon U_j, \Pi_2(X_j))_{j\in\beta}$$

is a base for an oriented C^∞-structure on Σ. Given this structure, Π_1 and Π_2 are orientation-preserving diffeomorphisms of M and $\mathscr{M}$ respectively onto Σ.

Let the composite manifold Σ be represented by setting

$$(4.5) \qquad\qquad \Sigma = [M, \mathscr{M}, \mu, W, \mathscr{W}]$$

To properly apply the preceding general theory to composite manifolds derived from submanifolds of $\mathbf{M}$ we need to prove the following.

An oriented differentiable structure on each non-singular level manifold f^a may be determined as follows by the oriented differentiable structure of $\mathbf{M}$.

Let V be an open subset of E_{n-1} with coordinates $v^1, \ldots, v^{n-1}$ and $(G; V, Y)$ an arbitrary admissible, coordinate presentation of an open domain of f^a. If $e > 0$ is sufficiently small, the interval $J = (a - e, a + e)$ is an interval of ordinary values of f. Let g_v be a subarc of the H-arc meeting the point $G(v)$ of f^a, restricted so that for p on g_v, $f(p) \in J$. Let the point q on g_v at which $f(p)$ has the value u^n be denoted by $h(u) = (u^1, \ldots, u^n)$, where we have set $(v^1, \ldots, v^{n-1}) = (u^1, \ldots, u^{n-1})$. We identify the product $V \times J$ with an open subset U of a euclidean space of coordinates $u^1, \ldots, u^n$. Then $(h\colon U, h(U))$ is an admissible presentation of $h(U)$ in the unoriented, differentiable structure of $\mathbf{M}$. If this coordinate presentation is admissible in the oriented structure of $\mathbf{M}$ we *prefer* $(G\colon V, Y)$ as a presentation of f^a. One shows readily that the coordinate presentations $(G\colon V, Y)$ thereby preferred are orientation consistent when they "overlap," and form an oriented differentiable structure on f^a.

We suppose f^a given the oriented differentiable structure determined as above from that of $\mathbf{M}$.

5. Composite manifolds formed from M

Let $[a, b]$ be a closed interval of ordinary values of f that includes no value taken on by f on the sets $X_z | (z \in \Omega)$ of Lemma 1.1. Let $c = (a + b)/2$. Set

$$M = p \in \mathbf{M} | f(p) < b)$$
$$M' = (p \in \mathbf{M} | f(p) > a)$$
$$W = (p \in \mathbf{M} | a < f(p) < b)$$

Corresponding to each point $p \in M'$ let $\theta(p)$ be a copy of p, regarded as distinct from p. So defined θ maps M' onto a set $\theta(M') = \mathcal{M}$, disjoint from M' and M. It is trivial that $\mathcal{M}$ can be so topologized and structured that θ is an orientation-preserving diffeomorphism of M' onto $\mathcal{M}$. The set $\theta(W)$ is an open subset of $\mathcal{M}$ to be denoted by $\mathcal{W}$.

In the notation of §4 a composite manifold Σ is defined by five elements

(5.0) $[M, \mathcal{M}, \mu, W, \mathcal{W}]$

of which $M, \mathcal{M}, W, \mathcal{W}$ have already been specially defined in this section. It remains to define the diffeomorphism μ of W onto $\mathcal{W}$.

Parameters (p, t) on W. Let p be an arbitrary point of f^c. Let $\mathbf{H}$ be the given family of f-arcs on $\mathbf{M} - \Omega$. Let g_p be the intersection with W of the H-arc meeting f^c in p. On g_p, $f(p)$ ranges over the interval (a, b). For $p \in f^c$ and $t \in (a, b)$ let $k(p, t)$ be the point $q \in W$ on g_p at which $f(q) = t$. Then the mapping

(5.1) $(p, t) \to k(p, t) : f^c \times (a, b) \to W$

is a diffeomorphism onto W.

Definition of μ. Let $p \to \lambda(p)$ be an orientation-preserving diffeomorphism of f^c onto f^c. Then λ can be extended as an orientation-preserving diffeomorphism $q \to \lambda^*(q)$ of W onto W, by making the point $q = k(p, t)$ in W correspond to the point $\lambda^*(q) = k(\lambda(p), t)$ in W. An orientation-preserving diffeomorphism

(5.2) $q \to \mu(q) = \theta(\lambda^*(q)) : W \to \mathcal{W}$

of W onto $\mathcal{W}$ is thereby defined.

The composite manifold $\mathbf{M}^\lambda$. The elements in (5.0) have been specially defined in this section. Let

(5.3) $\mathbf{M}^\lambda = [M, \mathcal{M}, \mu, W, \mathcal{W}]$

be the composite manifold thereby defined, with $\mathbf{M}^\lambda$ topologized and differentiably structured in terms of these elements and their oriented structures as in §4. The structure thereby defined on $\mathbf{M}^\lambda$ is an oriented differentiable structure. The diffeomorphisms

$$(5.4) \qquad \Pi_1 \colon M \to \mathbf{M}^\lambda \qquad \Pi_2 \colon \mathcal{M} \to \mathbf{M}^\lambda$$

are well-defined and are orientation-preserving.

A non-degenerate function f^* *on* $\mathbf{M}^\lambda$ *derived from* f *on* $\mathbf{M}$. Given $p \in M$ and $q \in \mathcal{M}$ set

$$(5.5) \qquad f^*(\Pi_1(p)) = f(p), \quad f^*(\Pi_2(q)) = f(\theta^{-1}(q))$$

The values $f^*(u)$ are defined for each point $u \in \mathbf{M}^\lambda$, twice at points u of $\Pi_1(W) = \Pi_2(\mathcal{W})$ but consistently, as one readily sees.

Recalling that the mappings $\Pi_1 \colon M \to \mathbf{M}^\lambda$ and $\Pi_2 \colon \mathcal{M} \to \mathbf{M}^\lambda$ are diffeomorphisms, one sees from (5.5) that f^* is non-degenerate. Set

$$M^a_- = (p \in \mathbf{M} | f(p) < a)$$
$$M^b_+ = (p \in \mathbf{M} | f(p) > b).$$

The critical points of f are in $M^a_- \cup M^b_+$. If z is a critical point of f in M^a_-, $\Pi_1(z)$ is a critical point of f^*. If z is a critical point of f in M^b_+, $\Pi_2(\theta(z))$ is a critical point of f^*.

Let Ω^* be the set of critical points of f^* in $\mathbf{M}^\lambda$.

A Riemannian metric $\mathcal{R}$ *on* $\mathbf{M}^\lambda$. In order that the basic Lemma 1.1 be extended to critical points z^* of f^*, it is necessary that a Riemannian metric $\mathcal{R}$ be defined on $\mathbf{M}^\lambda$, preferably in a manner closely related to the metric $\mathcal{R}^0$ on $\mathbf{M}$.

It is possible to define a Riemannian metric $\mathcal{R}$ on $\mathbf{M}^\lambda$ in such a manner that the restricted diffeomorphisms

$$\Pi_1 | M^a_-, \quad \Pi_2 | \theta(M^b_+)$$

into $\mathbf{M}^\lambda$ are isometries. We suppose $\mathcal{R}$ so defined. Each canonical neighborhood $X_z | (z \in \Omega)$ of Lemma 1.1 is included in one of the sets M^a_- and M^b_+. We draw the following conclusion.

If z is a critical point of f in M^a_- then $\Pi_1(z) = z^*$ is a critical point of f^* and Lemma 1.1 is satisfied if the elements

$$(5.6) \qquad \mathbf{M}, f, z, T_z, X_z, \mathcal{R}^0$$

are replaced respectively by

$$(5.7) \qquad \mathbf{M}^\lambda, f^*, z^*, \Pi_1(T_z), \Pi_1(X_z), \mathcal{R}$$

If z is a critical point of M^b_+ then $\Pi_2(\theta(z)) = z^*$ is a critical point of f^*, and Lemma 1.1 is satisfied if the elements (5.6) are replaced respectively by

$$(5.8) \qquad \mathbf{M}^\lambda, f^*, z^*, \Pi_2(\theta T_z) \Pi_1(\theta(X_z)), \mathcal{R}$$

An admissible family $\mathbf{H}^*$ *of* f^*-*arcs on* $\mathbf{M}^\lambda - \Omega^*$. A family $\mathbf{H}$ of f-arcs is given on $\mathbf{M} - \Omega$. By an H-arc on $\mathscr{M}$ we mean the θ-image of a maximal H-arc on M'. H^*-arcs on $\Pi_1(M)$ and $\Pi_2(\mathscr{M})$ shall be images under Π_1 and Π_2 of maximal H-arcs on M and $\mathscr{M}$ respectively. There exists a unique admissible family $\mathbf{H}^*$ of maximal f^*-arcs on $\mathbf{M}^\lambda - \Omega^*$ whose subarcs on $\Pi_1(M)$ and $\Pi_2(\mathscr{M})$ are respectively the H-arcs which we have just defined.

6. Diffeomorphisms of M onto the composite manifold $\mathbf{M}^\lambda$

The diffeomorphisms of $\mathbf{M}$ onto $\mathbf{M}^\lambda$ with which we are concerned are the special diffeomorphisms which arise naturally from the way in which the composite manifold $\mathbf{M}^\lambda$ is formed from $\mathbf{M}$.

Recall that $\Pi_1 | f^c$ is a diffeomorphism of the level manifold f^c of $\mathbf{M}$ onto the level manifold f^{*c} of $\mathbf{M}^\lambda$.

Diffeomorphisms of type λ. *An orientation-preserving diffeomorphism* φ *of* $\mathbf{M}$ *onto* $\mathbf{M}^\lambda$ *which induces an orientation-preserving diffeomorphism of* f^c *onto* $\Pi_1(f^c)$ *will be said to be of type* λ.

In this definition we do not require that $\varphi | f^c = \Pi_1 | f^c$.

Diffeomorphisms λ *of upper type*. If the diffeomorphism Π_1 of M into $\mathbf{M}^\lambda$ is extendable as a diffeomorphism φ of $\mathbf{M}$ onto $\mathbf{M}^\lambda$, φ will be termed an *upper diffeomorphism* of $\mathbf{M}$ onto $\mathbf{M}^\lambda$ of type λ, and λ *of upper type*.

Diffeomorphism λ *of lower type*. If the diffeomorphism $\Pi_2\theta$ of M' into $\mathbf{M}^\lambda$ is extendable as a diffeomorphism Ψ of $\mathbf{M}$ onto $\mathbf{M}^\lambda$, Ψ will be termed a *lower diffeomorphism of* $\mathbf{M}$ *onto* $\mathbf{M}^\lambda$ of type λ and λ *of lower type*.

The following theorems will be proved in [10].

THEOREM 6.1 (i). *A necessary and sufficient condition that there exists an upper diffeomorphism of* $\mathbf{M}$ *onto* $\mathbf{M}^\lambda$ *of type* λ *is that the diffeomorphism* λ^* *of* W *onto* W *be extendable as a diffeomorphism of* M' *onto* M'.

(ii) *A necessary and sufficient condition that there exist a lower diffeomorphism of* $\mathbf{M}$ *onto* $\mathbf{M}^\lambda$ *of type* λ *is that the diffeomorphism* λ^* *of* W *onto* W *be extendable as a diffeomorphism of* M *onto* M.

There may exist a diffeomorphism of $\mathbf{M}$ onto $\mathbf{M}^\lambda$ of type λ even when there exist no upper or lower diffeomorphisms of $\mathbf{M}$ onto $\mathbf{M}^\lambda$ of type λ. The basis for the positive part of this affirmation is Theorem 6.2.

THEOREM 6.2. *Let* λ_1 *and* λ_2 *be diffeomorphisms of* f^c *onto* f^c *of lower and upper types respectively. If* $\lambda = \lambda_2\lambda_1$ *there exists a diffeomorphism of* $\mathbf{M}$ *onto* $\mathbf{M}^\lambda$ *of type* λ.

COROLLARY 6.1. *Let λ_1 and λ_2 be given as in Theorem 6.2. If $\lambda = \lambda_1\lambda_2$ there exists a diffeomorphism of $\mathbf{M}$ onto $\mathbf{M}^{\lambda^{-1}}$ of type A^{-1}.*

Simple examples will show the following.

If λ is an orientation-preserving diffeomorphism of f^c onto f^c, the composite manifolds $\mathbf{M}^\lambda$ and $\mathbf{M}^{\lambda^{-1}}$ are not in general diffeomorphic.

We distinguish between the four following mutually exclusive cases. These cases presuppose the existence of an orientation-preserving diffeomorphism λ of f^c onto f^c.

Case I. There exist both an upper and lower diffeomorphism of $\mathbf{M}$ onto $\mathbf{M}^\lambda$ of type λ.

Case II. There exists an upper (lower) diffeomorphism of $\mathbf{M}$ onto $\mathbf{M}^\lambda$ of type λ, but no lower (upper) diffeomorphism of $\mathbf{M}$ onto $\mathbf{M}^\lambda$ of type λ.

Case III. There exists no diffeomorphism of $\mathbf{M}$ onto $\mathbf{M}^\lambda$ of type λ.

Case IV. There exists a diffeomorphism of $\mathbf{M}$ onto $\mathbf{M}^\lambda$ of type λ, but no upper or lower diffeomorphism of $\mathbf{M}$ onto $\mathbf{M}^\lambda$ of type λ.

Case I can be realized by taking λ as a diffeomorphism of f^c onto f^c differentiably isotopic on f^c to the identity.

Case III can be realized on making use of the classic Milnor example, taking $\mathbf{M}$ as a euclidean 7-sphere and f as a non-degenerate function on $\mathbf{M}$ with just two critical points.

To show that Cases II and IV are realizable in a proper setting we shall begin the following section with a study of a 3-sphere on which a function f with just four critical points has been specially defined. The composite manifolds thereby obtained include diffeomorphs of $\mathbf{M}$ in all cases in which $n = 3$ and f on $\mathbf{M}$ has fewer than six critical points.

7. The case of at most four critical points, $n = 3$

In this section we shall take $\mathbf{M}$ as a 3-sphere S_3 on which a non-degenerate function f has four critical points with indices 0, 1, 2, 3 and critical values 0, 1, 3, 4. The section f^c of S_3, will be taken as a surface of torus type at an f-level $c = 2$. As in the geometry of inversion, S_3 will be represented by a 3-plane E_3 closed at the point at infinity.

The manifold E_3^+. Let E_3 be a euclidean space of points x with coordinates (x^1, x^2, x^3). Let E_3^+ be obtained from E_3 by adding "a point Q at infinity" to E_3. We suppose E_3^+ structured so that it is the C^∞-diffeomorph of S_3. We shall define a non-degenerate function f on E_3^+.

The function f. The function f shall have its maximum at Q on E_3^+. We suppose f so defined on E_3^+ that the level manifold f^c, with $c = 2$, is a conventional torus τ. The critical points of f of index 0 and 1 shall be on the interior of τ and the critical point of f of index 2 on the exterior of τ at the point of the axis of the torus at the center of the torus.

The torus τ. Let $z = (u, v)$ be rectangular coordinates in a 2-plane Z. For arbitrary $z \in Z$ the ensemble of points (x^1, x^2, x^3) of the form

(7.1) $P(z) = [(2\text{-}\cos u) \cos v, \sin u, (2\text{-}\cos u) \sin v]$

is a torus τ generated by revolving the circle

$$x^1 = 2\text{-}\cos u, \ x^2 = \sin u, \ x^3 = 0 \qquad (-\infty < u < \infty)$$

about the x^2-axis. The mapping $P \to P(z)$ of Z into E_3 is real analytic, is onto τ and doubly periodic, with period 2π in u and v.

Mappings Λ *of* Z *onto* Z. Corresponding to any set $[p, q, r, s]$ of rational integers such that $ps - rq = 1$ we introduce the linear mapping $z \to \Lambda(z)$ of the form

(7.2) $$u' = pu + qv$$
$$v' = ru + sv$$

of Z onto Z, and the orientation-preserving diffeomorphism

(7.3) $p \to \lambda(p) = (P \Lambda P^{-1}((p)$ $(p \in \tau)$

of τ onto τ.

The composite manifold E_3^λ. Let Λ be an arbitrary diffeomorphism of Z onto Z of the form (7.2), and λ the corresponding diffeomorphism of τ onto τ given by (7.3). Regarding τ as the manifold f^c at the f-level 2 on the manifold E_3^+, let E_3^λ denote the corresponding composite manifold, constructed from E_3^+ and f^c as $\mathbf{M}^\lambda$ was more generally constructed from $\mathbf{M}$ and f^c in §4.

The composite differentiable manifolds E_3^λ include the topological types of the so-called *lens* spaces. Extending results in the topological case it is provable in the differentiable case that E_3^λ is the diffeomorph of a 3-sphere if and only if $|p| = 1$ in (7.2). The author has established the following.

CASE IV. Of the four Cases enumerated at the end of §6, Case IV can be realized by virtue of (a_1).

(a_1). *Necessary and sufficient condition that there exists a diffeomorphism of type* λ *of* E_3^+ *onto* E_3^λ *which is neither an upper nor a lower diffeomorphism of* E_3^λ *of type* λ *is that in* (7.2)

$$|p| = 1, \quad q \neq 0, \quad r \neq 0$$

CASE II. This case can be realized by virtue of (a_2).

(a_2). *Necessary and sufficient condition that* E_3^+ *admit a lower (upper) diffeomorphism of* E_3^+ *onto* E_3^λ *of type* λ *is that* $|p| = 1$ *and* $r = 0$ $(q = 0)$ *in* (7.2).

8. Homology 3-spheres

Let $c_1 < c_2 < \cdots < c_r$ be a set of ordinary values of f on $\mathbf{M}$, not in the subsets $f(X_z)$ of R (Cf. Lemma 1.1). Let λ_i be an orientation preserving diffeomorphism of f^{c_i} onto f^{c_i} $i = 1, \ldots, r$. Let the composite manifold, previously denoted by $\mathbf{M}^\lambda$, here be more explicitly denoted by $M(f, \lambda, c)$, recalling that λ was a diffeomorphism of f^c onto f^c. Generalizing $M(f, \lambda, c)$ in the obvious manner, we introduce the *composite manifold*

$$(8.1) \qquad M(f; \lambda_1, \ldots, \lambda_r; c_1, \ldots, c_r)$$

We are admitting only those polar non-degenerate functions f on $\mathbf{M}$ whose values at distinct critical points are distinct. It will be convenient to term a value of such an f at a critical point of index k a *critical value of index k*.

Diffeomorphic models for homology 3-spheres. Let Σ_3 be a differentiable manifold which is a homology 3-sphere. On Σ_3 let Φ be an admissible polar-non-degenerate function with r-critical values

$$(8.2) \qquad a_1 < a_2 < \cdots < a_r$$

of index 2. Let $c_1 < c_2 < \cdots < c_r$ be r ordinary values of Φ such that

$$(8.3) \qquad c_1 < a_1 < c_2 < a_2 < \cdots < c_r < a_r$$

so chosen that for $i = 1, \ldots, r$, (c_i, a) is an interval of ordinary values of Φ. There then exists a polar-non-degenerate function on a 3-sphere S_3 with the same critical values as Φ, with the same indices. We state the following theorem.

THEOREM 8.1. *For suitable choices of the diffeomorphisms* λ_i, $i = 1$, $\ldots, r$ *of the level manifolds* F^{c_i} *onto themselves the composite manifold*

$$(8.4) \qquad S_3(F; \lambda_1, \ldots, \lambda_r; c_1, \ldots, c_r) = \mathscr{S}_3$$

is a diffeomorph of Σ_3.

If F^* *is the polar-non-degenerate function on the manifold* $\mathscr{S}_3$ *"derived"* (Cf. §5) *from the function* F *on* S_3, *there exists a diffeomorphism* θ *of* Σ_3 *onto* $\mathscr{S}_3$ *such that*

$$\Phi(p) = F^*(\theta(p)) \qquad\qquad (p \in \Sigma_3)$$

Comment on Theorem 8.1. If Σ_3 is *not* a homology sphere, there may exist no polar-non-degenerate function F on S_3 with the same indexed critical values as those of Φ.

The numerical order of the critical values of Φ on the homology 3-sphere Σ_3 is far from arbitrary. If c is an arbitrary number, then

$$(8.5) \qquad N_1(c) \geq N_2(c)$$

where $N_k(c)$, $k = 1$, 2, is the number of critical values of Φ of index k less than c. This statement is not in general true if Σ_3 is not a homology sphere.

Consistent with (8.5) it is always possible to continuously modify Φ as a non-degenerate function on the homology 3-sphere Σ_3 so that the maximum critical value of index 1 is less than the minimum critical value of index 2. Such an order of the critical values is the least illuminating from the point of view of the next paragraph.

If the critical values of Φ on Σ_3 with indices 1 and 2 alternate as the critical values increase, and if Σ_3 is simply connected, it can be shown that Σ_3 is the diffeomorph of a 3-sphere in accord with the Poincaré conjecture. It follows that if Σ_3 is a simply-connected differentiable 3-manifold which is not the diffeomorph of a 3-sphere then any polar-non-degenerate function Φ on Σ_3 must have at least six critical points.

In justification of the principal hypothesis of Theorem 2.1 one can prove the following special theorem.

THEOREM 8.2. *In case* **M** *is 3-dimensional suppose that f has just four critical points. These critical points must include a critical point $\dot{w}$ of index 2, and a critical point w of index 1.*

Let **H⁰** *be the family of ortho-f-arcs on* **M**-Ω. *Then a necessary and sufficient condition that* **M** *be the diffeomorph of a 3-sphere is that $f(\dot{w}) > f(w)$ and that there exist an isotopic replacement* **H** *of* **H⁰** *such that the descending bowl B_- with pole $\dot{w}$, and the ascending bowl B_+ with pole w intersect regularly in an H-arc.*

9. An extension theorem

The problem of giving conditions sufficient that our n-manifold **M** be the diffeomorph of another such manifold $\dot{\text{M}}$, can be approached in terms of critical point theory. Such an approach leads to an extension problem, to be defined below, and an extension theorem, Theorem 9.1.

The data. We presuppose the existence on **M** and $\dot{\text{M}}$ of polar-non-degenerate functions f and $\dot{f}$ with the same indexed critical values. As previously we suppose that each value is assumed at a unique critical point of **M** and $\dot{\text{M}}$, respectively, with a common index k.

DEFINITION 9.1. $(f, \dot{f})$-diffeomorphisms. Let α be an ordinary value of f and $\dot{f}$. Set

$$f_\alpha = (p \in \mathbf{M} | f(p) \leq \alpha)$$

$$\dot{f}_\alpha = (p \in \dot{\mathbf{M}} | \dot{f}(p) \leq \alpha)$$

An orientation preserving diffeomorphism $p \to \theta(p)$ of f_α onto $\mathring{f}_\alpha$ such that

$$(9.1) \qquad\qquad f(p) = \mathring{f}(\theta(p)) \qquad\qquad (p \in f_\alpha)$$

will be called *an $(f, \mathring{f})$-diffeomorphism* of f_α onto $\mathring{f}_\alpha$.

DEFINITION 9.2. Let c be a critical value of f and $\mathring{f}$ of index k, with c interior to an interval $[a, b]$ of ordinary values of f and $\mathring{f}$. Suppose that there exists an $(f, \mathring{f})$-diffeomorphism

$$(9.2) \qquad\qquad \theta; f_a \to \mathring{f}_a \colon p \to \theta(p)$$

of f_a onto $\mathring{f}_a$. We suppose that $1 < k < n$.

PROBLEM P_c. *We seek sufficient conditions that θ admit an extension which is an $(f, \mathring{f})$-diffeomorphism of f_b onto $\mathring{f}_b$.*

In this definition we have referred to a diffeomorphism θ of a *closed set* f_a. We understand that such a diffeomorphism is well-defined only if it admits an *extension* as a diffeomorphism into $\mathring{M}$ of an open neighborhood of the given closed set.

Let z and $\mathring{z}$ be the critical points of f and $\mathring{f}$, respectively, such that $f(z) = \mathring{f}(\mathring{z}) = c$. We refer to isometric presentations,

$$(9.3) \qquad\qquad x \to T_z(x) \colon D_\sigma^x \to X_z$$

$$(9.4) \qquad\qquad y \to T_{\mathring{z}}(y) \colon D_\sigma^y \to X_{\mathring{z}}$$

of neighborhoods X_z and $X_{\mathring{z}}$ of z and $\mathring{z}$ on M and $\mathring{M}$, as characterized in Definition 1.3. Let B_- and $\mathring{B}_-$ be the k-bowls on M and $\mathring{M}$ respectively descending from the critical points z and $\mathring{z}$. Let B_-^a and $\mathring{B}_-^a$ be respectively the traces of these bowls on the level manifolds f^a and $\mathring{f}^a$. Let η be a constant such that $c - \sigma < \eta < c$. The trace B_-^η of the bowl B_- is included in X_z and the trace $\mathring{B}_-^\eta$ of the bowl B_- is included in $X_{\mathring{z}}$.

DEFINITION 9.3. *A canonical diffeomorphism π of B_-^a onto $\mathring{B}_-^a$*. The traces B_-^a and B_-^η of the bowl B_- on M are diffeomorphic, $\mathbf{H}$-related points corresponding. Similarly the traces $\mathring{B}_-^a$ and $\mathring{B}_-^\eta$ of the bowl $\mathring{B}_-^\eta$ on $\mathring{M}$ are diffeomorphic, $\mathring{\mathbf{H}}$-related points corresponding. The traces B_-^η and $\mathring{B}_-^\eta$ are diffeomorphic under a mapping in which points

$$(9.5) \qquad\qquad T_z(x) \in B_-^\eta \qquad T_{\mathring{z}}(y) \in \mathring{B}_-^\eta$$

correspond if $x = y$. There is thereby induced a *canonical diffeomorphism* π

$$B_-^a \leftrightarrow B_-^\eta \leftrightarrow \mathring{B}_-^\eta \leftrightarrow \mathring{B}_-^a$$

of B_-^a onto $\mathring{B}_-^a$.

The canonical diffeomorphism π of B_-^a onto $\mathring{B}_-^a$ can be extended by special diffeomorphism Π into $\mathring{f}^a$ of any sufficiently small open neighborhood N of B_-^a, relative to f^a.

Definition of Π. The definition of Π is similar to that of π. A sufficiently small open neighborhood N of B_-^a, relative to f^a, is the diffeomorph of an open neighborhood $\mathcal{N} \subset X_z$ of B_-^η relative to f^η, **H**-related points corresponding. This neighborhood $\mathcal{N}$ of B_-^η is the diffeomorph of a neighborhood $\mathcal{\dot{N}}$ of $\dot{B}_-^\eta$, relative to $\dot{f}^\eta$, under a mapping in which points

$$(9.6) \qquad\qquad T_z(x) \in \mathcal{N} \qquad T_{\dot{z}}(y) \in \mathcal{\dot{N}}$$

correspond if $x = y$. The neighborhood $\mathcal{\dot{N}}$, if sufficiently small, is the diffeomorph of a neighborhood $\dot{N}$ of $\dot{B}_-^a$ relative to $\dot{f}^a$, **H**-related points corresponding. Thus if N is a sufficiently small open neighborhood of B_-^a, relative to f^a, there results a diffeomorphism Π of N onto $\dot{N}$ extending π.

In order to satisfy condition (i) in Definition 2.10 we presented two admissible choices of T_w in the paragraph preceding Definition 2.10.

So here, in precisely the same manner we present two admissible choices of T_z.

The definition of π and Π will be affected by this choice of T_z. For example, if $k = 2$, the sense of the diffeomorphism π of the curve B_-^a onto the curve $\dot{B}_-^a$ will be reversed by a change from one of these presentations T_z to the other.

We state an extension theorem.

THEOREM 9.1. *In order that an* $(f, \dot{f})$-*diffeomorphism* θ *of* f *onto* $\dot{f}_a$ *admit an extension which is an* $(f, \dot{f})$-*diffeomorphism of* f_b *onto* $\dot{f}_b$, *it is sufficient that for one of the above two admissible choices of* T_z, *and for a sufficiently small neighborhood* N *of* B_-^a, *relative to* f^a, *the following be true.*

The diffeomorphism $\theta | f^a$ *of* f^a *onto* $\dot{f}^a$ *is differentiably isotopic among diffeomorphisms of* f^a *onto* $\dot{f}^a$ *to a diffeomorphism* φ *of* f^a *onto* $\dot{f}^a$ *such that*

$$(9.7) \qquad\qquad \varphi(p) = \Pi(p) \qquad\qquad (p \in N)$$

In case the index k of the critical value c is 1, Problem P_c always has a solution, as one sees readily.

When $k = n$ Problem P_c is undefined. If we understand that c is the maximum value of f and $\dot{f}$, and a an ordinary value exceeding each critical value other than c, one has the following problem. If θ is a $(f, \dot{f})$-diffeomorphism of f_a onto $\dot{f}_a$, what are sufficient conditions that θ admit an extension which is an $(f, \dot{f})$-diffeomorphism of $\mathbf{M}$ onto $\mathbf{\dot{M}}$? This problem is equivalent to the differentiable form of the Schoenflies extension problem for an $(n-1)$-sphere.

When $n = 3$ the only extension of the above types through a critical value c which is not always possible, occurs when the index $k = 2$, and in this case Theorem 9.1 can be reduced to the following.

Suppose that **M** *is 3-dimensional, and that the index* $k = 2$. *In order that an* $(f, \dot{f})$-*diffeomorphism* θ *of* f_a *onto* $\dot{f}_a$ *admit an extension which is an* $(f, \dot{f})$-*diffeomorphism of* f_b *onto* $\dot{f}_b$ *the following is sufficient.*

The diffeomorphism $\theta | f^a$ *of* f^a *onto* $\dot{f}^a$ *is differentiably isotopic among diffeomorphisms of* f^a *onto* $\dot{f}^a$ *to a diffeomorphism* φ *of* f^a *onto* $\dot{f}^a$ *such that*

(9.8) $$\varphi(p) = \pi(p)   (p \in B^a_-)$$

References

[1] M. MORSE, The existence of polar non-degenerate functions on differentiable manifolds, *Annals of Math.*, *71* (1960), p. 352–383.

[2] M. MORSE, The elimination of critical points of a non-degenerate function on a manifold, *Jour. D'analyse Math.* (to appear).

[3] W. HUEBSCH and M. MORSE, Schoenflies extensions without interior differential singularities, *Annals of Math.*, *76* (1962), p. 18–54.

[4] E. BAIADA and M. MORSE, Homotopy and homology related to the Schoenflies problem, *Annals of Math.*, *58* (1953), p. 142–165.

[5] M. MORSE, Quadratic forms Q and Q-fibre-bundles, *Annals. of Math.* To appear.

[6] N. STEENROD, *The Topology of Fibre Bundles*, Princeton University Press, 1951.

[7] M. MORSE, A model non-degenerate function. To be published.

[8] J. MILNOR, On manifolds homeomorphic to the 7-sphere, *Annals of Math.*, *64* (1956), p. 399–405.

[9] M. MORSE, Differentiable mappings in the Schoenflies theorem, *Compositio Mathematica*, *14* (1959), p. 83–151.

[10] M. MORSE, Diffeomorphisms of composite manifolds. To be published.

[11] S. SMALE, A survey of some recent developments in differential topology, *Bull. Amer. Math. Soc.*, *69* (1963), p. 131–145.

On Higher Dimensional Knots

MICHEL A. KERVAIRE[1]

Which groups π can be fundamental group of the complement of an imbedded n-sphere in $(n + 2)$-space?

A well-known necessary condition is for instance that π/π' be isomorphic to the group of integers. (π' denotes the commutator subgroup of π.)

In the case $n = 1$, further necessary conditions have been given by various authors. (For instance, the first elementary ideal of π in the integral group ring of π/π' must be principal, generated by the "Alexander polynomial" $\Delta_\pi(t)$, where t denotes a generator of π/π'. Moreover, $\Delta_\pi(t)$ must satisfy an equation $\Delta_\pi(t^{-1}) = t^m \cdot \Delta_\pi(t)$ with m even. Compare [12], [4], [6].) However, the problem of characterizing knot groups by algebraic conditions remains unsolved.

Let us define a (differential) n-knot to be a differential imbedding f: $S^n \to S^{n+2}$, and the group of the n-knot f: $S^n \to S^{n+2}$ to be $\pi_1(S^{n+2} - f(S^n))$.

For $n \geqq 3$, we get a complete algebraic characterization of the groups of n-knots. (See Theorem 1 below.)

For $n = 2$, we only give a set of sufficient conditions on the group π for the existence of an imbedding f: $S^2 \to \Sigma^4$ into a homotopy 4-sphere with $\pi \cong \pi_1(\Sigma^4 - f(S^2))$. A homotopy k-sphere is a closed differential k-manifold with the homotopy type of S^k. (See Theorem 2.) A "good" set of algebraic conditions for a group π to be the group of a 2-knot is unknown to me. Recall that the first elementary ideal of $\pi_1(S^4 - f(S^2))$ need not be principal. Compare [5], Example 12. On the other hand, if the ideal is principal, generated by $P(t)$, S. Kinoshita has proved that one can prescribe $P(t)$ arbitrarily, subject to the only, obviously necessary condition, that $P(1) = \pm 1$. See [11]. I do not know whether in Theorem 2 the manifold Σ^4 can be taken to be S^4. This question may of course be related to the 4-dimensional Poincaré problem.

The case $n = 1$ will not be considered. All groups in this paper are assumed to be finitely presentable. The proofs will rely on the technique of spherical modifications as expounded in [10], §5.

---

[1] The author holds an Alfred P. Sloan Fellowship.

1. Statement of results

Define the *weight* $w(\pi)$ of a group $\pi \neq \{1\}$ to be the smallest integer k with the property that there exists a set of k elements $\alpha_1, \ldots, \alpha_k \in \pi$ whose normal closure equals π. By convention the trivial group $\{1\}$ has weight 0.

It is easy to prove that for any differential imbedding $f: S^n \to S^{n+2}$ the fundamental group $\pi_1(S^{n+2} - f(S^n))$ is of weight 1. (See Lemma 2 below.)

THEOREM 1. *Given $n \geq 3$. The group π is isomorphic to $\pi_1(S^{n+2} - f(S^n))$ for some differential imbedding $f: S^n \to S^{n+2}$ if and only if $\pi/\pi' \cong \mathbf{Z}$, the weight of π is 1, and $H_2(\pi) = 0$.*

(Here $H_2(\pi)$ denotes the second homology group of π with integral coefficients and trivial action of π on $\mathbf{Z}$.)

Actually, the "only if" part of this theorem holds for $n \geq 1$:

LEMMA 1. *Let Σ^{n+2} be a homotopy $(n + 2)$-sphere, where $n \geq 1$. If*

$$\pi \cong \pi_1(\Sigma - f(S^n))$$

for some differential imbedding $f: S^n \to \Sigma^{n+2}$, then $\pi/\pi' = \mathbf{Z}$, $w(\pi) = 1$, and $H_2(\pi) = 0$.

For $n = 2$, the argument in the proof of Theorem 1 breaks down. We shall get a partial result by strengthening the algebraic conditions. Define the *deficiency* of a presentation $(x_1, \ldots, x_q; R_1, \ldots, R_r)$ of a group to be the integer $q - r$. Clearly, a group π with a presentation of deficiency 1 and such that $\pi/\pi' \cong \mathbf{Z}$ satisfies the condition $H_2(\pi) = 0$. [Let $K^{(1)}$ be the q-fold wedge of S^1, and attach $q - 1$ two-dimensional cells to $K^{(1)}$ using $R_1, \ldots, R_{q-1}$. The resulting 2-complex K satisfies $\pi_1 K \cong \pi$ and $H_2 K = 0$. Hence $H_2(\pi) = H_2 K/\rho(\pi_2 K) = 0$, where $\rho: \pi_2 K \to H_2 K$ is the Hurewicz homomorphism. Compare Hopf [7].]

THEOREM 2. *Given a group π of weight 1, with a presentation of deficiency 1, and such that $\pi/\pi' \cong \mathbf{Z}$. There exist a homotopy 4-sphere Σ^4 and a differential imbedding $f: S^2 \to \Sigma^4$ such that $\pi \cong \pi_1(\Sigma^4 - f(S^2))$.*

The condition of deficiency 1 is definitely stronger (for groups satisfying $\pi/\pi' \cong \mathbf{Z}$) than the condition $H_2(\pi) = 0$. For example, the group $\mathbf{G}$ with the presentation $(x, a; a^3 = 1, x = axa)$ considered by R. Fox in [5], Example 12, has vanishing second homology group because it is the group of some 2-knot. (Compare Lemma 1.) However, this group does not have deficiency 1 (it has therefore deficiency 0) because its Alexander ideal, which is easily computed to be $\mathscr{E}_1 = (3, 1 + t)$ fails to be principal.[2]

---

[2] This shows that the group with presentation $(x, a; a^3 = 1, x = axa)$ is not "efficient" in the sense of D. Epstein [3].

(For the notion of the Alexander ideal, compare [4]. If the group π, satisfying $\pi/\pi' \cong \mathbf{Z}$, has deficiency 1, one can find a presentation of π of the form $(x_1, \ldots, x_q; x_1 C_1 = 1, \ldots, x_{q-1} C_{q-1} = 1)$, where $C_1, \ldots, C_{q-1}$ belong to the commutator subgroup of the free group on $x_1, \ldots, x_q$. It follows that an Alexander matrix of π has its last column consisting of zeros only. Hence this matrix has only one non-zero minor of order $q - 1$, i.e., the Alexander ideal $\mathscr{E}_1$ is generated by a single element.)

The proof of Theorem 1 generalizes trivially to the case of links, i.e., unions of k disjointly imbedded n-spheres in S^{n+2}.

THEOREM 3. *Given $n \geq 3$. The group π is isomorphic to $\pi_1(S^{n+2} - L_k)$, where L_k is a union of k disjointly imbedded n-spheres if and only if π/π' is free abelian of rank k, the weight of π is equal to k, and $H_2(\pi) = 0$.*

The proof follows closely the pattern of the proof of Theorem 1 and will be left to the reader.

Similarly:

THEOREM 4. *If the group π of weight k and such that π/π' is free abelian of rank k has a presentation of deficiency k, then there exists a link L_k of k disjointly imbedded 2-spheres in some homotopy 4-sphere Σ^4, such that $\pi \cong \pi_1(\Sigma^4 - L_k)$.*

2. Proofs

We begin with the proof of a slight generalization of part of Lemma 1.

LEMMA 2. *Let M^{n+2} be a simply connected differential manifold, and V^n a connected submanifold. (Either or both manifolds possibly with boundary.) Then the weight of $\pi_1(M - V)$ is at most 1.*

Let $a: S^1 \to M - V$ be an imbedding such that $a(S^1)$ bounds a small 2-disc τ in M which intersects V transversally at exactly one point. Taking a base point $z_0 \in S^1$, let $a(z_0) = x_0$ be the base point in $M - V$. Let α be the homotopy class of $a: (S^1, z_0) \to (M - V, x_0)$. I claim that the normal closure of α in $\pi_1(M - V, x_0)$ is equal to $\pi_1(M - V, x_0)$. Let $\xi \in \pi_1(M - V, x_0)$ be an arbitrary element, and let $f: (S^1, z_0) \to (M - V, x_0)$ be a differential mapping representing ξ. Since M is simply connected, we can extend f to a map $F: D^2 \to M$ which may be assumed to be differential and transversal to V. (Compare [14].) Then $F^{-1}(V)$ is a finite set of points $u_1, \ldots, u_r \in D^2 - S^1$. Let $D_1, \ldots, D_r$ be small disjoint discs around $u_1, \ldots, u_r$ contained in $D^2 - S^1$. Joining $F(u_i)$ to $y_0 = \tau \cap V$ by a path on V, we can deform F in D_i, keeping it fixed in $D^2 - D_i$, so that the deformed map F satisfies $F(D_i^*) = \tau$, and $F(D_i - D_i^*) \cap V = \emptyset$, where D_i^* is concentric with D_i and of smaller positive radius. We do this for all $i = 1, \ldots, r$. Now the new map F restricted to the boundary of D_i^*

represents α^{ε_i}, where $\varepsilon_i = +1$ or -1. Let z_i be a base point on the boundary of D_i^*, i.e., a point such that $F(z_i) = x_0$. A path on $D^2 - \cup_i D_i^*$ from z_i to the base point z_0 on S^1 maps by F into a loop at x_0 representing some element $T_i \in \pi_1(M - V, x_0)$. Taking these paths on D^2 to be disjoint, we clearly have $\xi = \Pi_i T_i^{-1} \alpha_i^\varepsilon T_i$. Hence the weight of $\pi_1(M - V, x_0)$ is at most 1.

To complete the proof of Lemma 1 it remains to show that if $f: S^n \to \Sigma^{n+2}$ is a differentiable imbedding, where Σ^{n+2} is a homotopy $(n + 2)$-sphere, then $H_2(\pi) = 0$, where $\pi = \pi_1(\Sigma^{n+2} - f(S^n))$. This follows from the theorem of Hopf in [7] since $H_2(\Sigma^{n+2} - f(S^n)) = 0$ by Alexander duality.

The proofs of Theorem 2 and of the "if" part of Theorem 1 are based on the same construction. Thus we start proving them simultaneously. Eventually the proof will split into the two cases $n = 2$ and $n \geq 3$.

Let π be a given group of weight 1 and such that $\pi/\pi' \cong \mathbf{Z}$.

Suppose we have succeeded constructing a manifold M^{n+2} such that $\pi_1 M \cong \pi$, and $H_q M = 0$ for $2 \leq q \leq n$, where $n \geq 2$. Let $\alpha \in \pi$ be an element whose normal closure is equal to π, and let $\psi: S^1 \to M^{n+2}$ be a differential imbedding representing α (under some isomorphism $\pi \cong \pi_1(M, x_0)$, where $x_0 = \psi(z_0)$). Extending ψ to an imbedding $\varphi: S^1 \times D^{n+1} \to M^{n+2}$ and performing the spherical modification $\chi(\varphi)$, we obtain a Σ^{n+2} which is easily seen to be a homotopy sphere. We have

$$\Sigma^{n+2} = (M - \varphi(S^1 \times B^{n+1})) \cup D^2 \times S^n,$$

where B^{n+1} denotes the interior of D^{n+1}, and Σ^{n+2} is simply connected by the theorem of van Kampen. Using $\pi/\pi' \cong \mathbf{Z}$ and the fact that the homology class of α must be a generator of $H_1 M$, it follows that

$$H_2\Sigma = H_n\Sigma = 0.$$

Compare [10], §5, Lemma 5.6. The vanishing of $H_k\Sigma$ for $2 < k < n$ follows readily using a Mayer–Vietoris sequence.

Let $\varphi': D^2 \times S^n \to \Sigma^{n+2}$ be the inclusion map, and $f: S^n \to \Sigma^{n+2}$ the imbedding defined by $f(u) = \varphi'(0, u)$. Clearly, $\Sigma^{n+2} - f(S^n)$ and $\Sigma^{n+2} - \varphi'(D^2 \times S^n)$ have the same homotopy type. Hence

$$\pi_1(\Sigma^{n+2} - f(S^n)) \cong \pi_1(\Sigma^{n+2} - \varphi'(D^2 \times S^n))$$

$$\cong \pi_1(M - \varphi(S^1 \times D^{n+1})) \cong \pi_1 M \cong \pi,$$

since dim $M \geq 4$.

If $n = 2$, I do not know how to go any further. For $n \geq 3$ the connected sum $\Sigma \# (-\Sigma)$ is h-cobordant, and hence diffeomorphic to S^{n+2}. (Compare [13].) Considering S^n as imbedded in the first summand, we get an imbedding $f: S^n \to S^{n+2}$ such that $\pi_1(S^{n+2} - f(S^n)) \cong \pi$. (If $n = 3$, then Σ^5

is diffeomorphic to S^5 and we do not have to appeal to the connected sum $\Sigma \# (-\Sigma)$.)

It remains to construct the manifold M^{n+2} such that $\pi_1 M \cong \pi$ and $H_k M = 0$ for $2 \leq k \leq n$.

Let $\pi = (x_1, \ldots, x_q; R_1, \ldots, R_r)$ be a finite presentation of π (not necessarily of deficiency 1). We start with the manifold

$$M_0^{n+2} = S^1 \times S^{n+1} \# S^1 \times S^{n+1} \# \cdots \# S^1 \times S^{n+1},$$

i.e., the connected sum of q copies of $S^1 \times S^{n+1}$. Observe that M_0^{n+2} is S-parallelizable, i.e., the stabilized tangent bundle of M_0^{n+2} is trivial. (Compare [10].) It is convenient to choose as base "point" on M_0^{n+2} some contractible open subset $U \subset M_0$. The fundamental group $\pi_1(M_0, U)$ is a free group on q generators which we identify with $x_1, \ldots, x_q$. Let $f_j : (S^1, z_0) \to (M_0, U)$, where $j = 1, \ldots, r$ be r mutually disjoint differential imbeddings representing $R_j(x_1, \ldots, x_q)$. Since M_0 is orientable, we can extend f_j to disjoint differential imbeddings $\varphi_j : S^1 \times D^{n+1} \to M_0$, and then perform a polyspherical framed modification $\chi(\varphi_1, \ldots, \varphi_r)$. In other words, we consider the manifold M_1 obtained from the disjoint union $(M_0 - \bigcup_j \varphi_j(S^1 \times B^{n+1})) \cup (D^2 \times S^n)_1 \cup (D^2 \times S^n)_2 \cup \cdots \cup (D^2 \times S^n)_r$ by identifying $\varphi_j(u, v)$ for $u \in S^1$, $v \in S^n$ with $(u, v) \in (D^2 \times S^n)_j$, $j = 1, \ldots, r$. We denote by φ_j' the inclusion of $(D^2 \times S^n)_j$ into M_1. It is known that M_1 has a natural differential structure, and that the extensions φ_j of f_j can be chosen so that M_1 is S-parallelizable. (Compare [10], p. 521 and Lemma 5.4.) By the theorem of van Kampen, we have $\pi_1(M_1) \cong \pi$.

If the presentation $(x_1, \ldots, x_q; R_1, \ldots, R_r)$ of π has deficiency 1, i.e., if $r = q - 1$, then $\varphi_* : H_1(\bigcup_j(S^1 \times D^{n+1})) \to H_1(M_0)$ must be injective since $H_1 M_0 / \mathrm{Im}\, \varphi_* \cong H_1 M_1 \cong \mathbf{Z}$. Then $H_2 M_0 = 0$ implies

$$H_2(M_0, \bigcup_j \varphi_j(S^1 \times D^{n+1})) = 0,$$

and by excision we also have

$$H_2(M_1, \bigcup_j \varphi_j'(D^2 \times S^n)) = 0.$$

The exact sequence

$$\Sigma_j H_2(D^2 \times S^n) \xrightarrow{\varphi_*'} H_2 M_1 \to H_2(M_1, \bigcup_j \varphi_j'(D^2 \times S^n))$$

then yields $H_2 M_1 = 0$, at least for $n > 2$. For $n = 2$ the conclusion $H_2 M_1 = 0$ still follows since φ_* maps the generators of $\Sigma_j H_1(S^1 \times D^n)$ into primitive elements of $H_1 M_0$ and it follows that the map φ_*' of the above sequence is zero. (Compare [10], Lemma 5.6 and the "Assertion" on p. 516.) Hence, under the assumptions of Theorem 2, we can take $M = M_1$. This completes the proof of Theorem 2.

If the presentation of π is not necessarily of deficiency 1, and all we know is that $H_2(\pi) = 0$, we have to assume $n \geqq 3$ in order to be able to kill $H_2 M_1$ by spherical modifications.

Let $\rho \colon \pi_2 M_1 \to H_2 M_1$ be the Hurewicz homomorphism. Then $\rho(\pi_2 M_1)$ is the subgroup of spherical homology classes, and according to H. Hopf $H_2(\pi) = H_2 M_1 / \rho(\pi_2 M_1)$, where the homology of π is understood with integer coefficients and trivial action of π. (Compare [7].) Hence the assumption $H_2(\pi) = 0$ implies that $\rho \colon \pi_2 M_1 \to H_2 M_1$ is surjective. The assumption $n \geqq 3$ guarantees that every homology class $\xi \in H_2 M_1$ is representable by a differentiably imbedded 2-sphere. (Recall that according to [9] this is definitely false for $n = 2$.) Since M_1 is S-parallelizable, every differentiably imbedded 2-sphere in M_1 has a trivial normal bundle.

Following the discussion in §5 of [10], we construct a finite sequence $M_1, M_2, \ldots, M_k, \ldots$ of $(n + 2)$-manifolds. M_{k+1} is obtained from M_k by a spherical modification $\chi(\varphi_k)$ were $\varphi_k \colon S^2 \times D^n \to M_k$ represents a suitable class $\xi_k \in H_2 M_k$.

Since $M_{k+1} = (M_k - \varphi_k(S^2 \times B^n)) \cup D^3 \times S^{n-1}$, it follows from $n \geqq 3$, using the theorem of van Kampen, that $\pi_1 M_{k+1} \cong \pi_1 M_k \cong \pi$. Hence, at every stage of the construction, $\rho \colon \pi_2 M_k \to H_2 M_k$ is surjective (by Hopf's theorem [7]) and every class in $H_2 M_k$ is representable by a differentiably imbedded 2-sphere. Taking care of performing only *framed* spherical modifications (see §6 of [10]), all the manifolds M_k will be S-parallelizable, and every differentiably imbedded 2-sphere in M_k has a trivial normal bundle.

The choice of $\xi_k \in H_2 M_k$ is made as follows: (1) If $H_2 M_k$ is infinite, then $H_2 M_k$ contains a primitive element ξ_k. This means that there exists an element $\eta \in H_n M_k$ such that $\xi_k \cdot \eta = 1$. Then, killing ξ_k by a spherical modification also kills η and $H_2 M_{k+1} \cong H_2 M_k / (\xi_k)$. For the proof, see Lemma 5.6 of [10]. (2) If $H_2 M_k$ is finite (and non-zero) then n must equal 3. Killing an arbitrary element $\xi_k \in H_2 M_k$ by spherical modification introduces a new class $\xi' \in H_2 M_{k+1}$ necessarily of infinite order. More precisely, the sequence

$$0 \to \mathbf{Z} \to H_2 M_{k+1} \to H_2 M_k / (\xi_k) \to 0$$

is exact in this case, as proved in [10], p. 16. The next modification will be taken to kill a primitive element ξ_{k+1} in the newly introduced infinite cyclic summand of $H_2 M_{k+1}$. (In general $\xi_{k+1} \neq \xi'$.)

It is left to the reader to convince himself that the non-vanishing of the fundamental groups of M_k in the present situation does not invalidate Lemmas 5.6 and 5.8 of [10]. The proofs given in [10] apply word-for-word to the present case.

Hence, choosing $\xi_k \in H_2 M_k$ to be primitive if $H_2 M_k$ is infinite, and an arbitrary generator if $H_2 M_k$ is finite, the sequence $M_1, \ldots, M_k, \ldots$ leads in a finite number of steps to a manifold $M_l = M$ such that $\pi_1 M \cong \pi$ and $H_2 M = 0$.

If $n = 3$, then $H_2 M = 0$ implies $H_3 M = 0$ by Poincaré duality since $H_1 M \cong \pi/\pi' \cong \mathbf{Z}$ is free abelian. If $n > 3$, then $H_3 M = \cdots = H_{n-1} = 0$ because then $H_2 M_k$ is torsion free, and killing a primitive class of $H_2 M_k$ leaves the q-dimensional homology group unchanged for $3 \leqq q \leqq n - 1$. Moreover, $H_n M = 0$ again by Poincaré duality.

Thus the manifold M satisfies the requirements $\pi_1 M \cong \pi$ and $H_q M = 0$ for $q = 2, \ldots, n$. This completes the proof of Theorem 1.

REMARK. Of course, having an imbedding $f : S^3 \to S^5$ such that $\pi_1(S^5 - f(S^3)) \cong \pi$ it is easy to obtain an imbedding $f_n : S^n \to S^{n+2}$ with $\pi_1(S^{n+2} - f_n(S^n)) \cong \pi$ for all $n \geqq 3$ by the Artin "spinning" construction. (Compare Artin [1].)

3. Appendix

This last section contains some remarks which came up in discussions during the Symposium. They are due for the most part to M. Hirsch, J. Milnor, and J. Stallings. (However, except for Theorem III and Milnor's example under (3) below, the proofs given here are my own.)

The first question was: *What is the situation in the case of a differentiably imbedded homotopy n-sphere Σ^n in S^{n+2}?*

THEOREM I. *A homotopy n-sphere Σ^n can be imbedded in S^{n+2} (by a differential imbedding) if and only if Σ^n is the boundary of a parallelizable $(n + 1)$-manifold.*

PROOF. Suppose Σ^n is imbeddable in S^{n+2}, then Σ^n bounds a parallelizable $(n + 1)$-manifold. In fact, every $\Sigma^n \subset S^{n+2}$ bounds a parallelizable $V^{n+1} \subset S^{n+2}$. Let U be a tubular neighborhood of $\Sigma^n \subset S^{n+2}$ and

$$T = bU = \bar{U} - U.$$

Since Σ^n has a trivial normal bundle in S^{n+2}, we have a diffeomorphism $\Sigma^n \times D^2 \approx \bar{U}$. Let $\Sigma_1^n \subset T$ be the submanifold corresponding to $\Sigma^n \times (x_1)$, where $x_1 \in S^1 \subset D^2$. It is enough to show that Σ_1^n bounds a parallelizable $(n + 1)$-manifold V in $S^{n+2} - U$. The Pontrjagin–Thom construction applied to $\Sigma_1^n \subset T^{n+1}$ and a normal vector-field to Σ_1^n in T yields a map $\Phi_1 : T \to S^1$. We extend this map to a map $\Phi : S^{n+2} - U \to S^1$. The only obstruction to the extension is a cohomology class $\gamma \in H^2(S^{n+2} - U, T)$. (Coefficients in $\pi_1(S^1) \cong \mathbf{Z}$.) By the Hopf theorem [Proposition 13.1 on p. 189 of S. Hu, Homotopy Theory, Academic Press, 1959.], we have $\gamma = \delta\sigma$, where $\sigma \in H^1 T$ is the Poincaré dual of the homology class of Σ_1

in T. By the Alexander duality theorem, Σ_1 is homologous to zero in $S^{n+2} - U$, hence there exists a class $\xi \in H_{n+1}(S^{n+2} - U, T)$ such that $\partial \xi = (\Sigma_1)$, the homology class of Σ_1 (in $H_n T$). Using the diagram

$$
\begin{array}{ccccc}
H^1(S^{n+2} - U) & \xrightarrow{i^*} & H^1 T & \longrightarrow & H^2(S^{n+2} - U, T) \\
\updownarrow & & \updownarrow & & \updownarrow \\
H_{n+1}(S^{n+2} - U, T) & \xrightarrow{\partial} & H_n T & \longrightarrow & H_n(S^{n+2} - U)
\end{array}
$$

where the vertical isomorphisms are given by Poincaré duality, we see that the dual of ξ maps by i^* onto $\pm \sigma$. (The diagram is commutative up to sign.) Hence, $\delta \sigma = \gamma = 0$. Keeping $\Phi | T = \Phi_1$ fixed, we can approximate $\Phi : S^{n+2} - U \to S^1$ by a differential map, and assume that

$$
\Phi(\Sigma_1) = a \in S^1
$$

is a regular value of Φ. Then $\Phi^{-1}(a) = V^{n-1} \subset S^{n+2}$ or at least the component of Σ_1 in $\Phi^{-1}(a)$ is the desired manifold.

In particular, this shows that every higher knot has some sort of "generalized genus."

The converse is clear for $n = 1$ or 2. For $n = 3$, every compact orientable 3-manifold in imbeddable in S^5. [M. Hirsch, *Ann. of Math.*, 74 (1961), 494–497. Theorem 3.] If $n = 4$ we argue as follows. Every homotopy 4-sphere Σ^4 is the boundary of a contractible 5-manifold V. (Compare [10], Theorem 6.6.) Let Σ^5 be the double of V. The homotopy 5-sphere Σ^5 is the boundary of a contractible 6-manifold W, and according to Smale [13] W is diffeomorphic to the 6-disc D^6. Hence, Σ^5 is diffeomorphic to S^5, and so every homotopy 4-sphere is imbeddable in S^5. Let $n \geq 5$, and suppose that the homotopy n-sphere Σ^n is the boundary of a parallelizable $(n + 1)$-manifold. If n is even, then Σ^n is h-cobordant to S^n. (See [10], Theorem 6.6.) Hence, according to Smale [13], Σ^n is diffeomorphic to S^n. If n is odd, Σ^n is h-cobordant and hence diffeomorphic to the boundary of a $\frac{1}{2}(n - 1)$-connected manifold W^{n+1}, where W is the connected sum along the boundary of a finite number of copies of some manifold W_0. In Part II of [10] we give an explicit construction of W_0 as a "thickened" wedge of k-spheres, where $2k = n + 1$. Each S^k imbedded in W_0 has a stably trivial normal bundle. Now any wedge of k-spheres can be imbedded in S^{n+2}, and the imbeddability of W in S^{n+2} follows if we prove that every stably trivial SO_k-bundle over S^k can be realized by a normal field of k-planes over S^k in S^{2k+1}. Let f^{k+1} be a trivialization of the normal bundle of $S^k \subset S^{2k+1}$. If v is the field of normal vectors over S^k corresponding to a given map $\alpha : S^k \to S^k$, i.e., $v(x) = \Sigma_0^k \alpha_i(x) f_i(x)$ for all $x \in S^k$, where

$$
f^{k+1}(x) = \{f_0(x), \ldots, f_k(x)\},
$$

then the SO_k-bundle over S^k given by the field of normal k-planes orthogonal to v has a characteristic element $\chi \in \pi_{k-1}(SO_k)$ given by $\chi = \tau(\alpha)$,
where $\tau \colon \pi_k(S^k) \to \pi_{k-1}(SO_k)$ is the transgression homomorphism of the
fibration $SO_k \to SO_{k+1} \to S^k$ and (α) is the homotopy class of α. Stably
trivial SO_k-bundles over S^k are exactly those whose characteristic element
is in the image of τ. Hence, by a proper choice of (α), one can realize any
stably trivial SO_k-bundle over S^k by a field of normal k-planes in S^{2k+1}.
This completes the proof of Theorem I.

THEOREM II. (J. Milnor.) *If Σ^n is the boundary of a parallelizable
manifold, there exists a differential imbedding $f_0 \colon \Sigma^n \to S^{n+2}$ such that
$\pi_1(S^{n+2} - f_0(\Sigma^n)) \cong \mathbf{Z}$.*

PROOF.   The statement is trivial for $n = 1$, 2 and n even ≥ 6 since
then Σ^n is diffeomorphic to S^n as observed before. For $n = 4$ it follows
since every homotopy 4-sphere is imbeddable in S^5. (Compare the proof of
Theorem I.) If n is odd, let $W^{2k} \subset S^{2k+1}$, where $2k = n + 1$, be a connected submanifold of S^{2k+1} such that $bW = \Sigma^n$ and $S^{2k+1} - W$ is simply
connected. We shall prove that for such an imbedding $\Sigma^n \subset S^{n+2}$, we have
$\pi_1(S^{n+2} - \Sigma^n) \cong \mathbf{Z}$. The existence of a submanifold $W^{2k} \subset S^{2k+1}$ of the
required kind will be shown at the end of the proof. Let ℓ be a loop in
the complement of Σ^n. We can assume that ℓ is a differentiable curve,
transversal to W. Let $A(\ell)$ be the algebraic intersection number $I(\ell, W)$
$\in \mathbf{Z}$. Clearly, $A(\ell)$ depends only on the homotopy class of ℓ in
$\pi_1(S^{n+2} - \Sigma^n, x_0)$, where $x_0 = \ell(0)$, and provides a homomorphism
$A \colon \pi_1(S^{n+2} - \Sigma^n, x_0) \to \mathbf{Z}$. It is obvious that A is surjective. Suppose that
$A(\ell) = 0$. We show that ℓ is homotopic in $S^{n+2} - \Sigma^n$ in a loop in
$S^{n+2} - W$. Unless ℓ is already a loop in $S^{n+2} - W$, there exist a pair
$t < t'$ of values of t and small positive numbers ε, ε' such that $\ell[t + \varepsilon,
t' - \varepsilon']$ is contained in $S^{n+2} - W$, and

$$I(\ell[t - \varepsilon, t + \varepsilon], W) = -I(\ell[t' - \varepsilon', t' + \varepsilon'], W) \neq 0,$$

where the sets $\ell[t - \varepsilon, t + \varepsilon] \cap W$ and $\ell[t' - \varepsilon', t' + \varepsilon'] \cap W$ consist
of a single point. Since $S^{n+2} - W$ is simply connected, $\ell|[t + \varepsilon, t' - \varepsilon']$ is
homotopic in $S^{n+2} - W$ (and *a fortiori* in $S^{n+2} - \Sigma^n$) to a path ℓ' contained in a neighborhood of W. (Use a path on W connecting $\ell(t)$ and
$\ell(t')$.) Replacing the portion of ℓ between $t + \varepsilon$ and $t' - \varepsilon'$ by ℓ' and using
a field of normal vectors to W in S^{n+2} we can "push" the path

$$\ell([t - \varepsilon, t + \varepsilon]) \cdot \ell'([t + \varepsilon, t' - \varepsilon']) \cdot \ell([t' - \varepsilon', t' + \varepsilon'])$$

across W (keeping its endpoints fixed) without interesecting Σ^n, thus
removing the two intersection points $\ell(t)$ and $\ell(t')$ of ℓ and W. The
statement that ℓ is homotopic in $S^{n+2} - \Sigma^n$ to a loop in $S^{n+2} - W$ then

follows by induction on the cardinality of the finite set $\ell(I) \cap W$. Since $S^{n+2} - W$ is simply connected, $A(\ell) = 0$ implies $\ell \cong 1$, hence A is an isomorphism and $\pi_1(S^{n+2} - \Sigma^n) \cong \mathbf{Z}$.

If $n \geq 5$, we take for W a finite connected sum along the boundary of thickened wedge of k-spheres, and the imbedding $W^{2k} \subset S^{2k+1}$ whose existence has been shown in the proof of Theorem I. Since W retracts by deformation on a wedge of k-spheres, we clearly have

$$\pi_1(S^{2k+1} - W^{2k}) = \{1\}.$$

If $n = 3$, take an imbedding $\Sigma^3 \subset S^5$ which bounds a simply connected $W^4 \subset S^5$. (Compare Hirsch, *Ann. of Math.*, 74 (1961), 494–497, Theorem 3.) I claim that $S^5 - W$ is simply connected. Let $f: S^1 \to S^5 - W$ be a given differential imbedding and denote again by f an extension $f: (D^2, S^1) \to (S^5, S^5 - W)$. Firstly, we can push $f(D^2)$ away from $\Sigma^3 = bW^4$. To do this assume that f is transversal to W and Σ^3. If x, x' are two intersection points of $f(D^2)$ and Σ^3 with opposite intersection numbers, then x, x' are the endpoints of a path w in $f(D^2) \cap W$ and also endpoints of a path w' on Σ^3. Let $\varphi: Q \to W^4$ be an immersion of the 2-disc with two corners Q into W such that $\varphi|bQ = w' \cdot w^{-1}$. ($W$ is simply connected.) Keeping $\varphi|bQ$ fixed we can approximate φ by an imbedding into S^5 such that $\varphi(\text{int } Q) \cap \Sigma^3 = \emptyset$. Using a field of normal 3-frames on $\varphi(Q)$ we can push f along $\varphi(Q)$ using the method of H. Whitney [*Ann. of Math.*, 45 (1944), 220–246]. The effect of this operation is to remove the intersection points x, x' from $f(D^2) \cap \Sigma^3$. After a finite number of such operations we obtain a new mapping $f: (D^2, S^1) \to (S^5 - \Sigma^3, S^5 - W^4)$ with $f|S^1$ unchanged.

Now, assuming f still transversal to W, the intersection $f(D^2) \cap W$ consists of a finite number of disjoint closed curves. Let $C_1, \ldots, C_r$ be the corresponding curves in D^2. Let C_1 bound a disc D_1 on D^2. Since $f(C_1)$ is homotopic to a point in W, we can replace $f|D_1$ by a mapping into W. Using a normal vector-field on W, f can be pushed away from W in a neighborhood of D_1, thus reducing the number of components of $f(D^2) \cap W$ by at least 1. Hence the intersection $f(D^2) \cap W$ can also be removed in a finite number of steps, proving that $f|S^1$ is homotopic to a point in $S^5 - W$. Thus $\pi_1(S^5 - W) = \{1\}$. This completes the proof of Theorem II.

THEOREM III.   (M. Hirsch.) *Let* $f: \Sigma^n \to S^{n+2}$ *be a differential imbedding with* $n \geq 5$. *If* $S^{n+2} - f(\Sigma^n)$ *has the homotopy type of* S^1, *then* Σ^n *is diffeomorphic to* S^n.

PROOF.   Let $g: S^1 - S^{n+2} - f(\Sigma^n)$ be a differential imbedding which is a homotopy equivalence. Let U be a tubular neighborhood of $f(\Sigma^n)$ and set $V^{n+2} = S^{n+2} - U$. Extending g to an imbedding $g: S^1 \times D^{n+1} \to V^{n+2}$ using a trivialization of the normal bundle of $g(S^1)$. Then

$$V' = V - g(S^1 \times \text{int } D^{n+1})$$

provides a simple h-cobordism between $g(S^1 \times S^n)$ and $bU = bV$. It is easily seen that inclusions $g(S^1 \times S^n) \subset V'$ and $bU \subset V'$ are homotopy equivalences, and since the fundamental group is infinite cyclic, they are simple homotopy equivalences (compare J. H. C. Whitehead, *Proc. London Math. Soc.*, 45 (1939), 243–327). It follows by a theorem of B. Mazur [*Ann. of Math.*, 77 (1963), 232–249] that bU is diffeomorphic to $S^1 \times S^n$. Since Σ^n has a trivial normal bundle, bU is diffeomorphic to $S^1 \times \Sigma^n$. Hence there exists a diffeomorphism $h: S^1 \times \Sigma^n \to S^1 \times S^n$. Lifting h to the universal coverings, we get a diffeomorphism $H: R^1 \times \Sigma^n \to R^1 \times S^n \subset R^{n+1}$. Hence Σ^n can be differentially imbedded into R^{n+1}. The compact region W bounded by $H(0 \times \Sigma^n)$ in R^{n+1} is a contractible manifold with boundary Σ^n. Using the assumption $n \geq 5$, it follows by Smale [13] that W is diffeomorphic to D^{n+1}. In particular $\Sigma^n = bW$ is diffeomorphic to S^n.

THEOREM IV. *Given a homotopy n-sphere Σ^n which is the boundary of a parallelizable manifold, $n \geq 3$, and a finitely presentable group π of weight 1, such that $\pi/\pi' \cong \mathbf{Z}$ and $H_2(\pi) = 0$, there exists a differential imbedding $f: \Sigma^n \to S^{n+2}$ with $\pi \cong \pi_1(S^{n+2} - f(\Sigma^n))$.*

PROOF. Let $\Sigma^n \subset S^{n+2}$ be an imbedding such that $\pi_1(S^{n+2} - \Sigma^n) \cong \mathbf{Z}$ (Theorem II). Let $f_0: S^n \to S^{n+2}$ be an n-knot with $\pi_1(S^{n+2} - f_0(S^n)) \cong \pi$ (Theorem 1). Take the relative connected sum $(S^{n+2}, \Sigma^n) \# (S^{n+2}, f_0(S^n))$, and let $f: \Sigma^n \to S^{n+2}$ be the resulting differential imbedding. Then $\pi_1(S^{n+2} - f(\Sigma^n)) \cong \pi*\mathbf{Z}/(\alpha^{-1}\gamma)$, where γ generates $\mathbf{Z}$, and α is some element of π. Hence, $\pi_1(S^{n+2} - f(\Sigma^n)) \cong \pi$.

If the complement of a 1-knot $f: S^1 \to S^3$ has an infinite cyclic fundamental group, then $S^3 - f(S^1)$ and S^1 have the same homotopy type. This is a simple consequence of the Lemma of Dehn-Papakyriakopoulos [*Ann. of Math.*, 66 (1957), 1–26].

For which values of n can one imbed S^n into S^{n+2} so that $\pi_1(S^{n+2} - f(S^n))$ is infinite cyclic but $S^{n+2} - f(S^n)$ does not have the homotopy type of S^1?

THEOREM V. (J. Stallings) *For $n \geq 3$ there exist smooth imbeddings $f: S^n \to S^{n+2}$ such that $\pi_1(S^{n+2} - f(S^n)) \cong \mathbf{Z}$ and $\pi_2(S^{n+2} - f(S^n)) \neq 0$.*

For $n = 2$ the question remains open.

PROOF. Let $M_0 = S^1 \times S^{n+1} \# S^2 \times S^n$, and let J denote the multiplicative infinite cyclic group generated by the symbol t. Choosing some base point $x_0 \in M_0$ and a generator of $\pi_1(M_0, x_0)$, we identify $\pi_1(M_0, x_0)$

with J. Then, $\pi_2(M_0, x_0)$ is a free $\mathbf{Z}[J]$-module on one generator, where $\mathbf{Z}[J]$ is the integral group ring of J. Choosing a generator of $\pi_2(M_0, x_0)$, we can identify $\pi_2(M_0, x_0)$ with $\mathbf{Z}[J]$. Let $\varphi_0\colon S^2 \to M_0$ be a differential imbedding representing the element $(2 - t) \in \pi_2(M_0, x_0) = \mathbf{Z}[J]$. Clearly, φ_0 has a trivial normal bundle and we can extend φ_0 to an imbedding $\varphi\colon S^2 \times D^n \to M_0$. Let $M = \chi(M_0, \varphi)$ be the manifold obtained from M_0 by spherical modification. $M = (M_0 - \varphi(S^2 \times \operatorname{int} D^n)) \cup D^3 \times S^{n-1}$. Since the homology class of $\varphi_0(S^2)$ is a generator of $H_2 M_0$, it follows that $H_2 M = \cdots = H_n M = 0$. Since $n \geq 3$, $\pi_1 M \cong \mathbf{Z}$ and it is easily seen that $\pi_2 M$ is non-trivial. Indeed, M_0 and M are the two components of the boundary of a manifold W which is homotopy equivalent to $M_0 \cup e^3$ and $M \cup e^n$. Hence, the inclusions $M_0 \to W$ and $M \to W$ induce epimorphisms $i_*\colon \pi_2 M_0 \to \pi_2 W$ and $\pi_2 M \to \pi_2 W$. The kernel of i_* is the ideal of $\mathbf{Z}[J]$ generated by $2 - t$. Hence, $\pi_2 W = \operatorname{Im} i_* \neq 0$, and therefore $\pi_2 M \neq 0$.

Let $\psi\colon S^1 \times D^{n+1} \to M$ be an imbedding representing a generator of $\pi_1 M \cong \mathbf{Z}$. Then, the manifold

$$\chi(M, \psi) = (M - \psi(S^1 \times \operatorname{int} D^{n+1})) \cup D^2 \times S^n$$

is a homotopy $(n + 2)$-sphere Σ^{n+2}. Let $f\colon S^n \to \Sigma^{n+2}$ be the imbedding $S^n \to 0 \times S^n \subset D^2 \times S^n \subset \Sigma^{n+2}$. We have

$$\pi_1\big(\Sigma^{n+2} - f(S^n)\big) \cong \pi_1 M \cong \mathbf{Z},$$

and

$$\pi_2\big(\Sigma^{n+2} - f(S^n)\big) \cong \pi_2\big(\Sigma^{n+2} - D^2 \times S^n\big)$$

$$\cong \pi_2(M - \psi(S^1 \times D^{n+1})) \cong \pi_2 M \neq 0.$$

By suitably changing the differentiable structure of Σ^{n+2} in the complement of $f(S^n)$ we obtain a differential imbedding $f\colon S^n \to S^{n+2}$ with

$$\pi_1(S^{n+2} - f(S^n)) \cong \mathbf{Z} \qquad \text{and} \qquad \pi_2(S^{n+2} - f(S^n)) \neq 0.$$

Finally, we discuss the independence of the algebraic conditions:

    (i) $\pi/\pi' \cong \mathbf{Z}$;

    (ii) There exists an element $\alpha \in \pi$ whose normal closure is π;

    (iii) $H_2(\pi) = 0$.

(1) Any finite cyclic group satisfies (ii) and (iii) and does not satisfy (i).

(2) Let G be a non-trivial group such that $G = G'$, and suppose that G has a non-trivial finite dimensional unitary representation. We also assume that G has a presentation of deficiency 0. For instance, let G be

the group with the presentation $G = (\alpha, \beta; \alpha^2 = \beta^3 = (\alpha^{-1}\beta)^5)$. A representation $\rho: G \to U(5)$ into the group of 5×5 unitary matrices is given by

$$\rho(\alpha) = \begin{Vmatrix} 0 & 1 & 0 & 0 & 0 \\ 1 & 0 & 0 & 0 & 0 \\ 0 & 0 & 0 & 1 & 0 \\ 0 & 0 & 1 & 0 & 0 \\ 0 & 0 & 0 & 0 & 1 \end{Vmatrix} \qquad \rho(\beta) = \begin{Vmatrix} 0 & 0 & 1 & 0 & 0 \\ 0 & 1 & 0 & 0 & 0 \\ 0 & 0 & 0 & 0 & 1 \\ 0 & 0 & 0 & 1 & 0 \\ 1 & 0 & 0 & 0 & 0 \end{Vmatrix}$$

Under the above assumptions on G, the group $\pi = G * \mathbf{Z}$ satisfies (i) and (iii). It even satisfies the requirement stronger than (iii) of having deficiency 1. I claim that the weight of π is bigger than 1. We prove this for the above group $G = (\alpha, \beta; \alpha^2 = \beta^3 = (\alpha^{-1}\beta)^5)$. In the general case the proof is quite similar. Let $W(\alpha, \beta, \gamma)$ be a word representing an element ξ in $\pi = G * \mathbf{Z}$. (γ denotes a generator of $\mathbf{Z}$.) Claim: $\pi/(\xi) \neq \{1\}$.

The statement is trivial unless the sum of exponents of γ in $W(\alpha, \beta, \gamma)$ is equal to ± 1. (Look at the abelianized group of $\pi/(\xi)$.) We can then assume that the exponent-sum of γ in $W(\alpha, \beta, \gamma)$ is $+1$. Regard $W(A, B, X) = E$, where $A = \rho(\alpha)$ and $B = \rho(\beta)$ as an equation in $U(5)$ for the unknown matrix X. (E denotes the unit matrix of $U(5)$.) Following M. Gerstenhaber and O. Rothaus, consider the mapping $w: U(5) \to U(5)$ defined by $w(X) = W(A, B, X)$. (Compare *Proc. Nat. Acad. Sci.*, 48 (1962), 1531–1533. I am very grateful to W. Magnus and G. Baumslag for pointing out this paper to me.) Since $U(5)$ is connected, w is homotopic to the mapping $w_0: U(5) \to U(5)$ defined by

$$w_0(X) = W(E, E, X).$$

Since X enters into $W(A, B, X)$ with exponent-sum 1, we have

$$W(E, E, X) = X.$$

Hence, w_0 is the identity mapping, and w must be a surjective map since $U(5)$ is a finite dimensional manifold. In other words, the equation $W(A, B, X) = E$ has a solution $C \in U(5)$, i.e., $W(A, B, C) = E$. Now, let $\pi_* \subset U(5)$ be the subgroup of $U(5)$ generated by A, B, C. Then $\pi_* \neq \{1\}$ and $\pi/(\xi)$ maps surjectively onto π_* by $\rho_*: \pi/(\xi) \to U(5)$ defined by $\rho_*(\alpha) = A$, $\rho_*(\beta) = B$, $\rho_*(\gamma) = C$. It follows that $\pi/(\xi) \neq \{1\}$. Since this argument applies to any group element $\xi \in \pi$, the group π does not satisfy (ii).

(3) J. Milnor gave the following example of a group π satisfying (i) and (ii) but not (iii). Let A be a unimodular 2×2 matrix of determinant $+1$,

and let $\alpha\colon S^1 \times S^1 \to S^1 \times S^1$ be the corresponding automorphism of the torus:

$$\alpha(z_1, z_2) = (z_1^a z_2^b, z_1^c z_2^d),$$

where

$$A = \left\| \begin{matrix} a & b \\ c & d \end{matrix} \right\|.$$

$(a, b, c, d \in \mathbf{Z})$. Let E_A be the closed orientable 3-manifold obtained from $S^1 \times S^1 \times I$ by identifying $S^1 \times S^1 \times (0)$ with $S^1 \times S^1 \times (1)$ using α. Then E_A is the total space of a (locally trivial) fibration over S^1 with fibre $S^1 \times S^1$. It follows that $\pi_2 E_A = 0$. Since $\alpha(1, 1) = (1, 1)$, we can define a section $S^1 \to E_A$ by mapping each $z \in S^1$ into the point $(1, 1)$ of the fibre over z. This defines an element $\tau \in \pi_1(E_A, x_0)$, where x_0 is the point $(1, 1) \in S^1 \times S^1$ of the fibre over $1 \in S^1$. Let ξ, η be the generators of the fundamental group of the fibre over $1 \in S^1$ represented by $\xi(t) = (e^{2\pi i t}, 1)$ and $\eta(t) = (1, e^{2\pi i t})$. The group $\pi_1(E_A, x_0)$ is generated by τ, ξ, η and has the presentation $(\tau, \xi, \eta; [\xi, \eta] = 1, \tau^{-1}\xi\tau = \xi^a\eta^b, \tau^{-1}\eta\tau = \xi^c\eta^d)$. Hence, denoting $\pi_1(E_A, x_0)$ by π, we have $\pi/\pi' \cong \mathbf{Z}$ if and only if $(a - 1)(d - 1) - bc = \pm 1$. Then, $H_2(E_A) \cong \mathbf{Z}$ by Poincaré duality, and since $\pi_2(E_A) = 0$, it follows that

$$H_2(\pi) = H_2(E_A)/\rho\pi_2(E_A) \cong \mathbf{Z}.$$

Moreover, if $(a - 1)(d - 1) - bc = \pm 1$, the normal closure of τ in π is equal to π.

A simple example of a unimodular matrix satisfying the above requirements is

$$\left\| \begin{matrix} 1 & 1 \\ -1 & 0 \end{matrix} \right\|$$

The corresponding group, satisfying (i), (ii) but not (iii), has the presentation $(\tau, \xi, \eta; \xi^{-1}\eta^{-1}\xi\eta = 1, \tau^{-1}\xi\tau = \xi\eta, \tau^{-1}\eta\tau = \xi^{-1})$.

COURANT INSTITUTE OF MATHEMATICAL SCIENCES
NEW YORK UNIVERSITY

REFERENCES

[1] E. ARTIN, Zur Isotopie zweidimensionaler Flächen im R_4, *Abh. math. Seminar Hamburg. Univ.* Bd. 4 (1925), p. 174–177.

[2] R. CROWELL and R. FOX, *An Introduction to Knot Theory*, Boston: Ginn & Co., 1962.

[3] D. EPSTEIN, Finite presentations of groups and 3-manifolds, *Quarterly Journal of Math.*, Vol. 12 (1961), p. 205–212.

[4] R. Fox, Free differential calculus, II, *Annals of Math.*, *59* (1954), p. 196–210.

[5] ———, A quick trip through knot theory, *Proc. of the 1961 Topology Institute*, Georgia Univ.

[6] R. Fox and G. Torres, Dual presentations of the group of a knot, *Annals of Math.*, *59* (1954), p. 211–218.

[7] H. Hopf, Fundamentalgruppe und zweite Bettische Gruppe, *Comm. Math. Helv.*, *14* (1941), p. 257–309.

[8] E. van Kampen, On the connection between the fundamental groups of some related spaces, *Amer. J. of Math.*, *55* (1933), p. 261–267.

[9] M. Kervaire and J. Milnor, On 2-spheres in 4-manifolds, *Proc. Nat. Acad. Sci. U.S.A.*, *47* (1961), p. 1651–1657.

[10] ———, Groups of homotopy spheres, I, *Annals of Math.*, *77* (1963), p. 504–537.

[11] S. Kinoshita, On the Alexander polynomials of 2-spheres in a 4-sphere, *Annals of Math.*, *74* (1961), p. 518–531.

[12] H. Seifert, Über das Geschlecht von Knoten, *Math. Annalen Bd.*, *110* (1934), p. 571–592.

[13] S. Smale, Structure of differentiable manifolds, *Amer. Journal of Math.*, *84* (1962), p. 387–399.

[14] R. Thom, Singularities of differentiable mappings. Mimeographed notes, Bonn University, 1958.

On the Groups J(X)

J. FRANK ADAMS

1. Introduction

In another lecture [2], I have explained that certain problems of algebraic topology can be reduced to the calculation of the groups $J(X)$ defined by Atiyah [4]. In the same lecture I have tried to show that the best method which we possess at present to calculate the groups $J(X)$ is to try and sandwich them between two further groups $J'(X)$, $J''(X)$. All these groups will be defined below; but we may say at once that we shall define them as quotients of $K_R(X)$, where $K_\Lambda(X)$ denotes the "extraordinary cohomology theory" of Grothendieck–Atiyah–Hirzebruch [1, 6, 7]. That is, we shall give definitions of the form

$$J(X) = K_R(X)/U(X)$$
$$J'(X) = K_R(X)/V(X)$$
$$J''(X) = K_R(X)/W(X)$$

where $U(X)$, $V(X)$ and $W(X)$ are suitably defined subgroups of $K_R(X)$.

The group $J'(X)$ is a lower bound for $J(X)$, in the sense that $U(X) \subset V(X)$, so that the quotient map $K_R(X) \to J'(X)$ factors through the quotient map $K_R(X) \to J(X)$; this yields the following commutative diagram of epimorphisms.

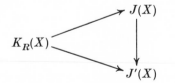

We hope to prove that $J''(X)$ is an upper bound for $J(X)$, in a similar sense; and this we have proved in some cases, notably those in which X is a complex projective space CP^n, or a sphere S^m with $m \not\equiv 0 \bmod 8$.

The main object of this paper is to prove the following result.

THEOREM 1.1.   For each finite CW-complex X we have $J'(X) = J''(X)$.

The precise sense in which the groups $J'(X)$ and $J''(X)$ are "equal" is the following. We shall prove that the subgroups $V(X)$ and $W(X)$ of $K_R(X)$, although differently defined, are in fact the same. Therefore the corresponding quotient groups $J'(X)$ and $J''(X)$ are (as a matter of logic) identical; that is, they are one and the same object.

The proof to be presented is extracted from a more complete account of these matters now in preparation [3], to which the reader is referred for a fuller exposition of the fundamentals of the theory, for the results of certain calculations (Lemmas 4.6 and 4.8 of this paper), and for a certain piece of number-theory (Lemma 4.7 of this paper). With these exceptions, it is hoped that the proof is as complete as can be expected in the present limited space.

The arrangement of this paper is as follows. Theorem 1.1 is proved in §4. The proof is completely dependent on the existence of a certain commutative diagram (Diagram 3.1), which is established in §3. In §2 we dispose of various necessary preliminaries.

2. Preliminaries

We have said that we shall give definitions of the following form:

$$J(X) = K_R(X)/U(X)$$
$$J'(X) = K_R(X)/V(X)$$
$$J''(X) = K_R(X)/W(X).$$

We define $U(X)$ to be the subgroup of $K_R(X)$ generated by elements of the form $\{\xi\} - \{\eta\}$, where ξ and η are real vector-bundles whose associated sphere-bundles are fibre homotopy equivalent.

It takes only a little longer to define the subgroup $W(X)$. The following definition is good if X is a finite CW-complex. Let $e(k)$ be a function which assigns to each integer k a non-negative integer $e(k)$. Let $W(e; X)$ be the subgroup of $K_R(X)$ generated by elements of the form

$$k^{e(k)}((\Psi^k x) - x);$$

here k runs over all integers, x runs over all elements of $K_R(X)$, and Ψ^k is the K-cohomology operation introduced in [1].

It is clear that if $e(k) \geq f(k)$ for all k, then $W(e; X) \subset W(f; X)$. We define

$$W(X) = \bigcap_e W(e; X);$$

here the intersection is taken as e runs over all functions $e(k)$.

At this point it is convenient to introduce some further notions. Let X be a finite-dimensional CW-complex; then by considering $SO(n)$-bundles over X (for $n = 1, 2, \ldots$) we can construct a Grothendieck group based on orientable bundles, which we may write $K_{SO}(X)$. The group $K_{SO}(X)$ is embedded in $K_R(X)$ as the subgroup of elements x whose first Stiefel–Whitney class $w_1(x)$ is zero. We may call such elements x "orientable elements."

The notation for each of our Grothendieck groups will contain the letter K; we agree that by substituting $\tilde{K}$ for K we indicate the corresponding subgroup of elements of virtual dimension zero. For example, we have

$$\tilde{K}_{SO}(X) = \tilde{K}_R(X) \cap K_{SO}(X).$$

In order to define the subgroup $V(X)$, we require the "cannibalistic characteristic classes" of Bott [8, 9] and Atiyah [private communication]. We shall call them ρ^k, although Bott uses the letter θ. For the moment we need only recall the following points.

(1) ρ^k assigns to suitable bundles over X a characteristic class lying in $K_R(X)$.

(2) ρ^k can be defined on suitable virtual bundles at the price of introducing denominators. More precisely, one defines Q_k to be the additive group of fractions of the form a/k^b, where a and b are integers. Then if $x \in K_R(X)$ is an orientable element whose virtual dimension is even, one defines $\rho^k(x)$ as an element of $K_R(X) \otimes Q_k$.

(3) ρ^k is "homomorphic from addition to multiplication," or more shortly "exponential," in the sense that

$$\rho^k(x + y) = \rho^k(x) \otimes \rho^k(y).$$

(4) If x has virtual dimension $2n$, then the virtual dimension of $\rho^k(x)$ is k^n.

(5) ρ^k bears the same relation to the K-cohomology operation Ψ^k that the total Stiefel–Whitney class $\sum\limits_{0}^{\infty} w_i$ does to the total Steenrod square $\sum\limits_{0}^{\infty} Sq^i$ in ordinary cohomology. In particular, we can carry over the proof that the Stiefel–Whitney classes are fibre-homotopy invariants; we find that ρ^k is invariant up to multiplication by a factor of the form

$$\frac{\Psi^k(1 + y)}{1 + y},$$

where $y \in \tilde{K}_R(X)$. (Note that for such y, $1 + y$ is invertible.)

These points are treated more fully in [3, 8, 9], and below. For the moment, we hope that they are sufficient to provide a heuristic justification for the following definition. We will place an element x of $K_R(X)$ in $V(X)$ if:

(1) x is an orientable element whose virtual dimension is even, and

(2) there exists $y \in \tilde{K}_R(X)$ (independent of k) such that

$$\rho^k(x) = \frac{\Psi^k(1 + y)}{1 + y}$$

in $K_R(X) \otimes Q_k$, for all k.

We note that $V(X) \subset \tilde{K}_{SO}(X)$. In fact, suppose we have

$$\rho^k(x) = \frac{\Psi^k(1 + y)}{1 + y};$$

since the right-hand side has virtual dimension 1, x must have virtual dimension 0.

We will check that $V(X)$ is a subgroup. In fact, let $1 + \tilde{K}_R(X)$ be the multiplicative group of elements of virtual dimension 1 in $K_R(X)$; and let $1 + \tilde{K}_R(X) \otimes Q_k$ be the multiplicative group of elements of virtual dimension 1 in $K_R(X) \otimes Q_k$.

Let us define

$$\delta^k: 1 + \tilde{K}_R(X) \to 1 + \tilde{K}_R(X) \otimes Q_k$$

by

$$\delta^k(1 + y) = \frac{\Psi^k(1 + y)}{1 + y};$$

then δ^k is a multiplicative homomorphism. We can now consider the following diagram of groups and homomorphisms; it will appear again later as part of a larger diagram.

$$
\begin{array}{ccc}
 & & \tilde{K}_{SO}(X) \\
 & & \downarrow \scriptstyle{\Pi\rho \atop k} \\
1 + \tilde{K}_R(X) \xrightarrow[k]{\Pi\delta^k} & \prod_k (1 & + \tilde{K}_R(X) \otimes Q_k)
\end{array}
$$

We have

$$V(X) = (\prod_k \rho^k)^{-1}(\prod_k \delta^k)(1 + \tilde{K}_R(X)).$$

This displays $V(X)$ as a subgroup of $\tilde{K}_{SO}(X)$.

In the present paper, we shall obtain our hold on the operations ρ^k by using representation-theory. If G is a compact Lie group we shall write $K'_\Lambda(G)$ for the Grothendieck ring of virtual representations of G over Λ. Our proof will involve establishing identities between composite operations such as $\rho^l\Psi^k$, $\Psi^l\rho^k$. We aim to establish these identities as universal formulae before we apply them to $K_\Lambda(X)$ for any particular X; that is, we aim to establish these identities as equations between virtual representations. Unfortunately, the correct formal setting for these equations is not the Grothendieck ring $K'_\Lambda(G)$. Just as we are forced to introduce denominators in defining ρ^k on virtual bundles, so here we are forced to introduce denominators in order to define ρ^k on virtual representations; this leads us to consider rings $K'_\Lambda(G) \otimes Q_k$. But actually one must go further and introduce the completion of a representation ring [cf. 5, 7]. Let S be a subring (containing 1) of the complex numbers; and let I be the ideal $\tilde{K}'_\Lambda(G) \otimes S$ in $K'_\Lambda(G) \otimes S$ (that is, the ideal of elements of virtual dimension zero). We define

$$\mathrm{Comp}\,(K'_\Lambda(G) \otimes S) = \mathop{\mathrm{Inv\ Lim}}_{n \to \infty} \frac{K'_\Lambda(G) \otimes S}{I^n}.$$

Suppose that θ is a virtual representation of G which can be written as a linear combination of representations into groups $SO(2n)$ for $n = 1, 2, \ldots$; then it is possible to define $\rho^k(\theta)$ as an element of $\mathrm{Comp}\,(K'_R(G) \otimes Q_k)$.

We note also that if ξ is a G-bundle over a finite-dimensional CW-complex X, and if $\hat{\rho}$ is an element of $\mathrm{Comp}\,(K'_\Lambda(G) \otimes S)$, then it is possible to define $\hat{\rho}(\xi)$ as an element of $K'_\Lambda(X) \otimes S$; for I^n will annihilate ξ if $n > \dim X$ [cf. 7].

One calculates with Grothendieck rings $K'_\Lambda(G)$ by using characters. We next explain the use of characters in calculating with $\mathrm{Comp}\,(K'_\Lambda(G) \otimes S)$ (where S is a subring of C). We shall follow Atiyah and Hirzebruch [7], except that we require more detailed information about a less general situation. In fact, we shall be almost exclusively concerned with the groups $G = SO(2n)$ and $G = SO(2n') \times SO(2n'')$.

We shall suppose that a maximal torus T is chosen in our compact connected Lie group G; the points of T are to be given by complex coordinates $(z_1, z_2, \ldots, z_n)$ with $|z_r| = 1$ for each r. For example, in $U(n)$ we consider the usual maximal torus consisting of the diagonal matrices with diagonal entries $z_1, z_2, \ldots, z_n$; by the usual embedding $U(n) \to SO(2n)$ we obtain a maximal torus in $SO(2n)$. The maximal torus in

$$SO(2n') \times SO(2n'')$$

is to be the product of those in $SO(2n')$ and $SO(2n'')$; we may give its points by complex coordinates $(z_1, \ldots, z_{n'}, z_{n'+1}, \ldots, z_{n'+n''})$.

The character $\chi(\theta)$ of an element θ in $K'_\Lambda(G) \otimes S$ is given by a polynomial in the letters z_r, z_r^{-1} $(r = 1, 2, \ldots, n)$; the coefficients of the polynomial lie in S. By writing $z_r = 1 + \zeta_r$, we can expand each such polynomial as a power-series in $\zeta_1, \zeta_2, \ldots, \zeta_n$ which is convergent in a neighbourhood of the origin. Let J be the ideal of power-series with zero constant term; we see that if $\theta \in I = \tilde{K}'_\Lambda(G) \otimes S$, then $\chi(\theta) \in J$. It follows that $\chi(I^m) \subset J^m$ for each m. Thus the character defines a map

$$\chi \colon \text{Comp } (K'_\Lambda(G) \otimes S) \to C[[\zeta_1, \zeta_2, \ldots, \zeta_n]],$$

where $C[[\zeta_1, \zeta_2, \ldots, \zeta_n]]$ is the ring of formal power-series in the variables $\zeta_1, \zeta_2, \ldots, \zeta_n$ (with complex coefficients). We shall use the letter J to denote also the ideal of formal power-series with zero constant term.

In the following lemma, we consider χ as defined on $K'_\Lambda(G) \otimes S$, so that $\chi^{-1}(J^r)$ means the set of elements $\theta \in K'_\Lambda(G) \otimes S$ whose characters are small of the nth order at the origin.

LEMMA 2.1 Suppose that $G = SO(2n)$ or $G = SO(2n') \times SO(2n'')$, and $\Lambda = R$ or C. Then given q there exists $r = r(n, q)$ or $r = r(n', n'', q)$ such that $\chi^{-1}(J^r) \subset I^q$.

PROOF. We must first describe the ring $K'_\Lambda(G) \otimes S$ in convenient terms. We will simply quote the results, which are well known in representation-theory. The description involves a choice; we choose each generator so that it lies in $\chi^{-1}(J^r)$ for as large an r as possible.

Consider first the case $G = SO(2n)$, $\Lambda = C$. Then there is an element τ_i of $K'_C(SO(2n))$ whose character is the ith elementary symmetric function of the expressions $(z_r - 2 + z_r^{-1})$; this element is in fact a polynomial in the exterior powers, and therefore real, i.e., in $K'_R(SO(2n))$. There is also an element ν of $K'_C(SO(2n))$ whose character is

$$\tfrac{1}{2}[\prod_{1 \leq r \leq n} (z_r - 2 + z_r^{-1}) + \prod_{1 \leq r \leq n} (z_r - z_r^{-1})].$$

(Note that this is a polynomial in the variables z_r, z_r^{-1} with integral coefficients.) The element ν is real if n is even. The ring $K'_C(SO(2n)) \otimes S$ is a free module on two generators $1, \nu$ over the polynomial ring $S[\tau_1, \tau_2, \ldots, \tau_n]$.

We now consider the case $\Lambda = R$. If n is even then

$$K'_R(SO(2n)) \otimes S = K'_C(SO(2n)) \otimes S.$$

If n is odd then

$$K'_R(SO(2n)) \otimes S = S[\tau_1, \tau_2, \ldots, \tau_n].$$

A similar description is valid for the case $G = SO(2n') \times SO(2n'')$. The (virtual) representations τ_i, ν of the two factors give representations of G which we may write τ'_i, ν', τ''_i, ν'' (with an obvious notation). By using the usual embedding of $SO(2n') \times SO(2n'')$ in $SO(2n' + 2n'')$, the representation ν of $SO(2n' + 2n'')$ yields a representation of G, which we will also write ν. These representations satisfy a relation:

$$\nu = 2\nu'\nu'' - \tau'_{n'}\nu'' - \nu'\tau''_{n''} + \tau'_{n'}\tau''_{n''}.$$

The ring $K'_C(G) \otimes S$ is a free module on four generators 1, ν', ν'', $\nu'\nu''$ over the polynomial ring $S[\tau'_1, \ldots, \tau'_{n'}, \tau''_1, \ldots, \tau''_{n''}]$.

We now consider the case $\Lambda = R$. If n' and n'' are even then

$$K'_R(G) \otimes S = K'_C(G) \otimes S.$$

If n' is even and n'' is odd then $K'_R(G) \otimes S$ is a free module on two generators 1, ν' over the polynomial ring $S[\tau'_1, \ldots, \tau'_{n'}, \tau''_1, \ldots, \tau''_{n''}]$; similarly if n' is odd and n'' is even. If both n' and n'' are odd then $K'_R(G) \otimes S$ is a free module over the same polynomial ring on the two generators 1, ν.

We have thus shown that in each of the cases to be considered the free S-module $K'_\Lambda(G) \otimes S$ admits an S-base consisting of certain monomials; for example, if $G = SO(2n)$ and $\Lambda = C$ we have the monomials

$$\tau_1^{a_1}\tau_2^{a_2} \cdot \cdot \cdot \tau_n^{a_n}\nu^\varepsilon,$$

where the a_i are non-negative integers and $\varepsilon = 0$ or 1.

We will next assign a weight to each of these monomials. We assign to τ_i, τ'_i and τ''_i the weight $2i$; we assign to ν, ν' and ν'' the weights n, n' and n''. Thus, for example, the monomial

$$\tau_1^{a_1}\tau_2^{a_2} \cdot \cdot \cdot \tau_n^{a_n}\nu^\varepsilon$$

is assigned the weight

$$2a_1 + 4a_2 + \cdot \cdot \cdot + 2na_n + \varepsilon_n.$$

We now reach the point of these proceedings. The character $\chi(\tau_i)$ is the ith elementary symmetric function of the variables $\zeta_1^2, \zeta_2^2, \ldots, \zeta_n^2$, plus a term in J^{2i+1}; similarly for the characters $\chi(\tau'_i)$ and $\chi(\tau''_i)$, using the variables $\zeta_1^2, \ldots, \zeta_{n'}^2$ or $\zeta_{n'+1}^2, \ldots, \zeta_{n'+n''}^2$. Similarly,

$$\chi(\nu) = 2^{n-1}\zeta_1\zeta_2 \cdot \cdot \cdot \zeta_n \bmod J^{n+1},$$
$$\chi(\nu') = 2^{n'-1}\zeta_1\zeta_2 \cdot \cdot \cdot \zeta_{n'} \bmod J^{n'+1},$$
$$\chi(\nu'') = 2^{n''-1}\zeta_{n'+1}\zeta_{n'+2} \cdot \cdot \cdot \zeta_{n'+n''} \bmod J^{n''+1}.$$

It follows that in each case, the monomials of weight exactly w map under χ into linearly independent elements of J^w/J^{w+1}. Therefore an element θ of $\chi^{-1}(J^r)$ can be expressed as a linear combination of monomials of weight $\geq r$. If $G = SO(2n)$ the maximum weight of a generator is $2n$; it follows that such an element θ lies in I^q, provided $r \geq 2nq$. Similarly for $G = SO(2n') \times SO(2n'')$; in this case the maximum weight of a generator is $\mathrm{Max}\,(2n', 2n'')$.

This completes the proof of Lemma 2.1.

COROLLARY 2.2.   Suppose that $G = SO(2n)$ or $G = SO(2n') \times SO(2n'')$ and $\Lambda = R$ or C; then the map

$$\chi \colon \mathrm{Comp}\,(K'_\Lambda(G) \otimes S) \to C[[\zeta_1, \zeta_2, \ldots, \zeta_n]]$$

is monomorphic.

This follows immediately from Lemma 2.1. It is this corollary which enables us to handle elements of $\mathrm{Comp}\,(K'_\Lambda(G) \otimes S)$ by means of their characters.

In order to state the next corollary, suppose given two subrings $S \subset T \subset C$. Then we have ideals

$$I_S = \tilde{K}'_\Lambda(G) \otimes S \subset K'_\Lambda(G) \otimes S$$
$$I_T = \tilde{K}'_\Lambda(G) \otimes T \subset K'_\Lambda(G) \otimes T.$$

COROLLARY 2.3.   Suppose that $G = SO(2n)$ or $G = SO(2n') \times SO(2n'')$ and $\Lambda = R$ or C. Then given q, there exists $r = r(n, q)$ or $r = r(n', n'', q)$ such that

$$(K'_\Lambda(G) \otimes S) \cap (I_T)^r \subset (I_S)^q.$$

This corollary follows immediately from Lemma 2.1. It is essential to the arguments of §3.

We will now introduce the virtual representations ρ^k. In the first instance these are representations of spinor groups. We take the maximal torus $\tilde{T}$ in Spin $(2n)$ to be the counterimage of our maximal torus T in $SO(2n)$. The symbol $(z_r)^{\frac{1}{2}}$ will indicate a function defined on a certain covering torus T_r of T, and taking the value $+1$ at the identity. Certain combinations of these symbols, such as $\prod_{1 \leq r \leq n} (z_r)^{\frac{1}{2}}$, indicate functions defined on $\tilde{T}$.

In the first instance, then, we define $(\rho^k)_n$ to be the virtual representation of Spin $(2n)$ whose character is

$$\prod_{1 \leq r \leq n} \frac{(z_r)^{\frac{1}{2}k} - (z_r)^{-\frac{1}{2}k}}{(z_r)^{\frac{1}{2}} - (z_r)^{-\frac{1}{2}}} = \prod_{1 \leq r \leq n} (z_r)^{\frac{1}{2}(k-1)} + (z_r)^{\frac{1}{2}(k-3)} + \cdots + (z_r)^{-\frac{1}{2}(k-1)}.$$

Two cases now arise. Consider first the case in which k is odd. In this case the given character is expressed in terms of integral powers of z_r; therefore it defines a virtual representation of $SO(2n)$. If n is even this representation is real, because $K'_R(SO(2n)) = K'_C(SO(2n))$. If $n = 2m - 1$ then we see that the restriction of $(\rho^k)_{2m}$ to $SO(4m - 2)$ is $k(\rho^k)_{2m-1}$. Now representation-theory shows that if k is odd and $k\sigma$ is real, then σ is real. It follows that $(\rho^k)_{2m-1}$ is real. When k is odd, then, we have

$$(\rho^k)_n \in K'_R(SO(2n)).$$

We consider next the case in which k is even. In this case we begin by remarking that the representation

$$2: SO(2n) \to SO(4n)$$

can be lifted into Spin $(4n)$. We can therefore form the composite

$$\rho^k.2 \in K'_C(SO(2n)).$$

This is a virtual representation whose character is

$$\prod_{1 \leq r \leq n} \left(\frac{(z_r)^{\frac{1}{2}k} - (z_r)^{-\frac{1}{2}k}}{(z_r)^{\frac{1}{2}} - (z_r)^{-\frac{1}{2}}} \right)^2.$$

Moreover, the virtual representation $\rho^k.2$ coincides with its complex conjugate; therefore

$$2(\rho^k.2) \in K'_R(SO(2n))$$

and

$$\rho^k.2 \in K'_R(SO(2n)) \otimes Q_k$$

(since k is divisible by 2). Since we expect ρ^k to be exponential we now seek to define ρ^k on $SO(2n)$ by extracting the square root of $(\rho^k.2)$. Since k is even, we can extract the square root of $\rho^k.2$ as an element of

$$\text{Comp } (K'_R(SO(2n)) \otimes Q_k);$$

and the result is unique, providing we specify that the virtual dimension of the square root is k^n rather than $-k^n$. When k is even, then, we can define $(\rho^k)_n$ as an element of Comp $(K'_R(SO(2n)) \otimes Q_k)$.

The character of $(\rho^k)_n$ is

$$\prod_{1 \leq r \leq n} \frac{(z_r)^{\frac{1}{2}k} - (z_r)^{-\frac{1}{2}k}}{(z_r)^{\frac{1}{2}} - (z_r)^{-\frac{1}{2}}};$$

of course this formula has to be interpreted as an element of

$$C[[\zeta_1, \zeta_2, \ldots, \zeta_n]],$$

by expanding the fractional powers of $z_r = 1 + \zeta_r$ as binomial series in ζ_r.

We will now discuss the sense in which the sequence of virtual representations $(\rho^k)_n$ is "homomorphic from addition to multiplication," or more shortly, "exponential." Let

$$\pi: SO(2n) \times SO(2m) \to SO(2n)$$
$$\tilde{\omega}: SO(2n) \times SO(2m) \to SO(2m)$$

be the projections of $SO(2n) \times SO(2m)$ onto its two factors. Let (σ_n) be a sequence of elements $\sigma_n \in \mathrm{Comp}\ (K'_\Lambda(SO(2n)) \otimes S)$. We will say that (σ_n) is "exponential" if we have

$$\sigma_{n+m}.(\pi \oplus \tilde{\omega}) = (\sigma_n.\pi) \otimes (\sigma_m.\tilde{\omega})$$

in $\mathrm{Comp}\ (K'_\Lambda(SO(2n) \times SO(2m)) \otimes S)$ for all n, m. (Cf. [1], pp. 607, 609.)

PROPOSITION 2.4.   The sequence of elements

$$(\rho^k)_n \in \mathrm{Comp}\ (K'_R(SO(2n)) \otimes Q_k)$$

is exponential.

This follows immediately from the characters given above; one has only to apply Corollary 2.2.

PROPOSITION 2.5.   If the sequence $\sigma_n \in \mathrm{Comp}\ (K'_\Lambda(SO(2n)) \otimes S)$ is exponential, then for any two representations $\alpha \colon G \to SO(2n)$, $\beta \colon G \to SO(2m)$ we have

$$\sigma_{n+m}.(\alpha \otimes \beta) = (\sigma_n.\alpha) \otimes (\sigma_m.\beta)$$

in $\mathrm{Comp}\ (K'_\Lambda(G) \otimes S)$. Moreover, for any two bundles ξ, η over a finite-dimensional CW-complex X, with groups $SO(2n)$, $SO(2m)$, we have

$$\sigma_{n+m}.(\xi \oplus \eta) = (\sigma_n.\xi) \otimes (\sigma_m.\eta)$$

in $K_\Lambda(X) \otimes S$.

This result is strictly analogous to those of [1], pp. 607–609, and so is its proof.

Given these propositions, one can define ρ^k on virtual representations so as to secure the following two properties.

(1) If the virtual representation is actually a representation α, then $\rho^k(\alpha)$ is the composite in the obvious sense.

(2) ρ^k is exponential, in the sense that

$$\rho^k(\theta + \phi) = (\rho^k\theta) \otimes (\rho^k\phi).$$

One can also define ρ^k on virtual bundles so as to enjoy similar properties. The details will be omitted from this paper.

3. An identity between virtual representations

The object of this section is to prove Theorem 3.2, which is vital to the proof of Theorem 1.1. The most important part of this theorem will state the commutativity of the following diagram.

(3.1)

$$
\begin{array}{ccc}
\tilde{K}_{SO}(X) & \xrightarrow{\ k^e(\Psi^k - 1)\ } & \tilde{K}_{SO}(X) \\
{\scriptstyle \theta^k}\big\downarrow & & \big\downarrow{\scriptstyle \rho^l} \\
1 + \tilde{K}_{SO}(X) & \xrightarrow{\ \delta^l\ } & 1 + \tilde{K}_{SO}(X) \otimes Q^l
\end{array}
$$

Here the groups are as in §2; those in the top row are additive, and those in the bottom row are multiplicative. The additive homomorphism $k^e(\Psi^k - 1)$ is defined by

$$k^e(\Psi^k - 1)x = k^e((\Psi^k x) - x).$$

(Thus the 1 in $\Psi^k - 1$ means the identity function.)

The existence of the homomorphism θ^k will be asserted as part of the theorem. The homomorphism ρ^l is as in §2. The multiplicative homomorphism δ^l is defined by

$$\delta^l(1 + y) = \frac{\Psi^l(1 + y)}{1 + y},$$

as in §2.

THEOREM 3.2 *Given integers q, k and a sufficiently large integer e (viz. $e \geq e_0 (q, k)$) there exists a function*

$$\theta^k = \theta^k(q, e) : \tilde{K}_{SO}(X) \to 1 + \tilde{K}_{SO}(X)$$

defined for CW-complexes of dimension $<q$ and having the following properties.

(1) *θ^k is homomorphic from addition to multiplication, that is, exponential.*
(2) *θ^k is natural for maps of X.*
(3) *The image of $\theta^k(x)$ in $1 + \tilde{K}_{SO}(X) \otimes Q_k$ is $\rho^k(k^e x)$.*
(4) *Diagram 3.1 is commutative.*

We will now give a heuristic plausibility argument for Theorem 3.2. For this purpose we will abandon the real K-theory and work instead with the complex K-theory, for simplicity. We now argue that in some suitable formal setting we may hope to have

$$(3.3) \qquad (\rho^l \Psi^k) \otimes \rho^k = \rho^{kl} = (\Psi^l \rho^k) \otimes \rho^l.$$

In fact, all three expressions are "exponential," that is, homomorphic from addition to multiplication; therefore it is presumably sufficient to check the result for a complex line bundle ξ. Here we have

$$\Psi^k \xi = \xi^k, \qquad \rho^k \xi = \frac{\xi^k - 1}{\xi - 1}.$$

Therefore

$$(\rho^l \Psi^k \xi) \otimes (\rho^k \xi) = \frac{\xi^{kl} - 1}{\xi^k - 1} \cdot \frac{\xi^k - 1}{\xi - 1},$$

$$\rho^{kl} \xi = \frac{\xi^{kl} - 1}{\xi - 1},$$

$$(\Psi^l \rho^k \xi) \otimes (\rho^l \xi) = \frac{\xi^{kl} - 1}{\xi^l - 1} \cdot \frac{\xi^l - 1}{\xi - 1}.$$

(The last line uses the fact that Ψ^l preserves both addition and multiplication.) The three results are equal. We may therefore agree to suspend disbelief in Equation 3.3. Rewriting this equation, we obtain

$$\rho^l(\Psi^k - 1) = \frac{\Psi^l \rho^k}{\rho^k}.$$

That is, if $x \in \tilde{K}_C(X)$, then $1 + y = \rho^k x$ is a formal solution of the equation

$$\rho^l(\Psi^k - 1)x = \frac{\Psi^l(1 + y)}{1 + y}.$$

Now this formal solution involves denominators, that is, coefficients in Q_k. However, we can remove these denominators, up to dimension q, by considering

$$1 + z = (1 + y)^{k^e},$$

where e is suitably large. Raising the equation

$$\rho^l(\Psi^k - 1)x = \frac{\Psi^l(1 + y)}{1 + y}$$

to the power k^e, we find

$$\rho^l k^e(\Psi^k - 1)x = \frac{\Psi^l(1 + z)}{1 + z}.$$

This completes the plausibility argument.

We turn now to a rigorous version of this argument for the real case. In order to state the first lemma, let α_n, $\beta_n \in \mathrm{Comp}\,(K'_\Lambda(SO(2n) \otimes S)$ be two exponential sequences.

LEMMA 3.4.   *If* $\chi(\alpha_1) = \chi(\beta_1)$, *then* $\alpha_n = \beta_n$ *for all* n.

PROOF.   Suppose that $\chi(\alpha_1) = \chi(\beta_1) = \phi(\zeta_1)$, where $\phi(\zeta_1)$ is a formal power series in ζ_1. Then by the exponential law,

$$\chi(\alpha_n) = \phi(\zeta_1)\phi(\zeta_2) \cdots \phi(\zeta_n) = \chi(\beta_n).$$

The result now follows from Corollary 2.2.

We will now apply this lemma. First we observe that (with an obvious notation)

$$K'_{SO}(SO(n)) = K'_R(SO(n)).$$

In fact, any representation $\gamma \colon SO(n) \to O(m)$ must map into $SO(m)$, since $SO(n)$ is connected. In particular, $(\Psi^k - 1) \in \tilde{K}'_{SO}(SO(2n))$. Thus

$\rho^l.(\Psi'^k - 1)$ is defined, and lies in Comp $(K'_R(SO(2n)) \otimes Q_l)$. Again, since $\Psi'^l: K'_R(G) \to K'_R(G)$ is a ring homomorphism, it induces

$$\Psi'^l: K'_R(G) \otimes S \to K'_R(G) \otimes S$$

and

$$\Psi'^l: \text{Comp } (K'_R(G) \otimes S) \to \text{Comp } (K'_R(G) \otimes S).$$

Thus $\Psi'^l.\rho^k$ is defined and lies in Comp $(K'_R(SO(2n)) \otimes Q_k)$. Since ρ^k is. invertible in this ring, $\delta^l.\rho^k = (\Psi'^l.\rho^k)/\rho^k$ is defined.

LEMMA 3.5. *Consider the sequences of elements*

$$\alpha_n = \rho^l.(\Psi'^k - 1)$$
$$\beta_n = \delta^l.\rho^k$$

in

$$\text{Comp } (K'_R(SO(2n)) \otimes Q_{kl}).$$

These sequences are exponential, and satisfy $\chi(\alpha_1) = \chi(\beta_1)$.

PROOF. It is easy to check that the sequences are exponential. In fact, α_n is exponential because $(\Psi'^k - 1)$ is additive and ρ^l is exponential; β_n is exponential because ρ^k is exponential and δ^l is multiplicative.

It remains to check that $\chi(\alpha_1) = \chi(\beta_1)$. The virtual representation Ψ'^k of $SO(2)$ is the representation $z \to z^k$. By definition $\rho^l.(\Psi'^k - 1)$ means the element $(\rho^l.\Psi'^k)/\rho^l$ of Comp $(K'_R(SO(2) \otimes Q_l)$. Its character is given by

$$\chi(\alpha_1) = \frac{(z_1)^{\frac{1}{2}kl} - (z_1)^{-\frac{1}{2}kl}}{(z_1)^{\frac{1}{2}k} - (z_1)^{-\frac{1}{2}k}} \cdot \frac{(z_1)^{\frac{1}{2}} - (z_1)^{-\frac{1}{2}}}{(z_1)^{\frac{1}{2}l} - (z_1)^{-\frac{1}{2}l}}.$$

(Of course, this expression is interpreted as an element of $C[[\zeta_1]]$.)

For any virtual representation θ of G, the character of $\Psi'^l.\theta$ is given by $\chi(\Psi'^l.\theta)g = \chi(\theta)g^l$ [1, p. 611]. Evidently this equation remains true when θ is replaced by an element of $K'_\Lambda(G) \otimes S$ or Comp $(K'_\Lambda(G) \otimes S)$. Therefore the character of $\delta^l.\rho^k = (\Psi'^l.\rho^k)/\rho^k$ is given by

$$\chi(\beta_1) = \frac{(z_1)^{\frac{1}{2}kl} - (z_1)^{-\frac{1}{2}kl}}{(z_1)^{\frac{1}{2}l} - (z_1)^{-\frac{1}{2}l}} \cdot \frac{(z_1)^{\frac{1}{2}} - (z_1)^{-\frac{1}{2}}}{(z_1)^{\frac{1}{2}k} - (z_1)^{-\frac{1}{2}k}}.$$

(Of course, this expression also is interpreted as an element of $C[[\zeta_1]]$.)
We have $\chi(\alpha_1) = \chi(\beta_1)$. This completes the proof of Lemma 3.5.

PROPOSITION 3.6. In Comp $(K'_R(SO(2n)) \otimes Q_{kl})$ we have

$$\rho^l.(\Psi'^k - 1) = \delta^l.\rho^k$$

and

$$\rho^l.(\Psi'^k - 1) = \frac{\Psi'^l(k^{-n}\rho^k)}{k^{-n}\rho^k}.$$

PROOF. The first assertion follows immediately from Lemmas 3.4, 3.5. The second follows by rewriting the first.

The element $k^{-n}\rho^k$ lies in Comp $(K'_R(SO(2n)) \otimes Q_k)$, and has virtual dimension 1.

LEMMA 3.7. *Given integers n, k, r and sufficiently large e*

$$(viz., \ e \geq e_0 \ (n, k, r))$$

we have

$$(k^{-n}\rho^k)^{k^e} = 1 + x \qquad in \qquad (K'_R(SO(2n)) \otimes Q_k)/I^r,$$

where $x \in \tilde{K}'_R(SO(2n))$.

PROOF. It is clear that if the conclusion holds for one value of e, then it holds for all larger values of e. We now proceed by induction over r. Suppose that we have found e such that

$$(k^{-n}\rho^k)^{k^e} = 1 + x \qquad in \qquad (K'_R(SO(2n)) \otimes Q_k)/I^r,$$

where $x \in \tilde{K}'_R(SO(2n))$. (The induction starts with $r = 1$.) Then in

$$(K'_R(SO(2n)) \otimes Q_k)/I^{2r}$$

we can write

$$(k^{-n}\rho^k)^{k^e} = 1 + x + k^{-f}y,$$

where

$$y \in K'_R(SO(2n)) \cap I^r.$$

Now we have

$$\begin{aligned}
(k^{-n}\rho^k)^{k^{e+f}} &= (1 + x + k^{-f}y)^{k^f} \\
&= (1 + x)^{k^f} + y(1 + x)^{k^f-1} \bmod I^{2r} \\
&= 1 + z \bmod I^{2r}
\end{aligned}$$

where $z \in \tilde{K}'_R(SO(2n))$. This completes the induction.

PROOF OF THEOREM 3.2. In what follows, X will always be a CW-complex of dimension $<q$. We can thus determine $n = n(q)$ so that there is a (1–1) correspondence between homotopy classes of maps $f: X \to BSO$ and homotopy classes of maps $f: X \to BSO(2n)$. That is, there is a (1–1) correspondence between the isomorphism classes of $SO(2n)$-bundles ξ over X and the elements of $\tilde{K}_{SO}(X)$; the correspondence is given by $\xi \to \{\xi\} - 2n$.

We will now invoke Lemma 3.7, and for this purpose we define an integer r depending only on q and n. (Thus r depends ultimately only on q.) We set

$$r = \text{Max} \ (q, r(n, q), r(n, n, q)),$$

where the functions $r(n, q)$ and $r(n', n'', q)$ are as in Corollary 2.3. We now employ Lemma 3.7 to choose elements

$$(\theta^k)_n \in K'_R(SO(2n))$$
$$(\theta^k)_{2n} \in K'_R(SO(4n))$$

such that the images of $(\theta^k)_n$, $(\theta^k)_{2n}$ in

$$(K'_R(SO(2n)) \otimes Q_k)/I^r,$$
$$(K'_R(SO(4n)) \otimes Q_k)/I^r$$

are $(k^{-n}\rho^k)^{k^e}$, $(k^{-2n}\rho^k)^{k^e}$. We can do this for all sufficiently large e (viz. for $e \geq e_0\,(q, k)$).

We shall use the element $(\theta^k)_n$ to define the function

$$\theta^k : \tilde{K}_{SO}(X) \to 1 + \tilde{K}_{SO}(X).$$

More precisely, we define

$$\theta^k(\{\xi\} - 2n) = (\theta^k)_n.\{\xi\},$$

where ξ runs over the $SO(2n)$-bundles. It is clear that this does define a function, which is natural for maps of X. Since $r \geq q$, it also follows that the image of $\theta^k(x)$ in $1 + \tilde{K}_{SO}(X) \otimes Q_k$ is $\rho^k(k^e x)$.

We shall use the element $(\theta^k)_{2n}$ to prove that the function θ^k is exponential. More precisely, let π, $\tilde{\omega}$ be the projections of $SO(2n) \times SO(2n)$ onto its first and second factors. Then in $(K'_R(SO(2n) \times SO(2n)) \otimes Q_k)/I^r$ we have the following equations.

$$(\theta^k)_{2n}.(\pi \oplus \tilde{\omega}) = (k^{-2n}\rho^k)^{k^e}.(\pi \oplus \tilde{\omega}),$$
$$(k^{-2n}\rho^k)^{k^e}.(\pi \oplus \tilde{\omega}) = (k^{-n}\rho^k)^{k^e}.\pi \otimes (k^{-n}\rho^k)^{k^e}.\tilde{\omega},$$
$$(k^{-n}\rho^k)^{k^e}.\pi \otimes (k^{-n}\rho^k)^{k^e}.\tilde{\omega} = (\theta^k)_n.\pi \otimes (\theta^k)_n.\tilde{\omega}.$$

We may now apply Corollary 2.3 with $G = SO(2n) \times SO(2n)$, $S = Z$, $T = Q_k$. The element

$$(\theta^k)_{2n}.(\pi \oplus \tilde{\omega}) - (\theta^k)_n.\pi \otimes (\theta^k)_n.\tilde{\omega}$$

lies in

$$[K'_R(SO(2n) \times SO(2n)) \otimes S] \cap (I_T)^r.$$

Since $r \geq r(n, n, q)$, Corollary 2.3 shows that

$$(\theta^k)_{2n}.(\pi \oplus \tilde{\omega}) - (\theta^k)_n.\pi \otimes (\theta^k)_n.\tilde{\omega}$$

lies in $(I_S)^q$. This shows that whenever ξ, η are $SO(2n)$-bundles over X, we have the equation

$$(\theta^k)_{2n}.(\xi \oplus \eta) = (\theta^k)_n.\xi \otimes (\theta^k)_n.\eta$$

in $K_R(X)$. It follows that the function

$$\theta^k \colon \tilde{K}_{SO}(X) \to 1 + \tilde{K}_{SO}(X)$$

is exponential.

We argue similarly to show that Diagram 3.1 is commutative. Proposition 3.6 states that

$$\rho^l.(\Psi^k - 1) = \frac{\Psi^l(k^{-n}\rho^k)}{k^{-n}\rho^k}$$

in Comp $(K'_R(SO(2n)) \otimes Q_{kl})$. Raising this equation to the power k^e, we have

$$\rho^l.k^e(\Psi^k - 1) = \frac{\Psi^l(k^{-n}\rho^k)^{k^e}}{(k^{-n}\rho^k)^{ke}}.$$

Thus

$$\rho^l.k^e(\Psi^k - 1) = \frac{\Psi^l.\theta^k}{\theta^k}$$

in

$$(K'_R(SO(2n)) \otimes Q_{kl})/I^r.$$

We will now apply Corollary 2.3 with $G = SO(2n)$, $S = Q_l$, $T = Q_{kl}$. Let us take a representative

$$y \in K'_R(SO(2n)) \otimes Q_l$$

for the element $\rho^l.k^e(\Psi^k - 1)$ in

$$(K'_R(SO(2n)) \otimes Q_l)/(I_S)^r.$$

Then we have

$$y \in K'_R(SO(2n)) \otimes S,$$
$$\frac{\Psi^l.\theta^k}{\theta^k} \in K'_R(SO(2n)),$$

and

$$y - \frac{\Psi^l.\theta^k}{\theta^k} \in (K'_R(SO(2n)) \otimes S) \cap (I_T)^r.$$

Since $r \geq r(n, q)$, Corollary 2.3 shows that

$$y - \frac{\Psi^l.\theta^k}{\theta^k} \in (I_S)^q.$$

That is, we have

$$\rho^l.k^e(\Psi^k - 1) = \frac{\Psi^l.\theta^k}{\theta^k}$$

in $(K'_R(SO(2n)) \otimes Q_l)/(I_S)^q$. It follows that Diagram 3.1 is commutative. This completes the proof of Theorem 3.2.

4. Proof of the main theorem

In proving Theorem 1.1, we shall have to work with square diagrams like Diagram 3.1. By a "square" S, we shall mean a commutative diagram of groups and homomorphisms which has the following form.

We shall call a square "special" if it has the following property: given $b \in B$ and $c \in C$ such that $hb = ic$, there exists $a \in A$ such that $fa = b$ and $ga = c$. This is equivalent to demanding the exactnesss of the following sequence:

$$A \xrightarrow{(f,g)} B \oplus C \xrightarrow{(h,-i)} D$$

By a "short exact sequence $0 \to S' \to S \to S'' \to 0$" of squares, we shall mean a commutative diagram composed of three squares S', S, S'' and four short exact sequences

$$0 \to A' \to A \to A'' \to 0$$
$$0 \to B' \to B \to B'' \to 0, \text{ etc.}$$

LEMMA 4.1. *Suppose that $0 \to S' \to S \to S'' \to 0$ is a short exact sequence of squares in which S' and S'' are special; then S is special.*

PROOF. Each square determines a sequence

$$A \xrightarrow{(f,g)} B \oplus C \xrightarrow{(h,-i)} D,$$

which we may regard as a chain complex. We now have a short exact sequence of chain complexes. This yields an exact homology sequence, which leads immediately to the required result.

Alternatively, one may give a direct proof by routine diagram-chasing.

Let X be a finite CW-complex, say of dimension $<q$. The main part of the proof of Theorem 1.1 will proceed by filtering X. Let us define F_r to be the image of $\tilde{K}_R(X/X^{r-1})$ in $K_R(X)$; then for $r \geq 2$ and sufficiently large e, Theorem 3.2 provides us with the following commutative square.

$$
\begin{array}{ccc}
F_r & \xrightarrow{k^e(\Psi^k - 1)} & F_r \\
\theta^k \downarrow & & \downarrow \rho^l \\
1 + F_r & \xrightarrow{\delta^l} & 1 + F_r \otimes Q_l
\end{array}
$$

(Since Q_l is torsion-free, $\otimes Q_l$ is an exact functor, and the image of $\tilde{K}_R(X/X^{r-1}) \otimes Q_l$ in $K_R(X) \otimes Q_l$ is $F_r \otimes Q_l$.) If we pass to a (restricted) direct sum over k and an (unrestricted) direct product over l, we obtain the following commutative square S_r (for $r \geq 2$).

(4.2)

$$
\begin{array}{ccc}
\displaystyle\sum_k F_r & \xrightarrow{\;\sum_k k^{e(k)}(\Psi^k-1)\;} & F_r \\[2ex]
{\scriptstyle\sum_k \theta^k}\Big\downarrow & & \Big\downarrow{\scriptstyle\prod_l \rho^l} \\[2ex]
1 + F_r & \xrightarrow[\;\prod_l \delta^l\;]{} & \displaystyle\prod_l 1 + F_r \otimes Q_l
\end{array}
$$

More precisely, we obtain this commutative square whenever the function $e(k)$ is sufficiently large, viz. for $e(k) \geq e_0(q, k)$, where q is our fixed upper bound for the dimension of the complexes X considered.

THEOREM 4.3.   *The square S_r displayed in Diagram 4.2 is special.*

PROOF.   We shall prove this result by downwards induction over r. For $r = q$ the result is trivial. Let us therefore assume as an inductive hypothesis that the square S_{r+1} is special, and prove that S_r is special. For this purpose, by Lemma 4.1, it is sufficient to construct a short exact sequence of squares

$$0 \to S_{r+1} \to S_r \to S_r/S_{r+1} \to 0$$

and prove that the square S_{r+1}/S_r is special. Since the square S_{r+1} is embedded in S_r, it is clear that the required quotient square exists. In order to establish its structure, let us recall that $F_r.F_s \subset F_{r+s}$; thus F_{r+1} is an ideal in F_r, and F_r/F_{r+1} is a ring in which the product is zero (assuming $r \geq 1$). Besides the short exact sequence of additive groups

$$0 \to F_{r+1} \to F_r \to F_r/F_{r+1} \to 0,$$

we have also a short exact sequence of multiplicative groups:

$$1 \longrightarrow 1 + F_{r+1} \longrightarrow 1 + F_r \longrightarrow 1 + (F_r/F_{r+1}) \longrightarrow 1.$$

Here the product in the last group is given by

$$(1 + a)(1 + b) = 1 + (a + b).$$

Similar results hold for the following short exact sequence of multiplicative groups.

$$1 \to 1 + F_{r+1} \otimes Q_l \to 1 + F_r \otimes Q_l \to 1 + (F_r/F_{r+1}) \otimes Q_l \to 1.$$

This shows that the square S_r/S_{r+1} has the following form.

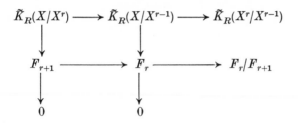

(4.4)

The maps of the square S_r/S_{r+1} are induced from those of the square S_r.

Theorem 4.3 will thus be proved once we have established the following lemma.

LEMMA 4.5. *The square displayed in Diagram 4.4 is special.*

PROOF. Consider the following diagram of exact sequences.

$$\begin{array}{ccccc}
\tilde{K}_R(X/X^r) & \longrightarrow & \tilde{K}_R(X/X^{r-1}) & \longrightarrow & \tilde{K}_R(X^r/X^{r-1}) \\
\downarrow & & \downarrow & & \\
F_{r+1} & \longrightarrow & F_r & \longrightarrow & F_r/F_{r+1} \\
\downarrow & & \downarrow & & \\
0 & & 0 & &
\end{array}$$

This shows that the quotient group F_r/F_{r+1} of Diagram 4.4 is isomorphic to a quotient group of a subgroup of

$$K_R(X^r/X^{r-1}) = K_R(\bigvee S^r).$$

Since this isomorphism is given by induced maps, the operations Ψ^k, ρ^k and θ^k on F_r/F_{r+1} are given by the same formulae that hold in S^r;

$$\Psi^k y = a(k, r)\, y$$
$$\rho^k y = 1 + b(k, r)\, y$$
$$\theta^k y = 1 + c(k, r, e)\, y$$

Here the coefficients a, b and c do not depend on X or y. To give the coefficients, we have to divide the cases. Unless $r \equiv 0, 1, 2$ or 4 mod 8 the group F_r/F_{r+1} is zero and there is nothing to prove. Consider first the case $r \equiv 0$ or 4 mod 8; say $r = 4t$, $t > 0$.

LEMMA 4.6. *We have*

$$\Psi^k y = k^{2t} y$$

$$\rho^k y = 1 + \frac{n(t)}{m(t)} (k^{2t} - 1)y$$

$$\theta^k y = 1 + \frac{n(t)}{m(t)} k^{e(k)}(k^{2t} - 1)y.$$

Here $n(t)/m(t)$ is a fraction in its lowest terms, of which the denominator $m(t)$ has the following property.

LEMMA 4.7. *For any function $e(k)$ the highest common factor of the numbers*

$$k^{e(k)}(k^{2t} - 1) \qquad (k = 0, \pm 1, \pm 2, \ldots)$$

divides $m(t)$. For sufficiently large functions $e(k)$ this highest common factor is exactly $m(t)$.

These two lemmas are quoted from [3].

We will now check that the square (4.4) is special for $r = 4t$. Suppose given $u, v \in F_r/F_{r+1}$ such that

$$\rho^l u = \frac{\Psi^l(1 + v)}{1 + v}$$

for all l. This yields

$$\frac{n(t)}{m(t)} (l^{2t} - 1)u = (l^{2t} - 1)v$$

in $(F_r/F_{r+1}) \otimes Q_l$ for all l. This means that for some exponent $f(l)$ we have

$$\frac{n(t)}{m(t)} l^{f(l)}(l^{2t} - 1)u = l^{f(l)}(l^{2t} - 1)v$$

in F_r/F_{r+1} (for each l). According to Lemma 4.7, by taking a suitable linear combination of these equations, we obtain

$$n(t)u = m(t)v.$$

Since the number $n(t)$, $m(t)$ are coprime we can choose $a(t)$, $b(t)$ so that

$$a(t)m(t) + b(t)n(t) = 1;$$

now define

$$w = a(t)u + b(t)v \in F_r/F_{r+1};$$

this ensures that

$$m(t)\, w = u, \qquad n(t)\, w = v.$$

Using Lemma 4.7 again, let us choose integers $c(k)$, zero except for a finite number of k, such that

$$\sum_k c(k)k^{e(k)}(k^{2t} - 1) = m(t).$$

Let σ be the element of $\Sigma_k F_r/F_{r+1}$ with components $c(k)w$. Then

$$\left(\sum_k k^{e(k)}(\Psi^k - 1)\right)\sigma = \sum_k c(k)k^{e(k)}(k^{2t} - 1)w$$
$$= m(t)w$$
$$= u.$$

Again,

$$\left(\sum_k \theta^k\right)\sigma = 1 + \sum_k \frac{n(t)}{m(t)}\, c(k)k^{e(k)}(k^{2t} - 1)w$$
$$= 1 + n(t)w$$
$$= 1 + v.$$

Therefore the square (4.4) is special if $r \equiv 0$ or $4 \bmod 8$.

We turn now to the case $r \equiv 1$ or $2 \bmod 8$, $r \geq 2$. In this case every element of F_r/F_{r+1} has order 2, so that

$$(F_r/F_{r+1}) \otimes Q_l \cong \begin{cases} F_r/F_{r+1} & (l \text{ odd}) \\ 0 & (l \text{ even}). \end{cases}$$

LEMMA 4.8.   *We have*

$$\Psi^k y = \begin{cases} 0 & (k \text{ even}) \\ y & (k \text{ odd}) \end{cases}$$

$$\left.\begin{aligned} \rho^k y &= 1 + y \\ \theta^k y &= 1 + y \end{aligned}\right\} (k \equiv \pm 3 \bmod 8).$$

This lemma is quoted from [3].

It follows from this lemma that the map $\Sigma_k k^{e(k)}(\Psi^k - 1)$ of Diagram 4.4 is zero (at least for $e(k) \geq 1$). The map $\Pi_l\,\delta^l$ is also trivial (with image 1). The map $\Sigma_k \theta^k$ is epimorphic. The map $\Pi_l \rho^l$ is monomorphic. It follow immediately that the square (4.4) is special.

This completes the proof of Lemma 4.5, and therefore of Theorem 4.3.

COROLLARY 4.9.   The following square is special

(4.10)

$$\begin{array}{ccc} \sum_k \tilde{K}_{SO}(X) & \xrightarrow{\;\sum_k k^{e(k)}(\Psi^k - 1)\;} & \tilde{K}_{SO}(X) \\ {\scriptstyle \sum_k \theta^k}\Big\downarrow & & \Big\downarrow{\scriptstyle \Pi_l \rho^l} \\ 1 + \tilde{K}_{SO}(X) & \xrightarrow[\;\Pi_l \delta^l\;]{} & \prod_l 1 + \tilde{K}_{SO}(X) \otimes Q_l \end{array}$$

This follows immediately from Theorem 4.3, by setting $r = 2$.

PROOF OF THEOREM 1.1. In proving Theorem 1.1, we may assume without loss of generality that X is connected. With the notation of §2, we require to prove that $V(X) = W(X)$.

We have defined $W(X) = \cap_e W(e, X)$, where $W(e, X)$ is the subgroup of $K_R(X)$ generated by elements of the form $k^{e(k)}(\Psi^k - 1)x$ as k runs over all integers and x runs over $K_R(X)$. I claim that for $e(k)$ sufficiently large (viz. for $e(k) \geq e_0(q)$) we can obtain the same subgroup $W(e, X)$ by letting x run over $\tilde{K}_{SO}(X)$. In fact, any element $x \in K_R(X)$ can be written as $x = y + z$, where $y \in \tilde{K}_{SO}(X)$ and z is a linear combination of real line bundles. A real line bundle ζ can be induced by a map $f \colon X \to RP^q$; from this we see that

$$2^{e_0(q)}(\Psi^k - 1)\zeta = 0 \quad (k \text{ even})$$
$$(\Psi^k - 1)\zeta = 0 \quad (k \text{ odd}).$$

Thus

$$k^{e(k)}(\Psi^k - 1)z = 0$$

if $e(k) \geq e_0(q)$, and hence

$$k^{e(k)}(\Psi^k - 1)x = k^{e(k)}(\Psi^k - 1)y.$$

We have thus shown that for each sufficiently large function $e(k)$ the group $W(e, k)$ is the image of the map $\Sigma_k k^{e(k)}(\Psi^k - 1)$ appearing in Diagram 4.10.

Again, we have defined

$$V(X) = (\prod_l \rho^l)^{-1}(\prod_l \delta^l)(1 + \tilde{K}_R(X)).$$

I claim that we can obtain the same subgroup by taking

$$(\prod_l \rho^l)^{-1}(\prod_l \delta^l)(1 + \tilde{K}_{SO}(X)).$$

In fact, any element $(1 + x) \in (1 + K_R(X))$ can be written in the form $(1 + y)\zeta$, where $(1 + y) \in (1 + \tilde{K}_{SO}(X))$ and ζ is a real line bundle over X. By dividing the cases "l even" and "l odd," as above, we see that

$$\frac{\Psi^l \zeta}{\zeta} = 1 \quad \text{in} \quad 1 + \tilde{K}_R(X) \otimes Q_l$$

for all l. Hence

$$(\prod_l \delta^l)(1 + x) = (\prod_l \delta^l)(1 + y)$$

and

$$(\prod_l \delta^l)(1 + \tilde{K}_R(X)) = (\prod_l \delta^l)(1 + \tilde{K}_{SO}(X)).$$

We have thus shown that the group $V(X)$ is the group

$$(\prod_l \rho^l)^{-1}(\prod \delta^l)(1 + \tilde{K}_{SO}(X)).$$

of Diagram 4.10.

The fact that Diagram 4.10 is commutative now shows that $W(e, X) \subset V(X)$ for sufficiently large functions $e(k)$, so that $W(X) \subset V(X)$. The fact that Diagram 4.10 is special shows that $V(X) \subset W(e, X)$ for sufficiently large functions $e(k)$, so that $V(X) \subset W(X)$. This completes the proof of Theorem 1.1.

MANCHESTER UNIVERSITY

REFERENCES

[1] J. F. ADAMS, Vector fields on spheres, *Annals of Mathematics*, 75 (1962), p. 603–632.

[2] ———, Applications of the Grothendieck-Atiyah-Hirzebruch functor K(X), *Proceedings of the International Congress of Mathematicians*, 1962.

[3] ———, On the groups J(X), I, II, III. In preparation for *Topology*.

[4] M. F. ATIYAH, Thom complexes, *Proc. London Math. Soc.*, (3) 11 (1961), p. 291–310.

[5] ———, Characters and cohomology of finite groups, *Publications Mathématiques de l'Institut des Hautes Etudes Scientifiques*, No. 9 (1961).

[6] ———, and F. HIRZEBRUCH, Riemann–Roch theorems for differentiable manifolds, *Bull. Amer. Math. Soc.* 65 (1959), p. 276–281.

[7] ——— ———, Vector bundles and homogeneous spaces, *Proc. Symp. Pure Maths.*, 3, *Differential Geometry*, p. 7–38: Amer. Math. Soc., 1961.

[8] R. BOTT, A note on the KO-theory of sphere-bundles, *Bull. Amer. Math, Soc.*, 68 (1962), p. 395–400.

[9] ———, Lectures on K(X), mimeographed notes, Harvard University.

Morse Theory

BARRY MAZUR

1. Introduction

The Classical Morse Theory studies functions with non-degenerate critical points on a differentiable manifold, and relates these functions and their properties to the geometry of the manifold. The key theorem for this program is something which we may call: "The Fundamental Theorem of Morse Theory," which establishes an "equivalence" between such functions and a specific kind of geometric decomposition of the manifold. These geometric decompositions we may call: Differentiable cell decompositions.

The fundamental work of Smale (see [7], [8], [9], [10]) in differential topology shows quite clearly the great importance of such differentiable cell decompositions in the study of manifolds. Smale's analysis has very little to do with the "original" functions, and is concerned only with a direct and vigorous simplification of particular differentiable cell decompositions.

In the context of [3] a close relationship may be seen between the Morse-Smale analysis, and the theory of simple homotopy types (of J. H. C. Whitehead [11]). The idea is that the Morse-Smale Theory and simple homotopy theory are "the same theory," only in two different categories. (Of course, the Morse-Smale setting is subtler than that of simple homotopy theory.) After one formalizes the relationship between these two theories, one may apply the deep theorems of J. H. C. Whitehead regarding simple homotopy types, to the differential topological setting.

Amusingly enough, one finds that the Whitehead theorems seem to be tailor-made to yield the Morse-Smale Theory. (In fact, without hypotheses of simple connectivity; but this is minor.)

The generality of this approach suggests that one should develop the foundations of theories of cell decomposition in the three contexts, differentiable, combinatorial, and topological. In the combinatorial and topological setting, the initial program of obtaining such geometric decompositions from real-valued functions must be dropped. In the

145

combinatorial category, one resorts to a brutal construction in order to be
certain that such geometric decompositions exist for all combinatoral
manifolds. In the topological category, one is not at all certain that every
topological manifold supports a "topological cell-decomposition."

Thus, in that category one must be content to restrict one's analysis to
the class of topological manifolds which are cell-decomposed.

Much of the theory can be comfortably performed with the aid of
relatively few foundational theorems. (That is, much of the theory is
"formal.") It is instructive to examine these few ingredients necessary
to nourish the techniques which are used.

They are isolated as four postulates in Sec. 4. These postulates are (of
course) known foundational results for differentiable manifolds, essentially
known for combinatorial manifolds, and virtually unknown for topological
manifolds. (It is quite interesting to peruse these postulates with the
purely topological case in mind. Postulate no. 4 seems related to the
well-known Annulus Problem.)

The object of this paper is to discuss the foundations of Morse-Smale
theory in terms of these postulates, putting the theory on functorial
ground. This was attempted in a confused and disorganized manner
in [3].

The idea of an *n-solid over* X is presented here. This is a slight modification of the notion of neighborhood, developed in [3], and is a kind of
generalization of Smale's handlebodies. We begin with objects X (which
are essentially CW decompositions, and are regarded in the realm of
simple homotopy theory; see Sec. 8). A differentiable n-solid over X is a
"lifting" of X to the realm of differential topology. The set of equivalence
classes of such n-solids over X is denoted $\mathscr{N}_0^n(X)$. This set is quite natural
and has natural functorial properties. (See Theorem I of Sec. 11.)

One application, for example, of Theorem I, Sec. 11, is that if M is a
differentiable or combinatorial manifold, we may speak unambiguously
of $\mathscr{N}_0^n(M)$ for $n \geq \dim M + 3$. A quite important problem would be
to identify this set. (After Theorem I, $\mathscr{N}_0^n(M)$ is dependent only upon
the simple homotopy type of M. If $M = S^k$, $\mathscr{N}_0^n(M)$ is related to the
differentiable isotopy classes of knotted $(k-1)$-sphere knots in S^{n-1} with
trivial normal bundle.)

Using Theorem I, a rather complete existence theorem may be obtained, describing (up to a slightly weaker equivalence) *all* cell decompositions of a compact oriented differentiable manifold without boundary
$M^n(n \geq 7)$ in terms of simple homotopy theory data. This generalizes a
fundamental result of Smale regarding the existence of Morse functions
with prescribed data.

2. The categories of manifolds

There are, primarily, four categories which will be of interest to us, and we shall denote them by $\mathscr{C}_O$, $\mathscr{C}_{PL}$, $\mathscr{C}_{TOP}$, $\mathscr{C}_H$ where the index, in each case, is meant only to be suggestive and refers to that group which has a lead-role in the analysis of the respective structures. (These groups will occur only fleetingly in this paper, and H never.) That is, $\mathscr{C}_O$: The category of (compact, bounded) differentiable manifolds and differentiable imbeddings. $\mathscr{C}_{PL}$: The category of (compact bounded) combinatorial manifolds and combinatorial imbeddings. (A combinatorial manifold may be defined as a topological space together with a maximal atlas, where, on overlaps, coordinate maps "compare" viz piecewise linear homeomorphisms of open subsets of euclidean space. Here piecewise linear means, of course, with respect to some *rectilinear* subdivision of euclidean space. It is easily seen that a compact combinatorial manifold M may be given a *combinatorial* triangulation (K, t) where K^n is a finite simplicial n-dimensional complex with the property that $St(\Delta)$ is combinatorially isomorphic with Δ^n, for all simplices Δ of K. One is free, of course, to regard this last fact as the starting point of a definition of combinatorial manifold, as well.) $\mathscr{C}_{TOP}$: The category of topological manifolds and topological imbeddings. Here some clarification is necessary:

DEFINITION 1. Let V^n, W^m be topological manifolds. Assume W^m without boundary. Let $\phi\colon V^n \to W^m$ be a homeomorphism into. Then ϕ will be called *locally flat* at $v \in V$ if one of the following holds:
(i) $v \in \operatorname{int} V$, and there is a coordinate homeomorphism h of some neighborhood U of $\phi(v) \in W$ such that

$$h\colon (R^m, R^n) \underset{\approx}{\to} (U, \phi(V^n) \cap U)$$

(ii) $v \in \partial V$, and there is a coordinate homeomorphism h of some neighborhood U of $\phi(v) \in W$ such that

$$h\colon (R^m, R^n_+, R^{n-1}) \underset{\approx}{\to} (U, \phi(V^n) \cap U, \phi(\partial V^n) \cap U)$$

Here $R^n_+ \subset R^m$ is half of a linear subspace and R^{m-1} is its boundary.
DEFINITION 2. A homeomorphism $\phi\colon V^n \to W^m$ will be called a *topological imbedding* if ϕ is locally flat at all points $v \in V^n$.
$\mathscr{C}_H$: The category of topological spaces and homotopy classes of continuous maps. In what follows, the letter $\mathscr{C}$ will ambiguously stand for one of the four categories above.

Let us remark that we have the natural structure-weakening functors:

$$\mathscr{C}_O \xrightarrow{\rho_{O,PL}} \mathscr{C}_{PL} \xrightarrow{\rho_{PL,TOP}} \mathscr{C}_{TOP} \xrightarrow{\rho_{TOP,H}} C_H$$

These will follow us throughout our work, and we reserve the letter ρ to denote structure-weakening.

DEFINITION 3. A *$\mathscr{C}$-isotopy* is a level-preserving map

$$f: X \times I \to Y \times I$$

(of the category $\mathscr{C}$). The $\mathscr{C}$-isotopy thus gives rise to maps $f_t: X \to Y$ for all $t \in I$, which are again of the category $\mathscr{C}$. The $\mathscr{C}$-isotopy f will be called a *$\mathscr{C}$-isotopy between f_0 and f_1*, and f_0, f_1 will be called *$\mathscr{C}$-isotopic* (denoted: $f_0 \underset{\mathscr{C}}{\approx} f_1$).

To avoid a possible clash with creased manifolds (in the case $\mathscr{C} = \mathscr{C}_0$) we may amend the above definition by saying that a $\mathscr{C}$-isotopy $\phi: X \times I \to Y \times I$ is a map obtained as the restriction of a level-preserving imbedding $\phi: X \times R \to Y \times R$.

REMARKS.

1. $\mathscr{C}_0$-isotopy is just differentiable isotopy.

2. $\mathscr{C}_H$-isotopy is just homotopy of continuous maps.

3. $\mathscr{C}_{PL}$-isotopy is one of numerous (not quite equivalent) definitions of isotopy for combinatorial manifolds. See the forthcoming works of C. Zeemann related to this problem.

3. Cell decompositions

An object M^n of the category $\mathscr{C}$ will be called *cell-decomposed in $\mathscr{C}$* if $M^n = \overset{\nu}{\underset{i=0}{\cup}} M_i$ where $M_0 \subset M_1 \subset \cdots \subset M_\nu = M$ is an increasing sequence, and

$$M_i = M_{i-1} \cup_{\phi_i} D^{n_i} \times D^{n-n_i}$$

where

(a) if $\mathscr{C} \neq \mathscr{C}_H$; the attaching map

$$\phi_i: \partial D^{n_i} \times D^{n-n_i} \to \partial M_{i-1}$$

is an imbedding of the category C.

(b) if $\mathscr{C} = \mathscr{C}_H$;

$$\phi_i: \partial D^{n_i} \times D^{n-n_i} \to M_{i-1}$$

is a continuous map for $i = 1, \ldots, \nu$.

We shall assume (in this paper) that $M_0 = \emptyset$. (More generally, let $\rho: \mathscr{C}_0 \to \mathscr{C}_1$ be any one of the $4 + 3 + 2 + 1$ possible structure-weakening functors, and V an object of $\mathscr{C}_0$. Then an object M of C_1 will be called *cell-decomposed in $\mathscr{C}_1$, rel V* if M is cell-decomposed in C_1, where $M_0 = \rho V$. This notion, in full generality, is essential for the "relative version" of the theory given here; see [4].)

The above definition of cell-decomposed objects makes sense immediately, except in $\mathscr{C}_0$, where if M_{i-1} is a differentiable manifold and ϕ_i a differentiable imbedding, then,

$$M_i = M_{i-1} \cup_{\phi_i} D^{n_i} \times D^{n-n_i}$$

is no longer a differentiable manifold. It is a differentiable manifold with creased boundary. (See [1].) One dignified manner of avoiding this difficulty is to identify $D^{n_i} \times D^{n-n_i}$ with (what may be termed) a *handle-region of type* $(n_i, n - n_i)$ in R^n. We shall digress, for a moment, to give a brief description of what this means.

DEFINITION 4. A *handle-region of type* (p, q) is a bounded region $D^{p,q}$ in $R^p \times R^q$ given by

$$D^{p,q} = \{(x, y) \in R^p \times R^q |\, \|x\| \leq 1,\, \|y\| \leq h(\|x\|)\}$$

where h is a real-valued homeomorphism $h \colon [0,1] \to [1/2, 1]$ satisfying these properties:

(1) h is differentiable on $[0, 1]$ and $\dfrac{dh}{dt}\bigg\}_{t=0} = 0$.

(2) h^{-1} is differentiable on $[1/2, 1]$ and $\dfrac{d(h^{-1})}{dt}\bigg\}_{t=1} = 0$.

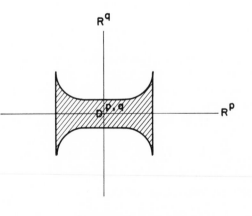

FIGURE 1

Let $\partial' D^{p,q} \subset D^{p,q}$ denote the set $\partial'^{p,q} = \{(x, y) \in D^{p,q} |\, \|x\| = 1\}$ and let $H \colon (D^p \times D^q, \partial D^p \times D^q)(D^{p,q}, \partial' D^{p,q})$ denote the homeomorphism given by $H(x, y) = (x, h(\|x\|)y)$. The mapping H is the "identity" on $\partial D^p \times D^q$.

Given two such homeomorphisms h_1, h_2, let $D_1^{p,q}$, $D_2^{p,q}$ be the handle-regions obtained. Then there is a homeomorphism

$$H_{1,2} \colon (D_1^{p,q}, \partial' D_1^{p,q}) \underset{\approx}{\to} (D_2^{p,q}, \partial' D_2^{p,q})$$

given by $H_{1,2} = H_2 H_1^{-1}$.

LEMMA 1.   *If M is a differentiable manifold,*

$$\phi \colon \partial D^p \times D^q = \partial' D^{p,q} \to \partial M$$

a differentiable imbedding. Then

$$M_\phi = M \cup_\phi D^{p,q}$$

is again a differentiable manifold which is independent of the handle-region chosen, in the following sense: if $M_\phi^{(j)} = M \cup_\phi D_{(j)}^{p,q}$, $j = 1$, 2 are differentiable manifolds obtained from distinct handle-regions, there is a diffeomorphism

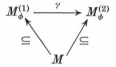

making the above commutative.

PROOF.   Evidently M_ϕ admits a differentiable atlas of local homeomorphisms into $R^n (n = p + q)$ exhibiting it as a differentiable manifold with boundary. The diffeomorphism γ is obtained by smoothing the homeomorphism

$$\gamma' \colon M_\phi^{(1)} \to M_\phi^{(2)}$$

given by $H_{1,2}$ extended via the identity. The map γ' is possibly non-differentiable at $\partial' D^{p,q}$.

We may now assume that for each pair (p, q), we have chosen a specific handle-region of type (p, q), $D_{(h)}$ via H.

DEFINITION 5.   If M is cell-decomposed, then we may refer to the data

$$X = \{(M_0, \ldots, M_\nu); \phi_1, \ldots, \phi_\nu\}$$

as a *cell-decomposition* (in $\mathscr{C}$).

If X is a cell-decomposition (of $\mathscr{C}$)

$$X = (X_0, \ldots, X_\nu)$$
$$X_i = X_{i-1} \cup_{\phi_i} D^{n_i} \times D^{n-n_i}$$

There is a natural inclusion homomorphism

$$\pi_{n_i}(X_i, X_{i-1}) \leftarrow \pi_{n_i}(D^{n_i}, \partial D^{n_i})$$

induced by inclusion. Since D_{n_i} possesses a natural orientation, there is a homomorphism

$$\pi_{n_i}(X_i, X_{i-1}) \xrightarrow{\phi_i} \mathbf{Z}$$

of the rational integers into $\pi_{n_i}(X_i, X_{i-1})$.

DEFINITION 6. Let $\nu \leq \mu$. An *imbedding* $f: X \to Y$ of *cell-decompositions* is given by a filtration-preserving continuous map $f: X_i \xrightarrow{\approx} Y_i$ (which is an isomorphism of the category $\mathscr{C}$) for $0 \leq i \leq \nu$, such that the induced diagrams

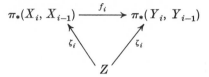

are commutative, for all $i < \nu$.

REMARK. Commutativity of the above diagram is a kind of orientation-preservation condition.

DEFINITION 7. *The category $\mathscr{D}$ of cell-decompositions of $\mathscr{C}$ is the category*, whose objects are:

cell-decompositions of $\mathscr{C}$;

and whose morphisms are:

imbeddings of cell-decompositions of $\mathscr{C}$.

If $\mathscr{C} = \mathscr{C}_O, C_{PL}, \mathscr{C}_{TOP}$ or $\mathscr{C}_H$, we denote the respective $\mathscr{D}$'s by

$$\mathscr{D} = \mathscr{D}_O, \mathscr{D}_{PL}, \mathscr{D}_{TOP} \text{ or } \mathscr{D}_H.$$

Again, we denote, ambiguously, any one of these categories by the letter $\mathscr{D}$.

Let X be a cell-decomposition

$$X = \{(X_0, \ldots, X_\nu); \phi_i: \partial D^{n_i} \times D^{n-n_i} \to X_{i-1}\}$$

DEFINITION 8. The dimension of X (dim X) is n. The *length of* X is ν. Also denote $\dim X = \max n_i, i = 1, \ldots, \nu$. Clearly, dim $X \leq$ dim X.

4. Postulates preliminary to a theory of cell decompositions

The aims of our analysis of cell decompositions will be to study problems of existence, classification and simplification of cell decompositions.

For examples of the types of theorems we are after, see Theorems I, II of Sec. 11. These are theorems proved only for $\mathscr{C}_O$, originally. An examination of the proof of Theorem I reveals that in uses only a small number of theorems peculiar to differential topology.

It seems to me to be instructive to isolate "all" the nonformal foundational results necessary to obtain a well-working theory of cell decompositions.

The postulates given below are sufficient to allow one to perform most
of the operations of cell decomposition theory in any category. (In
particular, Theorem I is dependent only upon these postulates.)

POSTULATES

POSTULATE 1. *$\mathscr{C}$-isotopy extension theorem (for spheres):* Let

$$S^k \times D^{n-k} \xrightarrow{\ \phi_t\ } M^n$$

be a $\mathscr{C}$-isotopy. Then there is a $\mathscr{C}$-isotopy $h_t \colon M^n \to M^n$ such that
  (i) $h_0 = 1$
  (ii) $h_t\phi_0 = \phi_t$.

To prepare for the second postulate, let us define transversal intersection of two imbeddings:

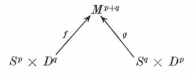

DEFINITION 9.   The maps f, g have *transversal intersection* if for each
$y \in M^{p+q}$ such that

$$y \in f(S^p \times \{0\}) \cap g(S^q \times \{0\}),$$

there is a homeomorphism

$$D^p \times D^q \xrightarrow{\ \gamma\ } f(S^p \times D^q) \cap g(D^p \times S^q)$$

such that $\gamma(0) = y$ and there are maps $\phi \colon D^p \to S^p$, $\psi \colon D^q \to S^q$ such that

$$f \cdot (\phi \times 1_q) = \gamma = g \cdot (1_p \times \psi)$$

Let

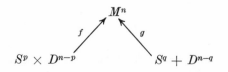

be two C-imbeddings where $n > p + q$. Then f, g have *transversal intersection* if their images are disjoint.

POSTULATE 2. *General Position Theorem (for spheres)*: Let

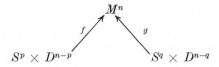

be two $\mathscr{C}$-imbeddings for $n \geq p + q$.

Then there is a $\mathscr{C}$-isotopy $f_t: S^p \times D^{n-p} \to M^n$ such that $f_0 = f$ and the imbeddings f_1, g have transversal intersection.

POSTULATE 3. *A Local Tubular Neighborhood Theorem*: Let

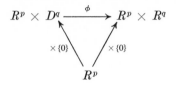

be a commutative diagram, where ϕ is an imbedding.

Then there is a $\mathscr{C}$-isotopy ϕ_t such that

(i) $\phi_0 = \phi$

(ii) $\phi_1 | D^p \times D^q$ is the identity.

POSTULATE 4. *Another Tubular Neighborhood Theorem*: Let M^n be a manifold with boundary (of $\mathscr{C}$), and assume $n \geq 5$. Let

$$f: (D^2, \partial D^2) \to (M, \partial M)$$

be an imbedding which is locally transversal to ∂M.

Then there is a tubular neighborhood of f in the strict sense that there is an imbedding

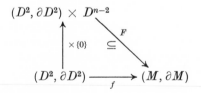

making the above commutative.

Naturally, C_O satisfies these postulates. Although it is not yet in the literature, it is to be expected that foundational work in combinatorial manifolds will soon validate these axioms for C_{PL}. (Postulate 2 poses no problem here.) In fact, these postulates are not entirely hopeless for $\mathscr{C} = \mathscr{C}_{TOP}$. In this connection, we may look forward to application of the newly developed techniques of Homma.

5. Ordering of cell decompositions

In our structure of cell decompositions we have taken into account the precise order of attached cells. Clearly, however, two cell decompositions which differ only because of the chosen order of attaching cells, are very much alike. We will call them *reordering-equivalent*. The precise definition is given below. In studying "reordering-equivalences" we must consider maps $f: X \to Y$ between cell decompositions which are not filtration-preserving. Such maps will be called *free* and will be denoted

$$f: X \dashrightarrow Y$$

So, let X, $Y \in \mathscr{D}$, both of dimension n, and length ν:

$$X = (X_0, \ldots, X\nu) \quad X_i = X_{i-1} \cup D^{n_i} \times D^{n-n_i}$$
$$Y = (Y_0, \ldots, Y\nu) \quad Y_i = Y_{i-1} \cup D^{m_i} \times D^{n-m_i}$$

Let $f: X_\nu \to Y_\nu$ be a $\mathscr{C}$-isomorphism between the total spaces of X and Y (i.e., $f: X \dashrightarrow Y$ is a *free* $\mathscr{C}$-isomorphism), and let $\omega: \{1, \ldots, \nu\} \to \{1, \ldots, \nu\}$ be a permutation such that these conditions hold:

(a) $m_{\omega(i)} = n_i \qquad i = 1, \ldots, \nu$

(b) $f(D^{n_i} \times D^{n-n_i}) \subseteq D^{m_{w(i)}} \times D^{n-m_{w(i)}} \subseteq Y_{\omega(i)}$

Then $f: X \underset{\sim}{\dashrightarrow} Y$ will be called a *re-ordering equivalence*.

DEFINITION 10. A cell decomposition X is called *properly ordered* if

$$X = \{(X_0, \ldots, X_\nu); X_i = X_{i-1} \cup_{\phi_i} D^{n_i} \times D^{n-n_i}\}$$

where $n_i \leq n_j$ if $i \leq j$.

6. $\mathscr{D}$-Equivalence

Since our isomorphisms must preserve the precise *decomposition* of a cell decomposition, we have an extremely rigid notion of isomorphism. For example, the two cell decomposition of length 3 in the plane, represented by the diagrams in Fig. 2 are non-isomorphic.

Thus, (it should be clear from Fig. 2) we must weaken our notion of isomorphism if we wish to obtain anything usable. We shall call the weakened notion of isomorphism "$\mathscr{D}$-equivalence."

Intuitively, a $\mathscr{D}$-equivalence will be given by a coherent one-parameter modification of cell decomposition (see Fig. 3).

DEFINITION 11. *A $\mathscr{D}$-equivalence of cell decompositions in $\mathscr{D}$ is an object of the form*

$$X = \{(X_0, \ldots, X_\nu); \phi_i\}$$

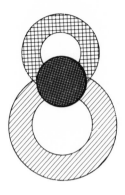 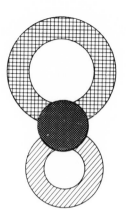

(a)   (b)

FIGURE 2

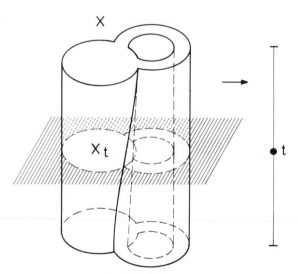

X

X_t

t

FIGURE 3

where there are also given projection mappings

$$\pi_i \colon X_i \to I \qquad\qquad i = 1, \ldots, \nu$$

The X_i are objects of $\mathscr{C}$ and we may define

(a) If $\mathscr{C} = \mathscr{C}_H$, $\partial^* X_i = X_i$

(b) If $\mathscr{C} \neq \mathscr{C}_H$, $\partial^* X_i = \partial X_i - \operatorname{int} \pi_i^{-1}\{\partial I\}$

then

$$X_i = X_{i-1} \cup_{\phi_i} D^{n_i} \times D^{n-n_i} \times I$$

and the ϕ_i are attaching imbeddings such that

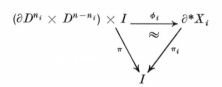

is commutative.

Thus we may regard X as a one-parameter family of cell decompositions. Restricting everything to any $t \in I$ we obtain an ordinary cell decomposition

$$X_t = \{(\pi_0^{-1}\{t\}, \pi_1^{-1}\{t\}, \ldots, \pi_\nu^{-1}\{t\}); \, \phi_i | \pi^{-1}\{t\}\}$$

Two cell decompositions X_0, X_1 which are linked by a $\mathscr{D}$-equivalence will be called $\mathscr{D}$-*equivalent*.

It would also be intuitively helpful if we could "realize" the $\mathscr{D}$-equivalence between two cell decompositions by an actual free $\mathscr{D}$-isomorphism between them. To this end we shall describe a class of free isomorphisms between cell decompositions.

DEFINITION 12. *The class of $\mathscr{D}$-equivalence mappings* between cell decompositions of $\mathscr{D}$ is the smallest class of free isomorphisms, $f \colon X \dashrightarrow Y$ between cell decompositions possessing the following properties:

(1) A $\mathscr{D}$-isomorphism is a D-equivalence.

(2) A free isomorphism $f \colon X \dashrightarrow Y$ which is $\mathscr{C}$-isotopic to a $\mathscr{D}$-equivalence is again a $\mathscr{D}$-equivalence.

(3) Let

$$Y^{(j)} = \{(Y_0^{(j)}, \ldots, Y_\nu, Y_{\nu+1}^{(j)}); \, \phi_i^{(j)}\} \quad j = 1, 2$$

be cell decompositions of $\mathscr{D}$.

Let $X^{(j)} \subseteq Y^{(j)}$ be the sub-cell decompositions of length ν.

Let $f \colon Y^{(1)} \dashrightarrow Y^{(2)}$ be a free isomorphism satisfying these properties:

(a) The map f induces an isomorphism (of $\mathscr{C}$)

$$f \colon (Y_{\nu+1}^{(1)}, Y_\nu^{(1)}) \underset{\approx}{\to} (Y_{\nu+1}^{(2)}, Y_\nu^{(2)})$$

such that

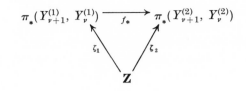

is commutative (i.e., f is an imbedding (rel $X^{(1)}$)).

(b) The restriction

$$f: X^{(1)} \to X^{(2)}$$

is a $\mathscr{D}$-equivalence.

We then obtain the following useful theorem (applying Postulate no. 1):

THEOREM 1. Two cell decompositions X, Y are $\mathscr{D}$-equivalent if and only if there is a $\mathscr{D}$-equivalence mapping $f: X \dashrightarrow Y$.

7. The "ground" category

In this section we shall discuss the category $\mathscr{D}_H$, the weakest of our four cell decomposition categories.

In $\mathscr{D}_H$ the "thickenings" of attached discs play no role whatever. We shall use this fact to aid us in the understanding of $\mathscr{D}_H$, by relating $\mathscr{D}_H$ to a category that may look a bit more familiar to those who study algebraic topology.

By an *ordinary CW-decomposition* let us mean a decomposition $X = \{(X_0, \ldots X_\nu); \phi_i\}$ where $X_i = X_{i-1} \cup_{\phi_i} D^{n_i}$, $i = 1, \ldots, \nu$, and the $\phi_i: \partial D^{n_i} \to X_{i-1}$ are continuous maps.

By an imbedding of ordinary CW-decompositions is meant $f: X \to Y$ a continuous filtration-preserving homotopy equivalence

$$f: (X_0, \ldots, X_\nu) \to (Y_0, \ldots, Y_\nu)$$

such that

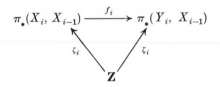

are, again, commutative for all i.

Denote by $\mathscr{D}_{CW}$ the category formed by these objects. Then, to each object $X \in D_H$ we will construct an object $\dot{X} \in \mathscr{D}_{CW}$ (its "unthickening") and a filtration preserving map $u: X \to \dot{X}$. The mapping u gives rise to a functor $u\colon \mathscr{D}_H \to \mathscr{D}_{CW}$ yielding an isotopy-equivalence between the two categories in the following sense:

PROPOSITION 1.   The mapping u is surjective on objects, and if uX_1 is isotopic to uX_2 in D_{CW}, then X_1 is $\mathscr{D}_H$-isotopic to X_2.

The unthickening functor may be defined inductively with respect to the length of X. Thus: assume $u\colon X \to \dot{X}$ defined, and let

$$Y = (X_0, \ldots, X_\nu, X_{\nu+1})$$

where

$$X_{\nu+1} = X_\nu \cup_{\phi_\nu} D^{n_\nu} \times D^{n-n_\nu}.$$

Define

$$\phi_\nu\colon \partial D^{n_\nu} \longrightarrow X_\nu$$

$$\downarrow {\scriptstyle \times\{0\}} \qquad\qquad \downarrow {\scriptstyle u}$$

$$\partial D^{n_\nu} \times D^{n-n_\nu} \xrightarrow[\ \dot\phi_\nu\ ]{} \dot X_\nu$$

by composition, giving us:

$$\dot Y = (\dot X_0, \ldots, \dot X_\nu, \dot X_{\nu+1})$$

where $\dot X_{\nu+1}$ is defined to be the space

$$\dot X_{\nu+1} = \dot X_\nu \cup_{\dot\phi_\nu} D^{n_\nu}$$

Furthermore, we may extend $u\colon X \to \dot X$ to a filtration-preserving map $u\colon Y \to \dot Y$, by setting $u\colon D^{n_\nu} \times D^{n-n_\nu} \dashrightarrow_{\pi_1} D^{n_\nu} \subseteq X_{\nu+1}$ to be the composite.

This unthickening map has the requisite properties.

A consequence of Proposition 1 is that we may replace the category $\mathscr{D}_H$ by $\mathscr{D}_{CW}$.

8. Simple homotopy theory in $\mathscr{D}_{CW}$

DEFINITION 13.   An *elementary expansion* $f\colon X \dashrightarrow Y$ is a mapping which is in the same homotopy class as a mapping f_0 which is a composite of the form:

$$f_0\colon X \underset{\subseteq}{\xrightarrow{\ e\ }} Y_0 \underset{\approx}{\dashrightarrow}{\ \scriptstyle s\ } Y_1 \dashrightarrow{\ \scriptstyle r\ } Y$$

where:

1. The cell decomposition $Y_0 \in \mathscr{D}_{CW}$ may be given as

$$Y_0 = X \cup_{\phi_0} D^{n-1} \cup_{\phi_1} D^n$$

with $\phi_0\colon \partial D^{n-1} \to \{x_0\} \subset X$ a constant map, and

$$\phi_1\colon \partial D^n \to D^{n-1}/\partial D^{n-1} \subseteq X \cup_{\phi_0} D^{n-1}$$

the natural identification. This might be termed an *irrelevant addition* in the category $\mathscr{D}_{CW}$. An object which is the result of k elementary expansions may be called a *k-fold expansion*, $X \subset X(k)$.

2. The map $e: X \to X \cup_{\phi_0} D^{n-1} \cup_{\phi_1} D^n = Y_0$ is the natural inclusion.

3. The map s is some $\mathscr{D}_{CW}$-equivalence.

4. The map r is some re-ordering equivalence. (Since r is not filtration-preserving, neither is f.)

REMARK. Any elementary expansion $f: X \dashrightarrow Y$ is a homotopy equivalence (between total spaces, of course).

DEFINITION 14. An *elementary contraction* $f: X \dashrightarrow Y$ is a map which has a two-sided homotopy inverse $g: Y \dashrightarrow X$ which is an elementary expansion.

DEFINITION 15. A *simple homotopy equivalence* $f: X \dashrightarrow Y$ is a free map such that there is a sequence

$$X = X_1 \xrightarrow{f_1} X_2 \xrightarrow{f_2} \cdots \xrightarrow{f_v} X_v = Y$$

of cell decompositions $X_j \in \mathscr{D}_{CW}$ and elementary expansions or contractions f_j such that f is homotopic to $f_v \circ \cdots \circ f_2 \circ f_1$.

The idea of "simple homotopy equivalence" is due to J. H. C. Whitehead. He originally defined this concept for simplicial complexes [11], and developed a rather beautiful "obstruction theory," relating this notion to the algebraic topology of the underlying spaces.

Whitehead defines a "torsion group" $W(G)$ which is an abelian group assignable to any group G. If X is a topological space he defines

$$W(X) = W(\pi_1(X)).$$

Whitehead then constructs an "obstruction" $\tau(f) \in W$ for any homotopy equivalence $f: X \to Y$ such that f is a simple homotopy equivalence if and only if $\tau(f) = 0$.

This clearly establishes the notion of simple homotopy type as an "algebraic" concept. In many cases, $W(G)$ may be computed to be trivial. (For example: $G = \{0\}$, $\mathbf{Z}_2$, $\mathbf{Z}_3$, $\mathbf{Z}_4$, $\mathbf{Z}$.) Thus, for spaces X having such a G as fundamental group, the concepts of simple homotopy equivalence and homotopy equivalence coincide.

The theory of Whitehead works just as well in $\mathscr{D}_{CW}$, for our definition of simple homotopy theory. (Or one may resort to the stopgap measure of [3] where our simple homotopy concept in $\mathscr{D}_{CW}$ was related directly to simple homotopy for simplicial complexes.)

Evidently one may mimic these definitions in all of our categories of interest, obtaining *simple homotopy equivalence* and irrelevant addition in $\mathscr{D}$. For $\mathscr{D}_O$, $\mathscr{D}_{PL}$, $\mathscr{D}_{TOP}$ one has the usual picture of a standard handle and cancelling cap, added on some microscopic portion of the boundary. We shall also make use of this notion of $\mathscr{D}_H$.

9. Solids over cell decompositions

As we have seen, an object X of $\mathscr{D}_H$ is a creature which may be understood "entirely" in the domain of algebraic topology. Since we regard algebraic topology as "known," we may think of elements $X \in \mathscr{D}_H$ as basically unmysterious objects. Thus, the first step in the program of studying a differentiable, combinatorial, or topological cell decomposition $X \in \mathscr{D}$, might be to apply the structure-weakening functor $\rho : \mathscr{D} \to \mathscr{D}_H$ to X, and analyze $\rho X \in \mathscr{D}_H$.

This program may be carried out (obliquely) by the inverse program: Starting with an $X \in \mathscr{D}_H$, study the collection of all $Y \in \mathscr{D}$ such that ρY is isomorphic with X.

This inspires the following definition.

DEFINITION 16. Let $X \in \mathscr{D}_H$. An *n-dimensional solid over* X *(in* $\mathscr{D}$*),* is a pair (M, π) where $M \in \mathscr{D}$ and $\pi : \rho M \dashrightarrow X$ is a $\mathscr{D}_H$-equivalence.

An *isomorphism*

$$\gamma : (M_1, \pi_1) \underset{\approx}{\overrightarrow{}} (M_2, \pi_2)$$

between two n-solids is a $\mathscr{D}$-equivalence; between some k-fold expansions

$$M_1(k) \xrightarrow{\ \gamma\ } M_2(k)$$

giving rise to the diagram,

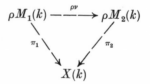

(commutative up to $\mathscr{C}_H$-isotopy).

Denote by $\mathscr{N}^n(X)$ the set of isomorphism classes of n-solids over X (in $\mathscr{D}$). (Here if $\mathscr{D} = \mathscr{D}_O, \mathscr{D}_{PL}, \mathscr{D}_{TOP}$ we give the respective sets $\mathscr{N}^n(X)$ the same indices.)[1]

Our structure-weakening functor ρ induces maps

$$\mathscr{N}_O^n(X) \xrightarrow[\rho_{O,PL}]{} \mathscr{N}_{PL}^n(X) \xrightarrow[\rho_{PL,TOP}]{} \mathscr{N}_{TOP}^n(X)$$

---

[1] Here we have changed our terminology from the ill-chosen word: "neighborhood" of [3] to "solid". It should also be remarked that the definition of "solid" differs slightly from the bad definition of "neighborhood" given in [3]. "Solid" seems to be, functorially, the correct notion. Everything said about "neighborhoods" in [3]

Let us also define a *free pull-back isomorphism* (or merely: *free isomorphism*) $\phi: \mathcal{N}^n(X) \rightleftharpoons \mathcal{N}^n(Y)$ as follows:

To each n-solid (M, π) over X, ϕ assigns an n-solid $\phi^!(M, \pi)$ over Y and a free $\mathscr{C}$-isomorphism, $\tilde{\phi}: \phi^! M \longmapsto M$. This assignation must satisfy the following property: It must induce a well-defined bijection

$$|\phi|: \mathcal{N}^n(X) \underset{\approx}{\to} \mathcal{N}^n(Y).$$

10. Examples

The "basic" elements in $\mathscr{D}$ are those which play the role of n-cells. In particular, let $D^{n,k}$ be the cell decomposition of length 3 in $\mathscr{D}_0$, unmistakeably recognized by the following description: $D^{n,k}$ is $(n + k)$-dimensional, built up with: (1) a thickened 0-cell, $D_1^{n,k}$, and (2) a thickened $(n - 1)$-cell, attached to the thickened 0-cell, by the natural unknotted and untwisted attaching map, forming $D_2^{n,k}$. That is, (identifying $D^{n,k}$ with $D^{n-1} \times D^{k+1}$) the attaching map

$$\phi_2: \partial D^{n-1} \times D^{k+1} \to \partial(D_1^{n,k}) = \partial(D^{n-1} \times D^{k+1})$$

may be taken to be the natural imbedding. Thus, we have a natural identification

$$D_2^{n,k} \approx S^{n-1} \times D^{k+1}$$

(3) a thickened n-cell, attached by a map

$$\phi_3: \partial D^n \times D^k \to \partial(D_2^{k,n}) \approx S^{n-1} \times S^k$$

which may be taken to be $1 \times i$ where $1: \partial D^n \underset{\approx}{\to} S^{n-1}$ is the standard identification, and $i: D^k \to S^k$ is the upper-hemisphere imbedding.

Then the total space $D_3^{n,k}$, evidently, is isomorphic with D^{n+k}. Thus, $D^{n,k}$ is one of the many cell decompositions of (circumlocutions for) the disc. D^n, in our category $\mathscr{D}_0$.

To avoid excess notation, let us use $D^{n,k}$ to denote the structure-weakened object $D^{n,k}$ in all categories $\mathscr{D}$.

---

translates immediately to "solids." The most grievous thing about a "neighborhood" in the sense of [3] is that it is not defined over a particular cell decomposition but rather over an equivalence class of cell decompositions. Lemma 3.2 of [3] is incorrect, and therefore the equivalence class described *makes no sense functorially*, and even if it did, it would yield no advantages. The urge to pass to equivalence classes was due to my utter inexperience with categories.

Now let us choose some *knotted* imbedding $\gamma: S^{n-1} \times D^k \to S^{n-1} \times S^k$ which is *homotopic* (i.e., $\mathscr{D}_H$-isotopic) to ϕ_3. Then let us proceed to construct the cell decomposition $D^{n,k}$, only using γ in place of ϕ_3. The resulting cell decomposition we shall denote by $D_\gamma^{n,k}$.

We easily have that $D^{n,k}$ and $D_\gamma^{n,k}$ are $\mathscr{D}_H$-equivalent. Let us denote by $\pi_\gamma: D_\gamma^{n,k} \to D^{n,k}$ a $\mathscr{D}_H$-isomorphism (any two such are $\mathscr{D}_H$-isotopic in

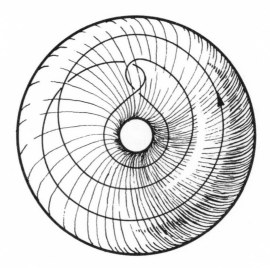

FIGURE 4

this case). Consequently, $(D_\gamma^{n,k}, \pi_\gamma)$ represents an $(n+k)$-solid over $D^{n,k}$. To see that these solids may be distinct, let $n = k = 2$ and let γ be some thickening of the knot pictured in Fig. 4. (See [2] which proves that $\partial D_\gamma^{2,2}$ for this γ is not simply connected, hence the solid $D_\gamma^{2,2} \in \mathscr{N}^4(D^{2,2})$ is distinct from the solid $D^{2,2} \in \mathscr{N}^4(D^{2,2})$.)

11. The main theorems

The geometric work of [3] succeeds in proving the following theorem. (The version "proved" in [3] was called the *nonstable neighborhood theorem*.)[1]

THEOREM I.   Let $M > 5$. Let $f: X \dashrightarrow Y$ be a simple homotopy equivalence between the properly ordered cell decompositions X, $Y \in \mathscr{D}_H$. Assume: $n \geq \max \{\dim X, \dim Y\} + 3$.

---

[1] The reader should be warned that the hypotheses on the nonstable neighborhood theorem [3] (and the relative theorem [4]) are inadequate.

Then f induces a free (pull-back) isomorphism $f^{(n)}: \mathcal{N}_0^n(X) \rightleftharpoons \mathcal{N}_0^n(Y)$ (which is indeed characterized by certain functorial properties).

This theorem is a generalization of the handlebody theorem of Smale [7].

It asserts that if $n \geq \dim X + 3$ then $\mathcal{N}^n(X)$ is dependent only upon the simple homotopy type of X. (It therefore allows us to simplify cell decompositions as follows: If we know that a differentiable manifold M admits a cell decomposition which exhibits it as a solid over X, then M admits a cell decomposition exhibiting it as a solid over Y for any Y of the same simple homotopy type as X.)

The theorem makes use of nothing more than postulates 1–4.

Concerning existence of cell decompositions of differentiable manifolds, there is a very strong result that may be obtained, the nature of which I shall sketch. Let M^n be an oriented connected compact differentiable manifold without boundary. Given any differentiable cell decomposition $\mathcal{M}$, of M, one may "turn $\mathcal{M}$ upside-down" and obtain a "dual" cell decomposition $\tilde{\mathcal{M}}$. If we set $\rho \mathcal{M} = X$; $\rho \tilde{\mathcal{M}} = \tilde{X}$, we obtain a pair of simple homotopy equivalences,

$$
\begin{array}{ccc}
M & \xrightarrow{\tilde{\pi}} & \tilde{X} \\
{\scriptstyle \pi}\Big\downarrow & & \\
X & &
\end{array}
$$

which necessarily obey a certain *algebraic topological* relationship.

Motivated by this observation (see [3], chapter 10) we define abstractly *a pairing into M* to be a pair $(\pi, \tilde{\pi})$ of simple homotopy equivalences

$$
\begin{array}{ccc}
M & \xrightarrow{\tilde{\pi}} & \tilde{X} \\
{\scriptstyle \pi}\Big\downarrow & & \\
X & &
\end{array}
$$

satisfying this relationship. If the "pairing" $(\pi, \tilde{\pi})$ is obtainable from a dual pair $(\mathcal{M}, \tilde{\mathcal{M}})$ of differentiable cell decompositions of M (in a certain weak sense; see [3]), then we may say $(\pi, \tilde{\pi})$ is *geometrically realizable*.

THEOREM II. Every pairing into-$M(\pi, \tilde{\pi})$ is geometrically realizable if $\dim M \geq 7$.

The question of geometric realizability of a pairing $(\pi, \tilde{\pi})$ is a very refined version of the problem of existence of Morse functions on M with prescribed data.

12. Stable theorems

Let $X \in \mathscr{D}_H$ and define a "suspension map" $\sigma \colon \mathscr{N}^n(X) \to \mathscr{N}^{n+1}(X)$ by $\sigma X = X \times I$.

Then we may form

$$\mathscr{N}(X) = \lim_{n \to \infty} \mathscr{N}^n(X)$$

with respect to this suspension. For simplicity, let $X = \rho M$, for $M \in \mathscr{D}_O$. Set $K(X)$ to be ambiguously the groups of stable differentiable vector bundles over X, $K_O(X)$, or stable PL-microbundles over (some smooth triangulation of) X, $K_{PL}(X)$ or $K_{TOP}(X)$. (See [5] for the concept of microbundle.)

Let $t^n \colon \mathscr{N}^n(X) \to K(X)$ be the map which assigns to each solid (M^n, π) the stable tangent microbundle (or bundle) of M regarded as a bundle over X (via pull-back by some homotopy-inverse to π).

The maps t^n commute with σ and induce a map $t \colon \mathscr{N}(X) \to K(X)$.

STABLE THEOREM.   The map t is a bijection of sets.

MASSACHUSETTS INSTITUTE OF TECHNOLOGY
CAMBRIDGE, MASSACHUSETTS

REFERENCES

[1] A. DOUADY, Variétés aux bords anguleux, *Séminaire Cartan, Exp. 3*, 1961/1962.

[2] B. MAZUR, A note on some contractible 4-manifolds, *Annals of Math., 73* (1961), p. 221–228.

[3] ———, *Theory of Neighborhoods*, mimeographed notes, Harvard University (published version to appear shortly in the Journal of the Institut des Hautes Etudes Scientifiques, under the title, "Differential Topology from the Point of View of Simple Homotopy Theory").

[4] ———, Relative neighborhoods and the theorems of Smale, *Annals of Math., 77* (1963), p. 232–249.

[5] J. MILNOR, *Microbundles and Differential Structures* (mimeographed notes), Princeton University, September 1961.

[6] ———, *Morse Theory*, Annals of Mathematics Study No. 51, Princeton University Press, 1962.

[7] S. SMALE, The generalized Poincaré conjecture in dimensions greater than four, *Annals of Math., 74* (1961), p. 391–406.

[8] ———, On the structure of manifolds, *Amer. J. of Math., 84* (1962), p. 387–399.

[9] ———, A diffeomorphism criterion for manifolds, *Annals of Math.* (to appear).

[10] ———, Differentiable and combinatorial structures on manifolds, *Annals of Math.*, *74* (1961), p. 391–406.

[11] J. H. C. WHITEHEAD, Simple homotopy types, *Amer. J. of Math.*, *72* (1950), p. 1–57.

[12] M. BROWN, Locally flat imbeddings of topological manifolds, *Annals of Math.*, *75* (1962), p. 331–341.

The Index Theorem for Homogeneous Differential Operators

RAOUL BOTT

---

1. Introduction

Let E and F be smooth complex vector bundles over the smooth compact manifold M. The notion of a linear elliptic differential operator, D, from E to F is then well defined and such an operator induces a linear map from the smooth sections of E to the smooth sections of F.

$$D\colon \Gamma E \to \Gamma F.$$

The elliptic character of D implies that both kernel and the cokernel of D are finite dimensional vector spaces over the complex numbers $\mathbf{C}$, and the index of D is defined as difference of their dimensions:

$$\text{index } (D) = \dim (\text{Ker } D) - \dim (\text{Coker } D)$$

Quite recently Atiyah and Singer obtained a formula for this index in terms of the topological data of the problem, that is, in terms of the characteristic classes of E, F, the tangent bundle of M and an auxiliary bundle $\sigma(D)$, the symbol of D, which is determined by the highest order infinitesimal effect of D.

Their result is the culmination of the pioneering work of Agranovic, Dynin, Seeley and Volpert in this direction, [see [1] for references], and may be interpreted as a far reaching generalization of the Riemann-Roch theorem of Hirzebruch both in statement and in the main lines of proof.

This note concerns itself with the following very special instance of the general index problem. We will call $D\colon \Gamma E \to \Gamma F$ a homogeneous operator if

H. 1.   The base manifold, X, is the coset space G/H of a compact connected Lie group G by a closed connected subgroup H.

H. 2.   Both E and F are induced by representations of H.

H. 3.   The differential operator $D\colon \Gamma E \to \Gamma F$ commutes with the induced action of G on ΓE and ΓF.

The original purpose for considering the homogeneous situation, was really to check the Atiyah-Singer formula in a concrete instance. Although this motivation does not exist anymore, we hope that this special case is nevertheless of some interest as a source of explicitly computable examples. From another point of view the present remarks may be thought of as an addendum to the Borel-Hirzebruch work on the consequences of the Riemann-Roch theorem for complex homogeneous spaces [2], and to my earlier paper on homogeneous vector-bundles [3].

For a *homogeneous* elliptic operator D, one would expect a formula for the index of D in terms of the H-modules which induce E and F, and some sort of infinitesimal invariant of D. However, and this is what makes this case so very simple, it turns out that due to the "Euler characteristic" nature of the index, this invariant depends only on the H-modules which induce E and F (and of course on the position of H and G) but does not involve the operator D at all. This lack of dependence on the operator already appears for a refined form of "index" which can be defined for homogeneous operators and which will be explained in a moment.

Recall first the definition of the ring, $R(G)$, of virtual G-modules. (The character-ring of G in the classical terminology.)

Following Grothendieck, this ring may be characterized by the following universal property. There is a canonical map: $A \to [A]$ from G-modules (finite dimensional representations of G on a complex vector-space) to $R(G)$, such that if f is any *additive* function from G-modules to an Abelian group $\mathscr{A}$, then f "extends" to a unique additive homomorphism $\tilde{f}\colon R(G) \to \mathscr{A}$, in the sense that for every G-module A, $f(A) = f([A])$. (An additive function on G-modules is one for which $f(A) + f(C) = f(B)$ whenever $0 \to A \to B \to C \to 0$ is an exact sequence of G-modules.)

In our situation G is compact and hence the G-modules completely reducible. It then follows easily that if $\{W_\alpha\}$, $\alpha \in \mathscr{I}(G)$ is any complete set of irreducible inequivalent G-modules, then the elements $\{w_\alpha = [W_\alpha]\}$ form a free basis for $R(G)$, *the canonical basis for $R(G)$.*

Indeed, the intertwining number of two-G-modules,

$$\tau(A, B) = \dim_C \operatorname{Hom}_G (A, B),$$

"extends" to a symmetric bi-linear form on $R(G)$, which we denote by $\langle\ ,\ \rangle_G$ and our canonical basis is orthonormal with respect to it:

$$\langle w_\alpha, w_\beta \rangle_G = \delta_{\alpha\beta} \qquad \alpha, \beta \in \mathscr{I}(G).$$

In short, we may identify $R(G)$ additively with the free group generated by the canonical basis. It is expedient to complete these remarks on $R(G)$ with the following additional easy properties which will be needed later:

(1.1)   The ring structure on $R(G)$ is induced by the tensor product of G-modules $[A] \cdot [B] = [A \otimes B]$.

(1.2)   If $\varphi \colon H \to G$ is a homomorphism, then the obvious H-module structure induced on a G-module by φ, extends to a ring homomorphism $\varphi^* \colon R(G) \to R(H)$.

(1.3)   The function $A \to \dim A$ extends to a ring homomorphism $\dim \colon R(G) \to \mathbf{Z}$.

(1.4)   The function $A \to A^*$ which assigns to the G-module A, its dual G-module extends to an involution or $R(G)$ which will also be denoted by *, and the following identities hold:

$$(1.5) \qquad \begin{cases} \langle x, y \rangle_G = \langle x^*, y^* \rangle_G \\ \langle xz, y \rangle_G = \langle x, z^*y \rangle_G \end{cases}$$

To return to our program of defining a refined index for a homogeneous elliptic operator $D \colon \Gamma E \to \Gamma F$. This is done simply as follows: clearly G acts naturally on Ker D and cokernel D. Because D is elliptic these spaces are finite dimensional, and hence are well determined G-modules. One now lets the "index" of D be the element $\chi(D)$ in $R(G)$ defined by

$$(1.7) \qquad \chi(D) = [\text{Ker } D] - [\text{Coker } D],$$

This element is clearly a refined form of the index because by (1.3):

$$(1.8) \qquad \text{index } (D) = \dim \chi(D).$$

In Theorem I below we state a formula for $\chi(D)$ which displays the independence of $\chi(D)$ on the particular elliptic operator D, and which, in view of the Weyl formulae, is explicitly computable. The proof of Theorem I as well as the precise definitions of induced representations, etc., is given in the next section. This proof is really a direct consequence of elementary facts concerning the action of G on the space of C^∞ functions on G, and the Peter-Weyl theorem.

We first define the "formal group" $\hat{R}(G)$, as the possibly infinite linear combinations $\Sigma a_\alpha w_\alpha$, $a_\alpha \in \mathbf{Z}$, of our canonical basis. Thus $R(G)$ is included in $\hat{R}(G)$ as the "finite" elements. Now, given a homomorphism $\varphi \colon H \to G$, we define the formal induced representation $\varphi_* \colon R(H) \to \hat{R}(G)$ as the extension to $R(H)$ of the function:

$$A \to \Sigma \langle \varphi^* w_\alpha, \lfloor A \rfloor \rangle_H w_\alpha, \qquad A \text{ an } H\text{-module}; \alpha \in \mathscr{I}(G).$$

With this terminology understood, we have the following theorem.

THEOREM I.   *Let* $D \colon \Gamma E \to \Gamma F$ *be a homogeneous elliptic operator over* $X = G/H$, *where the bundles* E *and* F, *are induced by the* H-modules M *and* N *respectively. Define the homogeneous symbol,* $\sigma(D)$, *of* D *to be the* element $[M] - [N]$ in $R(H)$. Then if $i_*: R(H) \to \hat{R}(G)$ is the formal induction homomorphism, the following holds:

(a) $i_*\sigma(D)$ is a finite element of $\hat{R}(G)$.

(b) $\chi(D) = i_*\sigma(D)$.

The situation is therefore as follows: For D to exist at all $i_*\sigma(D)$ has to be a finite element of $\hat{R}(G)$, i.e., an element of $R(G)$, and if D exists then this element is precisely $\chi(D)$. Thus the finiteness condition (a) may be thought of as a necessary condition on the homogeneous symbol of an elliptic operator, while (b) computes the index in terms of its homogeneous symbol. Some consequences of this theorem are:

THEOREM II. *Let rank $H <$ rank G. Then any homogeneous elliptic operator $D: \Gamma E \to \Gamma F$ over G/H has vanishing index: $\chi(D) = 0$.*

This is then the proper generalization of the well-known theorem that the Euler number of G/H vanishes when the rank of H is less than the rank of G.

In the maximal rank case the situation is completely reversed.

THEOREM III. *Let the rank of H equal the rank of G, and assume that $\pi_1(G)$ has no 2-torsion. Then for every G-module W, there exists a homogeneous elliptic operator $D_W: \Gamma E \to \Gamma F$, with $\chi(D) = [W]$.*

THEOREM IV. *Let rank $H =$ rank G, and let $D: \Gamma E \to \Gamma F$ be an arbitrary elliptic operator over G/H, then the formula of Atiyah-Singer for the index of D is valid.*

The proof of this last proposition proceeds by first finding a cohomological formula for dim $i_*(G/H)\sigma(D)$ and thus verifying the Atiyah-Singer formula for all homogeneous differential operators. Thereafter the invariance properties of D, imply that this same formula must be valid for all elliptic operators on G/H. Here the salient fact is that at least over the rationals the induced bundles generate all the bundles over G/H.

2. The induction process at various levels

Throughout this paper G denotes a compact Lie group and $H \to G$ a closed connected subgroup. By a G-vector space, M, we mean a complex vector-space M on which G acts as left C-automorphisms. If M and M' are two such objects $\text{Hom}_G(M, M')$ denotes the C-vector-space of linear maps from M to M' which commute with the action of G. If M is a finite dimensional G-vector space on which G acts continuously we call M a G-module.

Suppose now that M is a fixed H-module, and that $E \xrightarrow{\pi} X$ is a principal H-bundle. Thus H acts on the right of E and locally this action corresponds to the obvious right action of H on $U \times H$. We then let $E \times_G M$ denote the associated vector bundle to E by the H-module M. Precisely, $E \times_G M$—is the quotient space of $E \times M$ under the equivalence $(e, m) \sim (e \cdot h, h^{-1} \cdot m)$.

This situation is summarized by the standard mixing diagram:

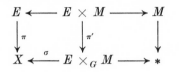

where π' is induced by the equivalence just described. From this point of view the H-module M, appears as a functor from principal H-bundles to vector bundles and we think of $E \times_G M$ as the value of this functor on E. For this reason we often write $M(G)$ for $E \times_G M$.

In our situation there is a canonical principal H-bundle singled out, namely the one described by the projection $\pi \colon G \to G/H$, of G on its space of left H-cosets. Thus for each H-module M, $G \times_H M = M(G)$ is a well-defined vector-bundle over G/H, and we call this the bundle induced by M. It is clear that the function $M \to M(G)$ is linear in M, i.e.;

$$(2.1) \quad (M + M')(G) = M(G) + M'(G), \quad M, M' = H\text{-modules.}$$

Another basic property of induction is the permanence law, which we state in the following form.

Consider the situation: $T \subset H \subset G$, and let $\pi \colon G/T \to G/H$ be the natural projection. Now let M be an H-module and N be a T-module, and let i^*M be the restriction of M to T. Then

$$(2.2) \quad \{N \otimes i^*M\}(G) \cong N(G) \otimes \pi^*M(G).$$

Observe that if $H = G$, then $\pi^*M(G)$ is just the trivial bundle on G/T, as then π projects G/T onto a point. The isomorphism (2.2) in this special case is induced by the map $G \times (M \times N) \to G \times (M \times N)$ given by $(g, m \otimes n) \to (g, m \otimes g^{-1}n)$. For the more general case see [5].

(2.3) G acts naturally (on the left) on $M(G)$ and on G/H, and these actions commute with the projection $\sigma \colon M(G) \to G/H$.

(Both actions are induced by the map $G \times M \to G \times M$, determined by $g'(g, m) = (g'g, m)$.)

The bundle $M(G)$ has a natural C^∞ structure which it inherits from $G \times M$, so that it makes sense to speak of the $\mathbf{C}$-vector space of C^∞ sections of $M(G)$. We denote this vector-space by $\Gamma M(G)$. In view of (2.3) a natural left G-action can be defined on $\Gamma M(G)$ in the following manner. If $g \in G$, $s \in \Gamma M(G)$ then

$$(2.4) \qquad (g \cdot s)(p) = g \cdot \{s(g^{-1} \cdot p)\}.$$

Thus the step from M to $\Gamma M(G)$ takes us from H-modules to G-vector-spaces, and in the case of a finite group G, this construction is precisely the induced representation ($\Gamma M(G)$) will then be finite dimensional).

Although ΓMG is in general an infinite dimensional space, its structure as a G-space, is quite transparent. Namely, it follows easily from the integration theory on G, that the following *Frobenius theorem* holds.

PROPOSITION 2.1. Let W be a G-module, let M be an H-module and denote by i^*W, the restriction of W to H. Then,

$$(2.5) \qquad \mathrm{Hom}_G\,(W,\,\Gamma MG) \cong \mathrm{Hom}_H\,(i^*W,\,M).$$

This isomorphism is quite canonical. First remark the following direct identifications. Let $\mathscr{F}(G, M)$ denote the vector-space of C^∞-functions from G to M. We define a left G-structure of $\mathscr{F}(G, M)$ by the formula:

$$(g \cdot f)(g') = f(g^{-1} \cdot g') \qquad\qquad g, g \in G.$$

Then the projection $G \times M \to M(G)$ is seen to identify the G-vector-space $\Gamma M(G)$ with the subset of $\mathscr{F}(G, M)$ characterized by:

$$(2.6) \qquad f(g \cdot h) = h^{-1} \cdot f(g) \qquad\qquad g \in G, h \in H.$$

Now then, if $\Phi\colon W \to \Gamma MG$ is a G homomorphism, then under the identification just described $\Phi(w)$ is a function $G \to M$. The value of $\Phi(w)$ at the identity $\mathscr{E}$, of G, thus defines an element of $\Phi(w)[\mathscr{E}] \in M$, and by (2.6) the correspondence $w \to \Phi(w)[\mathscr{E}]$ is seen to be an H-homomorphism, φ, of W into M. Conversely given an H-homomorphism $\varphi\colon W \to M$, define G-homomorphism $\Phi\colon W \to \mathscr{F}(G, M)$ by

$$\Phi(w)[g] = \varphi(g^{-1}w).$$

Then

$$\Phi w[gh] = \varphi(h^{-1}g^{-1}w) = h^{-1}\varphi(g^{-1}w),$$

so that $\Phi\colon W \to \Gamma(G, M)$ is indeed a G-homomorphism. The correspondences $\varphi \to \Phi$ and $\Phi \to \varphi$ are now seen to be inverses to each other and yield the isomorphism (2.5). We note that the step from φ to Φ yields C^∞ functions, because a continuous action of G is automatically C^∞, and in fact analytic.

3. The Peter-Weyl theorem and its consequences

We continue with the situation and notation of the last section. Also, we let $\{W_\alpha\}_{\alpha \in \mathscr{I}(G)}$ be a complete set of inequivalent irreducible G-modules. For each $\alpha \in \mathscr{I}(G)$ let $\Gamma_\alpha MG$ as the image of the homomorphism

$$i_\alpha: W_\alpha \otimes \mathrm{Hom}_G (W_\alpha, \Gamma MG) \to \Gamma MG$$

defined by $i_\alpha(w \otimes \varphi) = \varphi(w)$. Because W_α is irreducible i_α is clearly injective. The subspace $\Gamma_\alpha MG$ of ΓMG is thus precisely the subspace which under G transforms according to the irreducible representation W_α. The Peter-Weyl theorem now asserts that the spaces Γ_α, $\alpha \in \mathscr{L}(G)$ from a complete system of orthonormal subspaces in the Hilbert-space $\mathscr{L}_2(MG)$ which is obtained from ΓMG by completion with respect to a G-invariant inner product $\{\ \}$. Recall that this inner product is defined as follows:

Let ω be a left and right invariant volume on G, and let $[\ ,\ ]$ denote an H-invariant Hermitian inner product on M. Then if $f, g \in \Gamma M(G)$, we may think of f and g as maps of G into M, so that $\int_G [f, g] \omega$ is well-defined, and this complex number is by definition $\{f, g\}$. It is trivially checked that under this inner product the action of G on $\Gamma M(G)$ is unitary. To recapitulate

PETER-WEYL THEOREM. *Let $\mathscr{L}_2 M(G)$ be the Hilbert space obtained from $\Gamma M(G)$ by completion with respect to the norm inner product, $\langle\ ,\ \rangle$, just defined.*

The finite dimensional G-invariant subspaces $\Gamma_\alpha = \Gamma_\alpha MG$, then form a complete system of othogonal subspaces for $\mathscr{L}_2(MG)$.

Thus $\mathscr{L}_2(M, G)$ may be thought of as the sequences $\{X_\alpha\}$, $X_\alpha \in \Gamma_\alpha$, $\alpha \in \mathscr{I}(G)$, with $\sum_{\alpha \in \mathscr{I}(G)} \langle X_\alpha, X_\alpha \rangle < \infty$.

This theorem is well known. When H is the identity subgroup and M the trivial one dimensional representation our statement is precisely the usual Peter-Weyl theorem, and the present statement follows easily from it in view of the Frobenius formula. See [7].

4. The proof of Theorem 1

Let $\varphi: V \to W$ be a G-homomorphism of the G-modules V and W. Then we have the exact sequence of G-modules:

$$0 \to \mathrm{Ker}\,(\varphi) \to V \xrightarrow{\ \varphi\ } W \to \mathrm{Coker}\,(\varphi) \to 0$$

so that by the definition of $R(G)$, the identity:

(4.1) $$[\mathrm{Ker}\,(\varphi)] - [\mathrm{Coker}\,(\varphi)] = [V] - [W]$$

is valid. Thus if we denote the left-hand side by $\chi(\varphi)$, then $\chi(\varphi)$ is really quite independent of φ. This is the property of the index function, which by virtue of the Peter-Weyl theorem leads directly to Theorem I.

Let $D\colon \Gamma M(G) \to \Gamma N(G)$ be a homogeneous operator in the sense of H1, 2, 3, and let Γ_α denote the subspaces of type α in the two G-vector spaces. Then D must preserve these and hence induces linear maps:

$$D(\alpha)\colon \Gamma_\alpha MG \to \Gamma_\alpha NG, \qquad\qquad \alpha \in \mathscr{I}(G).$$

Now, by the general theory of elliptic operators, the kernel of D is finite dimensional. Hence by the Peter-Weyl theorem:

$$\mathrm{Ker}\,(D) = \sum_\alpha \mathrm{Ker}\,D(\alpha) \qquad\qquad \alpha \in \mathscr{I}(G)$$

and $D(\alpha)$ has to be injective for nearly all α.

Similarly the cokernel of D may be identified with orthogonal complement to the image of D in $\mathscr{L}_2\{N(G)\}$. Hence, again by the Peter-Weyl theorem:

$$\mathrm{Coker}\,(D) = \sum_\alpha \mathrm{Coker}\,D(\alpha) \qquad\qquad \alpha \in \mathscr{I}(G)$$

and $D(\alpha)$ must be surjective for nearly all α. It follows that

$$\chi(D) = [Ker\,(D)] - [\mathrm{Coker}\,(D)] = \sum_\alpha [Ker\,(D_\alpha)] - [\mathrm{Coker}\,(D_\alpha)]$$
$$\alpha \in \mathscr{I}(G).$$

Now applying (4.1), we obtain:

$$\chi(D) = \sum_\alpha \{[\Gamma_\alpha M(G)] - [\Gamma_\alpha N(G)]\} \qquad\qquad \alpha \in \mathscr{I}(G).$$

and the sumand on the right is 0 for nearly all α. But by the Frobenius formula (2.5) one has:

$$[\Gamma_\alpha M(G)] = \langle i^* w_\alpha, [M]\rangle_H w_\alpha$$
$$[\Gamma_\alpha N(G)] = \langle i^* w_\alpha, [N]\rangle_H w_\alpha$$

so that finally,

$$\chi(D) = \sum_\alpha \langle i^* w_\alpha, \sigma(D)\rangle_H w_\alpha \qquad \sigma(D) = [M] - [N],\ \alpha \in \mathscr{I}(G)$$

the sumand again vanishing for all but a finite number of α. By the definition of i_*, Theorem I follows: $\chi(D) = i_*\{\sigma(D)\}$.

5. The structure of $R(G)$; The proof of Theorem II

We start this section with a statement of two basic and well known facts, from the representation theory of compact groups, in the $R(G)$ terminology. It is of course a trivial problem to translate the classical formulae into this language, and, as we will see, certain of the expressions in the classical theory acquire a certain amount of geometric significance in this new guise. For example, the slightly mysterious fact that for a simply connected G "half the sum of the positive roots is a weight" becomes a consequence of the geometric fact that representation of such a group can be lifted to the Spinor group. This will be taken up later in Section 6. For the present we state the following two basic theorems.

Let $i: T \to G$ be the inclusion of a maximal torus into G, and let $W = W(G)$ be the group of automorphisms of T induced by inner automorphisms of G. Thus W acts on T and therefore also on $R(T)$, and we denote by $I(G)$, the ring of W-invariants in $R(T)$.

THEOREM A.   *Under the restriction $i^*: R(G) \to R(T)$, $R(G)$ is identified with the invariants $I(G)$, of $W(G)$ in $R(T)$.*

THEOREM B.   *Let $i^*: R(G) \to R(T)$ be as above. Also let g/t denote the tangent-space to G/T at the identity coset. This space is in a natural way a real T module. Let $\lambda^p(g/t)$ be its pth exterior power, and set*

$$\lambda_{-1}(G/T) = \Sigma(-1)^p[\lambda^p(g/t) \otimes \mathbf{C}].$$

Then, for $x, y \in R(G)$ we have:

(5.1) $$\{\#W(G)\}\langle x, y\rangle_G = \langle \lambda_{-1}(G/T)i^*x, i^*y\rangle_T$$

where $\#W$ denotes the order of the group W.

REMARK.   The formula (5.1) in which the weighting factor $\lambda_{-1}(G/T)$ acquires the Euler-characteristic interpretation is the sort of phenomenon which, in my mind, makes it worthwhile to re-think the old formulae in the language of virtual bundles. Note that by this interpretation, $\lambda_{-1}(G/T)$ is also the homogeneous symbol of the usual differential operator $d + \delta$ of the Hodge theory, interpreted as a homogeneous operator from the even forms to the odd forms. Now Theorem B easily implies that

$$i_*\lambda_{-1}(G/T) = \#W(G) \cdot 1,$$

so that by Theorem I, the Euler number of G/T is seen to equal the order of $W(G)$.

We now derive Theorem II from Theorems A and B, after some preliminary generalities concerning $R(G)$ and $\hat{R}(G)$. Recall that $\{w_\alpha\}$, $\alpha \in \mathscr{I}(G)$ is a base for $R(G)$ while $\hat{R}(G)$ is defined as the possibly infinite linear combinations $\Sigma a_\alpha w_\alpha$.

There is an obvious extension of $\langle\ ,\ \rangle_G$ to a pairing of $R(G)$ and $\hat{R}(G)$ to $\mathbf{Z}$, which we again denote by $\langle\ ,\ \rangle_G$. It is defined by:

$$\langle x, \Sigma a_\alpha w_\alpha\rangle_G = \Sigma a_\alpha\langle x, w_\alpha\rangle; \qquad x \in R(G), \Sigma a_\alpha w_\alpha \in \hat{R}(G).$$

Similarly we make $R(G)$ an $\hat{R}(G)$ module:

$$x \cdot (\Sigma a_\alpha w_\beta) = \sum_{\alpha,\beta} a_\alpha \langle w_\beta, x w_\alpha \rangle_G w_\beta, \quad x \in R(G), \Sigma a_\alpha w_\alpha \in \hat{R}(G).$$

The coefficient of w_β is then $\Sigma_\alpha a_\alpha \langle w_\beta x^*, w_\alpha \rangle$ and hence finite. Now if $i: H \to G$ is the inclusion of a closed subgroup, $i^*: R(G) \to R(H)$ is the ring homomorphism induced by restriction, while $i_* = i_*(G, H): R(H) \to R(G)$ was defined by:

$$i_*(x) = \Sigma \langle i^* w_\alpha, x \rangle_H w_\alpha, \quad x \in R(H), \alpha \in \mathscr{I}(G).$$

With the extended interpretation of $\langle \, , \, \rangle_G$, this formula is equally well expressed by:

(5.2) $$\langle y, i_*(x) \rangle_G = \langle i^* y, x \rangle_H \quad x \in R(H), y \in R(G)$$

and brings out the adjoint nature of i_*. The permanence relation encountered earlier, now has a formal analogue in this context, which is expressed by the formula:

(5.3) $$i_*(x \cdot i^* y) = i_*(x) \cdot y \quad x \in R(G), y \in R(G).$$

The proof follows from (5.2). Indeed if $z = i_*(xi^*y)$ then $z \in \hat{R}(G)$ is characterized by:

$$\langle u, z \rangle_G = \langle i^* u, xi^* y \rangle_H$$

while

$$\langle u, i_*(x)y \rangle_G = \langle uy^*, i_*(x) \rangle_G$$

by (1.5), and hence equals

$$\langle i^*(u \cdot y^*), x \rangle_H = \langle i^* u, xy \rangle_H.$$

An immediate consequence of (5.2) is:

PROPOSITION 5.1.   The image of i_* is perpendicular to the kernel of i^*. Theorem II is based on the following assertion.

PROPOSITION 5.2.   Let rank $H <$ rank G. Then 0 is the only element of $R(G)$ perpendicular to the kernel of $i^*: R(G) \to R(H)$.

PROOF.   Let T_1 be a maximal torus of H, and let T be the extension of T_1 to a maximal torus of G. We therefore have the commutative diagram

$$\begin{array}{ccc} R(H) & \longleftarrow & R(G) \\ \wr\wr & i^* & \wr\wr \\ I(H) & \longleftarrow & I(G) \end{array}$$

in which the vertical homomorphisms are isomorphisms by Theorem A, and i^* is the restriction: $R(T_1) \to R(T)$. We will now construct a series of elements in the kernel of $R(G) \to R(H)$, interpreted as a subring of $I(G) \subset R(T_1)$.

Because rank $H <$ rank G, there exists a character λ in T^* (the character group of T) with $\lambda \neq 1$, but $i^*\lambda = 1$. Hence $(1 - [\lambda])$ is in the kernel of i^*, but of course not necessarily in $I(G)$. We therefore consider the element $z = \Pi(1 - [\lambda])^\sigma$, $\sigma \in W(G)$ which clearly is in $I(G)$ and in the kernel of i^* and hence represents an element of the kernel $R(G) \to R(H)$. Hence zz^* is also in this kernel. Now this element is of the form

$$zz^* = a \cdot 1 + \Sigma a_\alpha[\lambda_\alpha] \qquad\qquad \lambda_\alpha \in T^*, \lambda_\alpha \neq 1$$

with

$$a = \langle 1, zz^* \rangle_T = \langle z, z^* \rangle_T > 0.$$

To proceed further it is convenient to imbed T^* as the lattice of integral points in the real Euclidean space of l dimensions, R^l, and to say that a subset U of R^l supports $x \in R(T)$ if the element $x = \Sigma a_i[\lambda_i]$, $\lambda_i \in T^*$, with all the λ_i contained in U. We also define: $U_\rho = \{x \in R^l \| |x| \geqslant \rho\}$.

Let $\psi_n \colon R(T) \to R(T)$ be the linear extension of the map induced on T^* by the nth power homomorphism of T into itself. It is then clear that ψ_n maps $I(G)$ into itself, and that when defined correspondingly on $R(T_1)$, ψ_n and i^* commute. Thus the kernel of $R(G) \to R(H)$ is also invariant under ψ_n. Furthermore it is evident that $y = zz^* - a$ is supported by $U_{1/2}$. Hence $\psi_n y$ will be supported by $U_{n/2}$. We conclude that:

(5.4)   *For every positive integer* n, *the kernel of* $R(G) \to R(H)$ *contains elements of the form* $x_n = a + y_n$, *with* y_n *supported by* U_n.

Suppose now that $u \in R(G)$ is perpendicular to the kernel of $R(G) \to R(T)$. Then $\langle u, x_n \cdot u \rangle_G = 0$ for all our elements x_n. By Theorem B, this implies:

$$(\#W)a\langle u, u \rangle_G + \langle \lambda_{-1}uu^*, y_n \rangle_T = 0 \qquad \lambda_{-1} = \lambda_{-1}(G/T)$$

On the other hand as $\lambda_{-1}uu^*$ is clearly supported by some finite S_n, (5.4) implies that for n large enough $\langle \lambda_{-1}uu^*, y_n \rangle_T = 0$. But then $\langle u, u \rangle_G = 0$, as was to be shown.

CStby. Theorem II is valid.

PROOF. We know that $\chi(D) \in R(G)$, and that by Theorem 1 $\chi(D)$ is in the image of i_*. Hence $\chi(D)$ is perpendicular to the kernel of i^* and hence by Proposition 5.2 equal to 0.

6. The Weyl formula, the proof of Theorem III

We come now to the central result of the representation theory of G, the Weyl formula, which gives a detailed description of the irreducible G-modules in terms of the irreducible T-modules, where T is a maximal torus of G.

An element $z \in R(T)$ is called alternating if

$$z^\sigma = (-1)^\sigma z, \qquad\qquad \sigma \in W(G).$$

where $(-1)^\sigma = -1$ if σ reverses the orientation of T, and $+1$ otherwise. The alternating elements form a module over $I(G)$ which we denote by $A(G)$. A nonzero element $u \in A(T)$ which is of the type $u = \Sigma(-1)^\sigma[\lambda^\sigma]$ where λ is a character on T is called a "principal alternating element" of $A(G)$.

THEOREM D.   *Assume that $\pi_1(G)$ has no 2-torsion, and let $i: T \to G$ in the inclusion of a maximal torus. Then*

(6.1) $A(T)$ *is a free module over $I(T)$.*

(6.2) *If Ω is a generator for $A(T)$ over $I(T)$, and if M is an irreducible G-module, then $[i*M]. \Omega$ is a principal alternating element of $A(T)$:*

$$[i*M]\Omega = \Sigma(-1)^\sigma[\lambda_M^\sigma] \qquad\qquad \sigma \in W(G).$$

(6.3)   *If $u = \Sigma(-1)^\sigma[\lambda^\sigma]$ is a principal alternating element, then there exists an irreducible G-module M_λ, such that*

$$\pm[i*M_\lambda] \cdot \Omega = \Sigma(-1)^\sigma[\lambda^\sigma].$$

This powerful theorem clearly gives one a good hold on the irreducible G-modules. The statement is usually given under the assumption that G be simply connected. The connection of that hypothesis to our condition on $\pi_1(G)$, will become apparent in the next section.

The Weyl formula fits very well with the formal induction from T to G, as is shown by the following corollary to Theorem D.

COROLLARY 6.1.   Let $i_*: R(T) \to \hat{R}(G)$ be the formal induction. Then i_* takes finite values on the ideal generated by $A(T)$ in $R(T)$, and if Ω is a generator of $A(T)$ the following identities are valid:

(6.4) $$\Omega \cdot \Omega^* = \lambda_{-1}(G/T)$$

(6.5) $$\Sigma(-1)^\sigma x^\sigma = \Omega \cdot i*i_*(\Omega^*x), \qquad x \in R(T).$$

Hence i_* maps $\Omega^*R(T)$ onto $R(G)$, and if λ is an irreducible T-module, then $i_*[\lambda]$ is 0 or $\pm$ an irreducible G-module.

PROOF.   Let M and N be irreducible G-modules. Then

$$\langle \Omega i*M, \Omega i*N \rangle_T = \Sigma(-1)^{\sigma\tau}\langle \lambda_M^\sigma, \lambda_N^\tau \rangle_T$$

by (6.2). Now the right-hand side is clearly $\#W$ if $M = N$, and 0 otherwise. Hence, in general, for $x, y \in R(G)$ we have

$$\langle \Omega i*x, \Omega i*y \rangle_T = \{\#W\}\langle x, y \rangle_G.$$

Comparing with (5.1) and observing that $\lambda_{-1}(G/T)$ as well as $\Omega \cdot \Omega^*$ are in $I(G)$ we obtain the identity (6.4).

Next consider $z = i_*\Omega^*x$. Then for all $y \in R(G)$ we have,

$$\langle y, z \rangle_G = \langle i^*y, \Omega^*x \rangle_T.$$

Now because Ω^* is alternating, and W preserves $\langle , \rangle_T$, as well as i^*y we may write

$$\langle i^*y, \Omega^*x \rangle_T = \frac{+1}{\{\#W\}} \cdot \langle i^*y, \Omega^*\Sigma(-1)^\sigma x^\sigma \rangle_T.$$

Next, it follows from (6.1) that

$$\Sigma(-1)^\sigma x^\sigma = \Omega \cdot i^*z' \qquad \text{for some } z' \in R(G).$$

Hence, we obtain the formula:

$$\langle y, z \rangle_G = \frac{1}{\{\#W\}} \langle i^*y, \Omega^*\Omega i^*z' \rangle_T = \langle y, z' \rangle_G$$

the last step being a consequence of (6.4). We conclude that $z = z'$. Now applying i^* we obtain (6.5). Finally this identity directly implies the rest of the corollary.

The corollary extends without difficulty to the case of an inclusion $\alpha: H \to G$ of maximal rank. We let $\beta: T \to H$ be the inclusion of a maximal torus into H and set $i = \alpha \circ \beta$. Now, the condition $\pi_1(G)$ is seen to be hereditary so that H is again of the same type. We let $\Omega(H)$ and $\Omega(G)$ be generators of $A(H)$ and $A(G)$ in $R(T)$ and in terms of these define

$$\Omega = \Omega(G/H) \subset R(H),$$

by the formula:

$$\Omega(H) \cdot \beta^*\Omega = \Omega(G).$$

Note that from $\Omega(G) \in A(G)$ it follows that $\Omega(G) \in A(H)$ and hence that $\Omega(G)$ is of the form $\Omega(H) \cdot \Omega$, with $\Omega \in I(H)$. Hence the desired Ω does exist and is given by $(\beta^*)^{-1}\Omega$.

With this definition of Ω one has the following analogues to (6.4) and (6.5).

(6.6) $$\langle x, y \rangle_G = \frac{\#W(H)}{\#W(G)} \cdot \langle \Omega^*\alpha^*x, \Omega^*\alpha^*y \rangle_T, \qquad x,y \in R(G)$$

(6.7) $$\Sigma(-1)^\sigma\{\Omega(H)\beta^*x\}^\sigma = \Omega(G)i^* \cdot \alpha_*(\Omega^*x) \qquad x \in R(H)$$
$$\sigma \in W(G)/W(H).$$

One obtains these by direct verification in $R(T)$. To obtain (6.7) we start with the formula:

$$(6.8) \qquad \alpha_* \{\Omega^* x\} = \frac{1}{\# W(H)} \, i_* \{\Omega^*(G) \cdot \Omega(H) \beta^*(x)\}$$

which is valid for the following reason. Let z be the left-hand side. Then z is characterized by $\langle y, z \rangle_G = \langle \alpha^* y, \Omega^* x \rangle_H$ for all $y \in R(G)$. Now by (6.4)

$$\langle \alpha^* y, \Omega^* x \rangle_H = \frac{1}{\# W(H)} \, \langle i^* y, \Omega(H) \Omega^*(H) \beta^*(\Omega^* x) \rangle_T$$

$$= \frac{1}{\# W(H)} \, \langle i^* y, \Omega^*(G) \cdot \Omega(H) \beta^* x \rangle_T$$

$$= \frac{1}{\# W(H)} \, \langle y, i_* \Omega^*(G) \Omega(H) \beta^* x \rangle_T$$

and so (6.8) is true. Now applying (6.5) we obtain

$$\frac{1}{\# W(H)} \cdot \Sigma (-1)^\sigma \{\Omega(H) \beta^*(x)\}^\sigma = \Omega(G) \cdot i^* \alpha_* \Omega^* x, \quad \sigma \in W(G).$$

Finally, remark that $\beta^*(x)$ is invariant under $W(H)$ and $\Omega(H)$ is alternating under $W(H)$. This implies (6.7). We leave (6.6) to the reader. As direct consequences we have:

COROLLARY 6.2. Let $\pi_1(G)$ have no 2-torsion. Then if $\alpha: H \to G$ is an inclusion of maximal rank, the induced formal induction $\alpha_*: R(H) \to \widehat{R(G)}$, maps the ideal generated by $\Omega^*(G/H)$ onto $R(G)$. Further if ξ is the class of an irreducible H module, then $i_*(\Omega^* \xi)$ is 0 or $\pm$ an irreducible G-module.

This corollary to the Weyl formula implies Theorem III, provided we can construct an elliptic homogeneous differential operator D on G/H, whose homogeneous symbol is $\Omega^* = \Omega(G/H)^*$. Indeed suppose that such an operator, defined on $\Gamma(E)$ with values in $\Gamma(F)$, where $E = M^+(G)$, $F = M^-(G)$ and $[M^+] - [M^-] = \Omega^*(G/H)$, can be found. Then if N is any other H-module, one may set $D_N: \Gamma\{E \otimes N(G)\} \to \Gamma(F \otimes N(G))$ equal to $D \otimes$ identity, and this operator has homogeneous symbol

$$\{[M^+] - [M^-]\} \otimes [N] = \Omega^*(G/H) \cdot [N].$$

Now

$$\chi(D_N) = i_* \{\Omega^*(G/H)[N]\}$$

by Theorem I, and so as N ranges over the H-modules, $\chi(D_N)$ ranges over all of $R(G)$.

In the next section we briefly indicate how the generalized Dirac-operator has this desired property. For greater detail see [6], [8].

7. The groups Spin and Spin^c, and the Dirac operator

We recall, that Spin (n) is a double covering of $SO(n)$, which for $n \geq 3$ is the simply connected covering group. Also that Spin (n) has a well determined complex representation M called the Spin-representation with the following properties:

(7.1) The generator of the kernel of π: Spin $(n) \to SO(n)$ acts as -1 on M.

(7.2) If V denotes the standard representation of Spin (n) i.e., the one determined by π on the n-dimensional number space then there is a pairing of Spin-modules

$$M \otimes V \xrightarrow{\ \mu\ } M$$

which is "elliptic" in the sense that the map $m \to \mu(m \times v)$, $m \in M$, is an isomorphism for each $v \neq 0$.

(7.3) If n is even, M splits into two irreducible modules M^+ and M^-, and the pairing (7.2) induces pairings:

$$M^+ \otimes V \to M^-, \ M^- \otimes V \to M^+.$$

(7.4) In $R\{\text{Spin } (n)\}$ one has the identity

$$\{[M^+] - [M^-]\}\{[M^+] - [M^-]\}^* = \lambda_{-1}[V]$$

where $\lambda_{-1}[V] = \Sigma(-1)^q[\wedge^q V]$.

Now suppose that X is a Riemannian manifold with principal orthogonal tangent bundle ξ. Then a Spin structure on X, is by definition a principal Spin (n)-bundle $\hat{\xi}$ over X which projects onto ξ under the homomorphism induced by the projection Spin $(n) \to SO(n)$.

Given such a Spin-structure $\hat{\xi}$ on X, one may define the Dirac operator D: $\Gamma M(\hat{\xi}) \to \Gamma M(\hat{\xi})$, as follows. The Riemannian torsion-free connection on ξ induces a connection on $\hat{\xi}$, and hence on the induced bundle $M(\hat{\xi})$. Properly interpreted such a connection is a map from $\Gamma M(\hat{\xi})$ to $\Gamma\{M(\hat{\xi}) \otimes V(\hat{\xi})\}$. If this is now composed with the pairing (7.2) one obtains the desired operator D: $\Gamma M(\hat{\xi}) \to \Gamma M(\hat{\xi})$. (This operator is elliptic as its symbol is nondegenerate by (7.2).)

We now wish to define a homogeneous Dirac operator on $X = G/H$, where H is of maximal rank in G. For this purpose consider the isotropy representation, ρ, of H on g/h, the tangent-space to G/H at the identity cosect. If G/H is equipped with a lef-invariant Riemann metric, the representation ρ will be orthogonal. Suppose that ρ admits a lifting $\tilde{\rho}$ to the corresponding spin group. Then $\tilde{\rho}$ determines a definite Spin structure on X. Indeed if η is the principal H-bundle $G \to G/H$, then the principal tangent bundle, ξ, of X is obtained from η by extending the structure group to the special orthogonal group via ρ. That is, $\xi = \rho_* \eta$. Hence the Spin-bundle $\tilde{\rho}_* \eta$ determines a Spin structure for X. We call this the homogeneous Spin structure for X, and note that it is unique if it exists. It is clear that the Dirac operator associated to such a Spin structure will then be homogeneous in the sense that $H(2)$ and $H(3)$ will be satisfied, and the homogeneous symbol of this operator is given by

$$\sigma(D) = \tilde{\rho}^*[M^+] - \tilde{\rho}^*[M^-],$$

where $M\pm$ are the Spin-representations.

As an application of this remark we have:

PROPOSITION 7.1. Let T be a maximal torus of G and assume that $\pi_1(G) = 0$. Then G/T has a homogeneous Spin structure, and the homogeneous symbol of the corresponding Dirac operator, D, generates the alternating elements of $R(T)$: $\sigma(D) = \pm\Omega$.

PROOF. Because T acts trivially on its own Lie-agebra we have the commutative diagram:

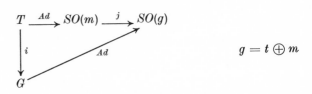

$$g = t \oplus m$$

where $SO(m)$ and $SO(g)$ denotes the isometries of these Euclidean spaces and

$$SO(m) \xrightarrow{\ j\ } SO(g)$$

is induced by the inclusion $m \to g$. Now, because j_* is an isomorphism in π_1, it follows that $\pi_1(G) = 0$ implies that $(Ad)_*: \pi_1(T) \to \pi_1\{SO(m)\}$ is trivial, i.e., G/T has a homogeneous Spin structure, given by lifting Ad to $\widetilde{Ad}: T \to \text{Spin}(m)$. It is now not difficult to see that the element $\Omega = (\widetilde{Ad})^*\{[M^+] - [M^-]\}$ in $R(T)$, is alternating under $W(G)$ and in view of (7.3)—satisfies the identity $\Omega \cdot \Omega^* = \lambda_{-1}(G/T)$. This is then, up to sign, the generator which occurs in the Herman Weyl formula (Theorem D).

In the general case one proceeds quite analogously, once the notion of Spin structure is extended a little.

For this purpose let $\varepsilon \in \text{Spin}(n)$ generate the kernel of the covering $\text{Spin}(n) \to SO(n)$. Also let S denote the multiplicative group of complex numbers of norm 1. Now define $\text{Spin}^c(n)$ as the quotient group $\text{Spin}(n) \times S/(\varepsilon, -1)$. We let $\pi: \text{Spin}^c(n) \to SO(n)$ be the obvious projection.

One now essentially rewrites the preceding discussion with $Spin^c(n)$ replacing Spin (n) throughout and thus obtains an extended notion of the Dirac operator which is an elliptic operator defined on a manifold X once a $Spin^c$ structure exists on X. If this is done it is not difficult to show that if $\pi_1(G)$ has no 2-torsion and H is of maximal rank in G, then G/H always admits a homogeneous $Spin^c$ structure such that the homogeneous symbol of the corresponding Dirac operator is precisely $\Omega(G/H)$.

REMARKS 1. If $\lambda: G \to SO(n)$, $n \geq 3$ then λ can be factored through $\pi: Spin^c(n) \to SO(n)$, if and only if $\lambda_*: \pi_1(G) \to \pi_1\{SO(n)\}$ can be covered by a homomorphism $\lambda'_*: \pi_1(G) \to \mathbf{Z}$, with $\lambda_* = \lambda'_*$ mod 2. This is a straightforward application of covering theory, and explains how our condition on $\pi_1(G)$ enters.

2. If M is the Spin-representation of Spin (n) then the action of Spin (n) on M may be extended to Spin $(n) \times S$, simply by letting S act by complex multiplication. In view of (7.1), the resulting action induces the structure of a $Spin^c(n)$ module on M. This explains why the earlier construction of the Dirac operator carries over to the present situation.

8. Relations with the Chern character of induced bundles

In this section we obtain a formula for dim $i_*\{\Omega^*x\}$ in terms of the Chern-character of the bundle induced by x over G/H and a correction factor. This formula is essentially the link between our results on i_*, which are all consequences of the Weyl formula, and the formulae of Borel-Hirzebruch, which were obtained by means of the Riemann-Roch theorem. Although we will not give the details, one may also check the formula of Atiyah-Singer with this expression quite easily and so obtain a proof of Theorem IV. The following proposition in the theory of characteristic classes will be needed.

PROPOSITION 8.1. There is a natural transformation T, from principal $Spin^c(2n)$ bundles to rational cohomology:

$$T: H^1(X, Spin^c(2n)) \to H^*(X; \mathbf{Q})$$

such that:

(8.1) $\qquad T(\xi) = 1 +$ higher degree terms.

(8.2) If $\xi_1 + \xi_2$ denotes the direct sum of two $Spin^c$-bundles, then $T(\xi_1) \cdot T(\xi_2) = T(\xi_1 + \xi_2)$.

(8.3) If M^+ and M^- are the Spin representations E denotes the Euler class and ch the Chern character then T satisfies the equation:

$$ch\{M^+(\xi)\} - ch\{M^-(\xi)\} = E(\xi) \cdot T^{-1}(\xi).$$

We briefly indicate the construction of T. In the usual way it suffices to define T as a cohomology class in $X = B_{\text{Spin}^c(2n)}$ the universal base space of $\text{Spin}^c(2n)$. Let T be a maximal torus of $\text{Spin}^c(2n)$, B_T the universal base space of T, and $\pi: B_T \to X$ the usual fibering. Then π^* imbeds $H^*(X; \mathbf{Q})$ onto the invariants of the Weyl group in $H^*(B_T; \mathbf{Q})$.

Next let $\sigma: \text{Spin}^c(2n) \to SO(2n) \times S^1$ be the double-covering, and let $T' = T_1 \times S^1$ be the maximal torus of $SO(2n) \times S^1$ on which T projects. There is induced a map $B_T \overset{\sigma}{\longrightarrow} B_{T'}$. Now let $x_1, \ldots, x_n$ denote the pre-image under σ of the "usual" basis of $H^2(B_{T_1}; \mathbf{Z})$ and let u stand for the pre-image of the generator of $H^2(B_{S^1})$. In terms of these classes T is defined by the expression

$$\Pi \left(\frac{x_i}{e^{x_i/2} - e^{-x_i/2}} \right) e^{-u/2}.$$

As is suggested by this formula, T may be considered as a generalized Todd genus. Indeed if ξ is a real vector-bundle then every complex structure, J, on ξ, defines a Spin^c structure $\hat{\xi}$ on the bundle, and $T(\hat{\xi})$ then is precisely the Todd genus of the complex bundle determined by J and ξ. On the other hand, T is also defined for any Spin structure on ξ, and then agrees with the $\widehat{\mathfrak{A}}$ class of Hirzebruch.

To describe the relation we have in mind, it is convenient to denote induction on the bundle level, by $i_!$. Thus if $i: H \to G$, and M is an H-module, we write $i_! M$ for the induced bundle, $M(G)$, over G/H. It is then clear that the linear extension of $i_!$ induces an additive homomorphism $i_!: R(H) \to K(G/H)$ of $R(H)$ into the group of virtual bundles over X. The formulae (2.1), (2.2) of Section 2 then clearly imply that $i_!: R(H) \to K(G/H)$ is a ring homomorphism and that the following identity is valid:

$$(8.4) \qquad\qquad i_!(x \cdot i^*y) = (i_! x) \dim (y) \qquad x \in R(H), y \in R(G)$$

PROPOSITION 8.2. Let $\pi_1(G)$ be free of 2-torsion and let $\alpha: H \to G$ be an inclusion of maximal rank. Let ξ be a homogeneous Spin^c structure on G/H, and let Ω be the homogeneous symbol of the associated Dirac operator. Then there is an orientation $[G/H]$ of G/H, such that the following identity holds for all $x \in R(H)$.

$$(8.5) \qquad\qquad \langle T(\xi), ch(\alpha_! x), [G/H] \rangle = \dim \alpha_* \{\Omega^* x\}.$$

Here $\langle u, [G/H] \rangle$ denotes the value of the cohomology class u on the orientation class $[G/H]$.

Proof. Let $\beta: T \to H$ be the inclusion of a maximal torus, and set $i = \alpha \circ \beta$. Also write $\pi: G/T \to G/H$ for the natural projection with fiber H/T. Let E_H be the Euler class of the tangent bundle along the fibers in this fibering. Then $\langle (\pi^* u) \cdot E_H, [G/T] \rangle = \chi(H/T) \langle u, [G/H] \rangle, u \in H^*(G/H)$.

Further as $\chi(H/T) = \#W(H)$ (this is well known and also follows from Theorem I and Theorem C) we may transfer our problem to G/T and attempt to compute the expression

$$A = \frac{1}{\#W(H)} \langle \pi^*(ch(x) \cdot T(\xi)) \cdot E_H, G/T \rangle.$$

Now let ξ_H be a Spin^c structure of the bundle along the fibers, and ξ_G the induced Spin-structure on G/T. We then have

$$\pi^* T(\xi) = T(\xi_G) \cdot T^{-1}(\xi_u).$$

It follows that

$$\begin{aligned}\#W(H) \cdot A &= \langle \pi^*\{ch(\alpha_! x) T(\xi)\} E_H, [G/T] \rangle \\ &= \langle ch\, i_!(\beta^* x) T(\xi_G) ch\, i_!(\Omega_H), [G/T] \rangle \\ &= \langle T(\xi_G) ch\, i_!\{(\beta^* x)\Omega_H\}, [G/T] \rangle \end{aligned}$$

where

$$i_!\Omega_H = M^+(\xi_H) - M^-(\xi_H),$$

so that Ω_H is a principal alternating element for H in $R(T)$.

Now the Weyl group acts on G/T and $[G/T]$ is alternating under this action while $T(\xi_G)$ is invariant, as follows from (8.3). Hence we may write:

$$\#W(H) \cdot A = \frac{1}{\#W(G)} \langle T(\xi_G) ch\, i_! \Sigma(-1)^\sigma \{(\beta^* x)\Omega^*_H\}^\sigma, [G/T] \rangle.$$

Applying (6.1) one obtains

$$A = \frac{1}{\#W(G)} \langle T(\xi_G) ch\, i_! \Omega(G) i^* \alpha^*(\Omega^* x), G/T \rangle$$

so that finally, by (8.4)

$$\begin{aligned}A &= \frac{1}{\#W(G)} \langle T(\xi_G) \cdot ch\, i_! \Omega(G), [G/T] \rangle \dim \alpha_*(\Omega^* x) \\ &= \frac{1}{\#W(G)} \langle E(\xi_G), [G/T] \rangle \dim \alpha_*(\Omega^* x) \\ &= \dim \alpha_*(\Omega^* x).\end{aligned}$$

This is the desired formula.

HARVARD UNIVERSITY

References

[1] M. F. Atiyah and I. M. Singer, The index of elliptic operators on compact manifolds (to be published).

[2] A. Borel and F. Hirzebruch, Characteristic classes and homogeneous spaces, *Amer. J. of Math.*, *80* (1958), p. 458–538; *81* (1959, p. 315–382; *82* (1960), p. 491–504.

[3] R. Bott, Homogeneous vector bundles, *Ann. of Math.*, *vol. 66*, p. 203–248.

[4] ———, A note on the KO-theory of sphere-bundles, *Bull. Amer. Math. Soc.*, *vol. 68* (1962), p. 395–400.

[5] ———, Lectures on $K(X)$, mimeographed notes, Harvard University.

[6] C. Chevalley, *Theory of Spinors*. New York, Columbia University Press. 1954, p. 213.

[7] A. Shapiro, R. Bott, and M. Atiyah, Clifford modules (to appear).

[8] A. Weil, *L'integration dans les groupes topologiques et ses applications*, Paris, 1938.

Minimal Surfaces in an Euclidean Space of N Dimensions[1]

SHIING-SHEN CHERN

1. Introduction

A classical theorem of S. Bernstein [1] asserts that a minimal surface of class C^2, which can be globally represented in the form $z = f(x, y)$, is a plane. This theorem has been generalized by R. Osserman to the following more geometrical form [9]:

A complete simply connected minimal surface in 3-space whose normal mapping into the unit sphere omits a neighborhood of some point is a plane.

A major tool in the study of such problems is complex function theory. We wish to show that the work of Bernstein-Osserman has a complete generalization to minimal surfaces in euclidean spaces of higher dimensions. The over-riding facts are the following: (1) The Grassmann manifold $SO(n + 2)/SO(2) \times SO(n)$, (where $SO(n) = SO(n; R)$), of all oriented planes through a point 0 in an euclidean space of dimension $n + 2$ has a complex structure invariant under the action of $SO(n + 2)$; (2) with the complex structure on the minimal surface defined by its induced riemannian metric, the Gauss mapping, which assigns to a point p of the minimal surface the oriented plane through 0 parallel to the tangent plane at p, is anti-holomorphic. This makes it possible to apply the theory of holomorphic curves to derive geometrical consequences on minimal surfaces.

2. The complex hyperquadric

The Grassmann manifold mentioned above is an irreducible symmetric hermitian manifold ([7], p. 354) and is complex analytically equivalent to the non-degenerate complex hyperquadric. We propose to describe some of its geometrical properties, to the extent that they will be needed in our problem.

[1] Work done under partial support by National Science Foundation grant No. G-21938 and ONR contract 3656(14).

We write

(1) $Q_n = SO(n + 2)/SO(2) \times SO(n),$

where the right-hand side stands for the space of right cosets. Then Q_n is a compact homogeneous manifold of real dimension $2n$. To give it a complex structure let $SO(n + 2; C)$ be the complex properly orthogonal group, i.e., the group of all $(n + 2) \times (n + 2)$ matrices A with complex entries such that

(2) $A \cdot {}^t\!A = I,$ $\det A = 1,$

where ${}^t\!A$ denotes the transpose of A and I is the unit matrix. Throughout this paper we will agree on the following ranges of indices:

(3) $1 \leq \alpha, \beta, \gamma \leq n + 2,$ $3 \leq a, b, c \leq n + 2.$

Let

(4) $A = (a_{\alpha\beta}).$

Introduce the vector

(5) $Z = (z_1, \ldots, z_{n+2}).$

Then $SO(n + 2; C)$ acts on the vector space V_{n+2} of the vectors Z according to

(6) $Z \to ZA.$

It therefore acts on the complex projective space $P_{n+1}(C)$ of dimension $n + 1$ obtained from $V_{n+2} - 0$ by identifying the vectors which differ from each other by a non-zero factor. This action is intransitive; in fact, it leaves invariant the hyperquadric

(7) $z_1^2 + \cdots + z_{n+2}^2 = 0.$

On the other hand, its induced action on (7) is transitive.

Let N be the subgroup of $SO(n + 2; C)$, which leaves invariant the point $(1, i, 0, \ldots, 0)$ of (7). The hyperquadric (7) can then be regarded as a right coset space $SO(n + 2; C)/N$. From the inclusion

$$SO(n + 2) \subset SO(n + 2; C)$$

and the easily checked fact that

$$N \cap SO(n + 2) = SO(2) \times SO(n),$$

it follows that (7) is isomorphic to Q_n. Henceforth we will identify these two manifolds.

To find the relation between the complex coordinates z_α on Q_n and its representation by (1), let A be a real properly orthogonal matrix. Then A maps the point $(1, i, 0, \ldots, 0)$ to $(a_{11} + ia_{21}, \ldots, a_{1,n+2} + ia_{2,n+2})$, so that we have

$$(8) \qquad z_\alpha = a_{1\alpha} + ia_{2\alpha},$$

where $a_{1\alpha}$, $a_{2\alpha}$ are real and satisfy the relations

$$(9) \qquad \sum_\alpha a_{1\alpha}^2 = \sum_\alpha a_{2\alpha}^2 = 1, \qquad \sum_\alpha a_{1\alpha}a_{2\alpha} = 0.$$

The Plücker coordinates of the plane are then given by

$$(10) \qquad p_{\alpha\beta} = a_{1\alpha}a_{2\beta} - a_{1\beta}a_{2\alpha} = \frac{i}{2}(z_\alpha \bar{z}_\beta - z_\beta \bar{z}_\alpha).$$

The topology of Q_n is well known ([2], [5], [8]). Q_n is simply connected, has no torsion, and has all its odd-dimensional homology groups equal to zero. Its even-dimensional Betti numbers are given by

$$(11) \qquad b^{2h} = 1, \qquad 2h \neq n; b^n = 2, \text{ if } n \text{ is even.}$$

For $n \geq 3$ a generator of the homology group $H_{2n-2}(Q_n)$ is given by the section of Q_n by a hyperplane of $P_{n+1}(C)$. For $n = 2$, Q_2 is complex analytic-ally equivalent to $P_1(C) \times P_1(C)$, the equivalence being established as follows: Q_2 has two families of projective lines, such that: (1) distinct lines of the same family do not meet; (2) lines of different familes meet in exactly one point; (3) through a point of Q_2 there passes one line from each family. Let $q_0 \in Q_2$ be a fixed point, and let L_1, L_2 be the lines through q_0. Define the mapping $Q_2 \to L_1 \times L_2$ by assigning to each point $q \in Q_2$ the points where the lines through q meet L_1, L_2 respectively. This establishes the complex analytic equivalence stated above. It follows that the lines of Q_2 define cycles which are generators of $H_2(Q_2)$.

To study the geometry of Q_n we take the right-invariant linear differential forms of $SO(n + 2)$. These are the entries of the skew-symmetric matrix

$$(12) \qquad \varphi = (\varphi_{\alpha\beta}) = dA \cdot A^{-1} = dA \cdot {}^tA.$$

Explicitly they are given by

$$(13) \qquad \varphi_{\alpha\beta} = \sum_\gamma da_{\alpha\gamma}a_{\beta\gamma}.$$

They satisfy the structure equations

$$(14) \qquad d\varphi_{\alpha\beta} = \sum_\gamma \varphi_{\alpha\gamma} \wedge \varphi_{\gamma\beta}.$$

From (13) and (8) we get

$$(15) \qquad \varphi_{1b} + i\varphi_{2b} = \sum_{\gamma} a_{b\gamma} \, dz_{\gamma}$$

Thus the forms at the left-hand side of (15), to be denoted by θ_b, are the complex-valued linear differential forms, which define the almost complex structure on Q_n. The integrability of this almost complex structure follows from the expression in (15), but can also be verified directly by using the structure equations (14).

On Q_n we now introduce the hermitian structure

$$(16) \qquad ds^2 = \tfrac{1}{2} \sum_a \theta_a \bar{\theta}_a.$$

The latter is obviously invariant under the action of $SO(n + 2)$. By (15), (8), and making use of the relation

$$(17) \qquad \sum_{\alpha} z_{\alpha} \, dz_{\alpha} = 0,$$

we find

$$(18) \qquad \tfrac{1}{2} \sum \theta_a \bar{\theta}_a = \tfrac{1}{2} \sum dz_{\alpha} \, d\bar{z}_{\alpha} - \tfrac{1}{4} (\sum \bar{z}_{\alpha} \, dz_{\alpha})(\sum z_{\beta} \, d\bar{z}_{\beta}).$$

In this formula z_{α} are normalized by the condition

$$(19) \qquad \sum_{\alpha} z_{\alpha} \bar{z}_{\alpha} = 2,$$

in view of (9).

Now the standard hermitian structure on $P_{n+1}(C)$ with the homogeneous coordinates z- is given by (see [3]):

$$(20) \qquad \frac{1}{(\sum z_{\alpha} \bar{z}_{\alpha})^2} \{ (\sum z_{\alpha} \bar{z}_{\alpha})(\sum dz_{\beta} \, d\bar{z}_{\beta}) - (\sum \bar{z}_{\alpha} \, dz_{\alpha})(\sum z_{\beta} \, d\bar{z}_{\beta}) \}.$$

This reduces to (18), when the normalization (19) holds. This means that the hermitian structure (16) on Q_n is induced from the hermitian structure (20) of its ambient space $P_{n+1}(C)$. It is known, and can be easily verified, that the associated two-form of the latter can be written

$$(21) \qquad \Omega = \frac{i}{2} \, d' \, d'' \log \left(\sum_{\alpha} z_{\alpha} \bar{z}_{\alpha} \right).$$

In the open set $z_1 \neq 0$ of P_{n+1} we have

$$(22) \qquad \Omega = \frac{i}{2} \, d' \, d'' \log \left(1 + \frac{|z_2|^2 + \cdots + |z_{n+2}|^2}{|z_1|^2} \right).$$

This reduces to the associated two-form of the hermitian structure (16) of Q_n by restriction; the latter is by definition

$$\Omega = \frac{i}{4} \sum_a \theta_a \wedge \bar{\theta}_a.$$

For later applications to minimal surfaces we wish to find other expressions for the associated two-form Ω on Q_n for $n = 1,2$. In the case $n = 1$, the conic Q_1, with the point $(1, -i, 0)$ deleted, has the parametric representation

$$(23) \qquad z_1 = 1 + t^2, \qquad z_2 = i(1 - t^2), \qquad z_3 = 2it,$$

and we get

$$\sum_\alpha z_\alpha \bar{z}_\alpha = 2(1 + t\bar{t})^2.$$

It follows that

$$(24) \qquad \Omega = i \, d' \, d'' \log \left(1 + \frac{1}{|t|^2} \right), \qquad t \neq 0.$$

Similarly, for $n = 2$ the quadric Q_2 has the parametric representation

$$(25) \qquad z_1 = 1 + t\tau, \quad z_2 = i(1 - t\tau), \quad z_3 = -t + \tau, \quad z_4 = -i(t + \tau),$$

and we find

$$(26) \qquad \Omega = \frac{i}{2} d' \, d'' \log \left\{ \left(1 + \frac{1}{|t|^2} \right) \left(1 + \frac{1}{|\tau|^2} \right) \right\}, \quad t\tau \neq 0.$$

By a holomorphic curve in Q_n we mean a holomorphic mapping $f : M \to Q_n$, where M is a Riemann surface (i.e., a complex manifold of one dimension). The mapping f, followed by the inclusion on Q_n in P_{n+1}, defines a holomorphic curve in P_{n+1}. The latter is called non-degenerate, if it does not lie in a linear space of lower dimension. A classical theorem of E. Borel can now be stated as follows [11]:

Let $g : M \to P_{n+1}$ be a non-degenerate holomorphic curve, where M is the gaussian plane. To $n + 3$ hyperplanes in P_{n+1}, in general position, the image $g(M)$ meets one of them.

Let P^*_{n+1} be the dual projective space of P_{n+1}, i.e., the manifold of all the hyperplanes of P_{n+1}. Under the hypotheses of Borel's theorem let S be the set of all hyperplanes which have non-void intersections with $g(M)$. Then Borel's theorem has the consequence that S is dense in P^*_{n+1}.

3. Geometry of surfaces

Consider now the euclidean space E of dimension $n + 2$ and an oriented surface M immersed in E defined by the C^∞-mapping

$$(27) \qquad\qquad\qquad x \colon M \to E.$$

To the surface is associated the Gauss mapping

$$(28) \qquad\qquad\qquad f \colon M \to Q_n,$$

where $f(p)$, $p \in M$, is the oriented plane through a fixed point 0 of E and parallel to the tangent plane to $x(M)$ at $x(p)$.

We consider the bundle B of orthonormal frames $x e_1 \cdots e_{n+2}$ such that $x \in x(M)$ and e_1, e_2 are tangent vectors at $x = x(p)$, $p \in M$. In the bundle B we have

$$(29) \qquad \begin{aligned} dx &= \omega_1 e_1 + \omega_2 e_2, \\ de_i &= \sum_\alpha \varphi_{i\alpha} e_\alpha. \end{aligned}$$

In these and in later formulas we will agree on the following range of indices:

$$(30) \qquad\qquad\qquad 1 \leqq i, j, k \leqq 2.$$

We consider the following diagram of mappings:

$$(31) \qquad \begin{array}{ccc} B & \xrightarrow{\ F\ } & SO(n + 2) \\ {\scriptstyle \psi} \downarrow & & \downarrow {\scriptstyle \pi} \\ M & \xrightarrow{\ f\ } & Q_n = SO(n + 2)/SO(2) \times SO(n). \end{array}$$

In this diagram ψ is the projection which sends the frame $x e_1 \cdots e_{n+2}$ to its origin x; F maps the frame to the matrix whose rows are the components of e_α; and π is the natural projection. The diagram (31) is clearly commutative. Our notation is essentially consistent with those of §2; use of $\varphi_{i\alpha}$ in (29) means that we have omitted the dual mapping F^*.

By taking the exterior derivative of the first equation of (29) and considering the terms involving e_a, we get

$$\sum_i \omega_i \wedge \varphi_{ia} = 0.$$

From this it follows that

$$(32) \qquad\qquad\qquad \varphi_{ia} = \sum_k l_{iak} \omega_k,$$

where

$$(33) \qquad\qquad\qquad l_{iak} = l_{kai}.$$

The quadratic differential forms

$$(34) \qquad \Phi_a = \sum_i \omega_i \varphi_{ia} = \sum_{i,k} l_{iak} \omega_i \omega_k$$

are the second fundamental forms of the surface.

The normal vector

$$(35) \qquad l_a = \sum_k l_{kak} = l_{1a1} + l_{2a2}$$

is called the mean curvature vector. Its vanishing defines the minimal surfaces. The Gaussian curvature of the induced metric on M is given by

$$(36) \qquad K = \sum_a (l_{1a1} l_{2a2} - l_{1a2}^2).$$

The complex structure defined by the induced metric on M is given by the differential form $\omega_1 + i\omega_2$. For a minimal surface we find

$$(37) \qquad \varphi_{1a} + i\varphi_{2a} = (l_{1a1} + il_{1a2})(\omega_1 - i\omega_2).$$

This proves the result: *If M is a minimal surface, the Gauss mapping* (28) *is anti-holomorphic.* For $n = 2$ this result was first proved by M. Pinl [10].

4. Generalization of the theorem of Bernstein-Osserman

The theorem we wish to establish is the following:

Let $x: M \to E$ be a complete simply-connected minimal surface immersed in a euclidan space E of dimension $n + 2$ (≥ 3) and not lying in a linear space of lower dimension. Let $f: M \to Q_n \subset P_{n+1}$ be the Gauss mapping. Then the subset of P_{n+1}^* whose sections with Q_n meet $f(M)$ is dense in P_{n+1}^*.

For $n = 2$ write $Q_2 = L_1 \times L_2$ as a product of two projective lines and denote by π_1, π_2 respectively the projections on the two factors. Then either $\pi_1 \circ f(M)$ is dense in L_1 or $\pi_2 \circ f(M)$ is dense in L_2. For $n = 1$ the set $f(M)$ is dense in Q_1.

The theorem can be interpreted as a description of the set $f(M)$ relative to the generating cycles of $H_{2n-2}(Q_n)$. The statements in the second part of the theorem correspond to the fact that, for $n = 1, 2$, these generating cycles are not given by the hyperplane sections of Q_n. The last statement is the Bernstein-Osserman theorem quoted in §1.

First of all, M is non-compact ([4]). By the Riemann mapping theorem, M, with the conformal structure induced from the metric of E, is conformally equivalent to the gaussian plane (parabolic type) or to the unit disk (hyperbolic type). We will prove that, under the assumption that the assertions in the theorem are not true, M is necessarily of parabolic type. The proof is based on the following lemma of Osserman [9]:

Let M be a complete, non-compact, simply-connected riemannian manifold of two dimensions. Let K be its gaussian curvature and Δ the second Beltrami operator. Suppose there exists a real-valued function $u \geqq \varepsilon > 0$ ($\varepsilon = $ const.) satisfying the condition

$$(38) \qquad\qquad \Delta \log u = K.$$

Then M, with the conformal structure defined by its riemannian metric, is parabolic.

Before applying the lemma, we will formulate the condition (38) in a different form. Let x, y be the isothermal parameters of the riemannian metric, so that $z = x + iy$ is a local coordinate of the induced complex structure and that the riemannian metric can be written

$$ds^2 = h^2 \, dz \, d\bar{z}, \qquad h > 0.$$

Then

$$\Delta = \frac{1}{h^2} \left(\frac{\partial^2}{\partial x^2} + \frac{\partial^2}{\partial y^2} \right)$$

and

$$2i \, d' \, d'' \log u = (\Delta \log u) \frac{i}{2} h^2 \, dz \wedge d\bar{z},$$

where the last expression after the parentheses is the element of area of M. Hence condition (38) can be written

$$(39) \qquad\qquad 2i \, d' \, d'' \log u = K \cdot \frac{i}{2} h^2 \, dz \wedge d\bar{z}.$$

Suppose that the assertions in the theorem are not true. In the general case there is a neighborhood in P^*_{n+1} whose hyperplanes do not meet $f(M)$; we can suppose this to be a neighborhood of the hyperplane $z_1 = 0$. Then the function

$$(40) \qquad\qquad u = \left\{ \frac{|z_1|^2}{|z_1|^2 + \cdots + |z_{n+2}|^2} \right\}^{\frac{1}{4}}$$

is $\geqq \varepsilon$ on M, for a certain constant $\varepsilon > 0$. Since f is antiholomorphic, we have

$$d' \, d'' f^* = f^* \, d'' \, d'$$

and we find, by (22) and (36),

$$2i \, d' \, d'' f^* \log u = -2if^* \, d' \, d'' \log u = 2f^* \Omega = K\omega_1 \wedge \omega_2,$$

so that the function $u \circ f$ satisfies the condition (39).

In the case $n = 1$ we suppose that $f(M)$ omits a neighborhood of the point $t = 0$ in the parametric representation (23), and put

$$(41) \qquad u = \frac{|t|^2}{1 + |t|^2}$$

For $n = 2$ we can consider t and u as the non-homogeneous coordinates on the projective lines L_1, L_2 respectively. Suppose $\pi_1 \circ f(M)$ omits a neighborhood of $t = 0$ and $\pi_2 \circ f(M)$ omits a neighborhood of $\tau = 0$. Choose

$$(42) \qquad u = \left\{ \frac{|t|^2 |\tau|^2}{(1 + |t|^2)(1 + |\tau|^2)} \right\}^{\frac{1}{2}}$$

Then, in view of (24) and (26), these functions u satisfy the conditions in Osserman's lemma. It follows that in all cases M is of parabolic type.

It is now easy to get a contradiction to our assumption. In the general case it follows from Borel's theorem that the holomorphic curve $f(M)$ is degenerate. Suppose P_{m+1}, $m < n$, be the linear subspace of least dimension in P_{n+1}, which contains $f(M)$. Then P_{m+1} is not a point, because $x(M)$ is not a plane. Borel's Theorem, when applied to $f(M) \subset P_{m+1}$, $0 \leqq m < n$, has the consequence that the set of hyperplanes in P_{m+1}, which meet $f(M)$, is dense in P_{m+1}^* (= space of hyperplanes in P_{m+1}). This in turn implies that the set of hyperplanes in P_{n+1}, which meet $f(M)$ is dense in P_{n+1}^*. But this contradicts our assumption. Similarly, we get contradictions in the other cases. Thus our main theorem is completely proved.

It should be remarked that our proof gives also the following theorem: *Let* $x \colon M \to E$ *be a complete simply-connected minimal surface immersed in a euclidean space* E *of four dimensions. If* $\pi_i \circ f(M)$ *is not dense in* L_i, $i = 1, 2$, *then the surface* $x(M)$ *is a plane.*

As a result of the relation between minimal surfaces and holomorphic curves pointed out in this paper, it seems clear that further works are called for to extend the quantitative results on minimal surfaces in the direction initiated by E. Heinz [6] and developed by E. Hopf, Nitsche, Osserman, etc.

Appendix[2]

The idea mentioned at the end of this paper has been partially carried out, and such an inequality has been found. In fact, following the notation of this paper, let $x \colon M \to E$ be a simply-connected minimal surface and let $D \subset M$ be a finite piece of geodesic radius s about a point $p_0 \in M$. The image $f(D)$ under the Gauss mapping being a subset of P_{n+1}, let δ

---

[2] Added November 1, 1963.

be the distance, in the hermitian metric in P_{n+1}, of $f(D)$ from a fixed hyperplane of P_{n+1}. Then we have the following inequality

$$(43) \qquad |K(p_0)| \leqq \frac{2(n+1)}{s^2} \cot^2 \delta \cos^2 \delta (1 + 2n \cot^2 \delta)$$

for the Gaussian curvature $K(p_0)$ at p_0. A similar inequality has been obtained by Osserman.

Denote the fixed hyperplane by λ. The homogeneous coordinates in P_{n+1} being $z_1, \ldots, z_{n+2}$, we suppose λ to be defined by $z_1 = 0$. The distance $d(z, \lambda)$ from a point $z \in P_{n+1}$ to λ is then given by the formula

$$(44) \qquad \sin d(z, \lambda) = \frac{|z_1|}{\sqrt{|z_1|^2 + \cdots + |z_{n+2}|^2}}.$$

Since the inequality (43) is automatically valid when $\delta = 0$, we will suppose $\delta > 0$, i.e., that $f(D)$ does not meet the hyperplane λ. In $P_{n+1} - \lambda$ let

$$(45) \qquad \zeta_\rho = z_\rho/z_1, \qquad\qquad 2 \leqq \rho, \sigma \leqq n+2$$

The mapping which assigns to $z \in P_{n+1} - \lambda$ the number $\zeta_\rho \in C$ (= complex field) we will denote by ψ_ρ. The formula for $d(z, \lambda)$ can be written

$$(46) \qquad \sin^2 d(z, \lambda) = \frac{1}{1 + |\zeta|^2},$$

where

$$(47) \qquad |\zeta|^2 = |\zeta_2|^2 + \cdots + |\zeta_{n+2}|^2.$$

The condition $d(z, \lambda) \geq \delta$ is equivalent to $|\zeta|^2 \leqq R^2$, with $R = \cot \delta$.

With the function

$$(48) \qquad u = (1 + |\zeta|^2)^{-\frac{1}{2}}$$

defined in (40), the Gaussian curvature K can be calculated according to the formula

$$(49) \qquad -2if^* \, d' \, d'' \log u = 2i \, d' \, d'' f^* \log u = K\omega_1 \wedge \omega_2.$$

By calculation we get

$$(50) \quad 2i \, d' \, d'' \log u = \frac{-i}{(1 + |\zeta|^2)^2} \left\{ \sum_\rho d\zeta_\rho \wedge d\bar\zeta_\rho + \sum_{\rho < \sigma} (\zeta_\rho \, d\zeta_\sigma - \zeta_\sigma \, d\zeta_\rho) \wedge \right.$$
$$\left. (\bar\zeta_\rho \, d\bar\zeta_\sigma - \bar\zeta_\sigma \, d\bar\zeta_\rho \} \right.$$

Formula (49) shows that $(f^*u) \, ds$, where ds is the element of arc on M, has zero Gaussian curvature. With this fact as analytical basis, Osserman showed ([9], p. 230), by making use of the uniformization theorem, that there exists a holomorphic mapping h of M into the complex t-plane, such that

$$(51) \qquad h^*|dt| = (f^*u)\, ds.$$

Moreover,[3] if $|\zeta|^2 \le R^2$ in D, the image $h(D)$ contains an unbranched disk Δ of radius $r = s/(1 + R^2)^{\frac{1}{2}}$ about $h(p_0)$.

Taking the elements of area of both sides of (51), we get

$$(52) \qquad h^*\left(\frac{i}{2}\, dt \wedge d\bar{t}\right) = \frac{1}{1 + |\zeta|^2}\, \omega_1 \wedge \omega_2.$$

We now map Δ into C by the composition $\psi_\rho \circ f \circ h^{-1}$. The latter is an anti-holomorphic mapping, under which ζ_ρ is a holomorphic function of $\bar{t}$. Combining (49), (50), (52), we get the following formula for the Gaussian curvature K:

$$(53) \qquad |K| = \frac{2}{(1 + |\zeta|^2)^3}\left\{\sum_\rho \left|\frac{d\zeta_\rho}{d\bar{t}}\right|^2 + \sum_{\rho<\sigma}\left|\zeta_\rho \frac{d\zeta_\sigma}{d\bar{t}} - \zeta_\sigma \frac{d\zeta_\rho}{d\bar{t}}\right|^2\right\}.$$

The image of Δ under $\psi_\rho \circ f \circ h^{-1}$ belongs to a disk of radius R. By supposing the center of Δ to be the point $t = 0$, it follows from Schwarz Lemma that

$$\left|\frac{d\zeta_\rho}{d\bar{t}}\right|_{t=0} \le \frac{R}{r}.$$

Since $|\zeta_\rho| \le R$, we get, at $t = 0$,

$$\left|\zeta_\rho \frac{d\zeta_\sigma}{d\bar{t}} - \zeta_\sigma \frac{d\zeta_\rho}{d\bar{t}}\right| \le \frac{2R^2}{r}.$$

Substituting into (53), we find

$$|K(p_0)| \le 2\left\{(n+1)\frac{R^2}{r^2} + \left(\frac{n+1}{2}\right)\frac{4R^4}{r^2}\right\},$$

which gives (43) on simplification.

Allowing $s \to \infty$ and utilizing the fact that a minimal surface with zero Gaussian curvature is a plane, we get the following corollary:

Let $x: M \to E$ be a complete, simply-connected minimal surface in an euclidean space E of dimension $n + 2$, such that $x(M)$ is not a plane. Then the set of hyperplanes of P_{n+1} which meet the image $f(M) \subset P_{n+1}$ under the Gauss mapping f is dense in P_{n+1}^*.

Actually this corollary also follows from the proof in §4 of this paper, although the main theorem was stated there under stronger hypotheses.

---

[3] R. Osserman, An analogue of the Heinz-Hopf inequality, *J. Math. and Mech.*, 8 (1959) p. 383–385.

References

[1] S. Bernstein, Sur un théorème de géométrie et ses applications aux équations aux dérivées partielles du type elliptique, *Comm. Inst. Sci. Math. Mech. Univ. Kharkov, 15* (1915–17), p. 38–45.

[2] E. Cartan, Sur les propriétés topologiques des quadriques complexes, *Publ. math. Univ. Belgrade, 1* (1932), p. 55–74; or *Oeuvres*, Partie I, vol. 2, p. 1227–1246.

[3] S. Chern, Characteristic classes of Hermitian manifolds, *Annals of Math., 47* (1946), p. 85–121.

[4] S. Chern and C. C. Hsiung, On the isometry of compact submanifolds in euclidean space, *Math. Annalen, 149* (1963), p. 278–285.

[5] C. Ehresmann, Sur la topologie de certains espaces homogènes, *Annals of Math., 35* (1934), p. 396–443.

[6] E. Heinz, Über die Lösungen der Minimalflächengleichung, *Nachr. Akad. Wiss. Göttingen* 1952, p. 51–56.

[7] S. Helgason, *Differential Geometry and Symmetric Spaces*, Academic Press, New York, 1962.

[8] W. V. D. Hodge and D. Pedoe, *Methods of Algebraic Geometry*, Vol. 2, Book 4, Cambridge University Press, 1952.

[9] R. Osserman, Proof of a conjecture of Nirenberg, *Comm. on Pure and Applied Math., 12* (1959), p. 229–232.

[10] M. Pinl, *B*-Kugelbilder reeller Minimalflächen in R^4, *Math. Zeits., 59* (1953), p. 290–295.

[11] H. Weyl, *Meromorphic Functions and Analytic Curves*, Princeton University Press, 1943.

On Homotopy Spheres of Low Dimension

MORRIS W. HIRSCH

---

1. Introduction

Poincaré conjectured that every simply connected closed 3-manifold is homeomorphic to the 3-sphere S^3. A more general conjecture is that every *homotopy n-sphere* (i.e., n-manifold having the homotopy type of S^n) is homeomorphic to S^n. This problem is still open for $n \geq 3$. However, S. Smale [6, 7] has proved that every combinatorial homotopy n-sphere M is combinatorially equivalent to S^n (symbolized by $M \equiv S^n$) if $n > 5$ and homeomorphic to S^5 if $n = 5$; moreover, every smooth homotopy 5-sphere is diffeomorphic to S^5 (symbolized by $M \approx S^5$). Zeeman [9] has proved that if M is a combinatorial homotopy 5-sphere, then $M - x \equiv$ Euclidean 5-space R^5.

In this paper we obtain a condition on M^5 implying $M^5 \equiv S^5$ (Theorem 4, below). We show that homotopy spheres of dimension 3 and 4 exhibit behavior similar to that of S^3 and S^4 when certain operations are performed upon them. An interesting result of this sort is this:

THEOREM 1. *The suspension of a smooth homotopy 4-sphere M is homeomorphic to S^5. The homeomorphism can be taken to be diffeomorphism on the complement of the two suspension points.*

This follows from Theorem 6 (b) below, which states that

$$M \times R^1 \approx S^4 \times R^1.$$

V. Poénaru has pointed out that a theorem of this kind leads to the study of critical points, since Theorem 1 has the following corollary.

THEOREM 2. *Every homotopy 4-sphere is diffeomorphic to a level surface of a smooth real valued function on S^5 having only two critical points.*

Theorem 1 leads to an obvious connection between Poincaré's conjecture in dimension 4 and the Hauptvermutung for arbitrary triangulations of S^5.

In the next section Theorem 1 and related results are proved. In section 3 we prove

THEOREM 3. *Let M be a smooth homotopy 4-sphere. Then*

$$M \times M - \Delta(M) \approx S^4 \times S^4 - \Delta(S^4),$$

where Δ is the diagonal embedding.

The last section is independent from the others. In it we prove the following result.

THEOREM 4. *Let M be a combinatorial homotopy 5-sphere which bounds a compact, orientable, combinatorial 6-manifold. Then $M \equiv S^5$.*

2. Trivializations

For this section and the next we consider only *smooth* manifolds.

A homotopy k-sphere M^k is *trivialized by V* if V is a manifold such that $M^k \times V \approx S^k \times V$.

A *homotopy k-cell* is a compact contractible k-manifold A^k with simply connected boundary ∂A^k. We say A^k is trivialized by V if V is unbounded and $A^k \times V \approx D^k \times V$, where D^k is the closed k-disk.

A manifold is *closed* if it is compact and unbounded. The *interior* of X is Int $X = X - \partial X$.

THEOREM 5. *Let A^5 be a homotopy 5-cell and V^j a closed manifold. Then A^5 is trivialized by V^j if $j \geq 1$.*

PROOF. Let $D^5 \subset$ Int A^5 be a smoothly embedded disk. It is clear that A^5 is a *simple neighborhood* of D^5 in the sense of Mazur, and that $A^5 \times V^j$ is a simple neighborhood of $D^5 \times V^j$. Unfortunately the s-cobordism theorem of Mazur [4] and Stallings (unpublished) is not valid in dimension five. It is valid in higher dimensions, however. Therefore Mazur's "simple neighborhood theorem" shows that $A^5 \times V^j \approx D^5 \times V^j$.

THEOREM 6. *A homotopy 4-sphere M^4 is trivialized by V^j if any one of the following conditions holds:*

    (a) $j \geq 1$ and V^j is closed;

    (b) $j \geq 1$ and $V^j = R^j$;

    (c) $j \geq 2$ and $V^j = D^j$.

PROOF. It is known that M^4 bounds a homotopy 5-cell; this is the theorem of Kervaire and Milnor [3] that $\theta^4 = 0$. Therefore (a) is implied by Theorem 5. In particular, $M^4 \times S^1 \approx S^4 \times S^1$, and consequently $M^4 \times R^1 \approx S^4 \times R^1$, proving (b).

To prove (c), observe that $\partial(M^4 \times D^j) = M^4 \times S^{j-1} \approx S^4 \times S^{j-1}$ by (a). Therefore $S^4 \times D^j$ can be diffeomorphically embedded in the interior of $M^4 \times D^j$, and the simple neighborhood theorem [4] applies if $j \geq 2$, proving $M^4 \times D^j \approx S^4 \times D^j$.

THEOREM 7.   *A homotopy 4-cell A^4 is trivialized by the closed manifold V^j if either*

(a) $j \geq 2$, *or*
(b) $j = 1$ *and* $\partial A^4 = S^3$.

PROOF.   If $j \geq 2$, we see that $A^4 \times V^j$ is a simple neighborhood of $D^4 \times V^j$, where $D^4 \subset \operatorname{Int} A^4$. If $j = 1$ and $\partial A^4 = S^3$, let M^4 be a homotopy 4-sphere obtained by gluing the boundary of a 4-disk B^4 onto ∂A^4 diffeomorphically. We may assume $V^j = S^1$.

By Theorem 6, we know that $M^4 \times S^1 \approx S^4 \times S^1$. Observe that

$$A^4 \times S^1 = M^4 \times S^1 - \operatorname{Int}(B^4 \times S^1),$$

and we may think of $B^4 \times S^1$ as being a tubular neighborhood of $0 \times S^1$ in $M^4 \times S^1$. Similarly, $D^4 \times S^1$ is the complement of the interior of a tubular neighborhood of $x \times S^1 \subset S^4 \times S^1$, for some $x \in S^1$. Thus to prove (b), it suffices to prove that if $f, g: S^1 \to S^4 \times S^1$ are homotopic embeddings, there is a diffeomorphism of $S^4 \times S^1$ carrying a tubular neighborhood of $f(S^1)$ onto a tubular neighborhood of $g(S^1)$. Because of the dimensions involved, f and g are isotopic, and by the isotopy extension theorem of Thom (unpublished) and Palais [5], the isotopy can be extended to all of $S^4 \times S^1$. Now (b) follows from the uniqueness of tubular neighborhoods.

The next two theorems present similar facts about homotopy 3-spheres and 3-cells. Some of these are merely particular cases of theorems of Smale, and are included for the sake of completeness.

THEOREM 8.   *A homotopy 3-sphere M^3 is trivialized by*

(a) S^j *for* $j \geq 2$;
(b) D^j *for* $j \geq 3$.

If M^3 bounds a homotopy 4-cell, then M^3 is trivialized by

(c)   *the closed manifold V^j for* $j \geq 2$.

PROOF.   Clearly (b) implies (a). To prove (b), first embed S^3 in $M^3 \times D^j$ by a smooth embedding which is a homotopy equivalence; this can be done if $j \geq 3$ according to Haefliger [1]. Now observe that the normal bundle of S^3 in $M^3 \times D^j$ is trivial, and apply the simple neighborhood theorem [4]. Part (c) follows from Theorem 7 (a).

REMARK.   It is easy to see that Poincaré's conjecture in dimension 3 is true if it is true for boundaries of homotopy 4-cells.

THEOREM 9. *A homotopy 3-cell A^3 is trivialized by*
(a)   *a closed manifold V^j if $j \geq 3$;*
(b) S^2.

PROOF. The proof is similar to that of Theorem 7, and is omitted.

3. Complements of manifolds

For any space Y, let $\Delta: Y \to Y \times Y$ be the diagonal embedding
$\Delta(y) = (y, y)$.

THEOREM 10. *Let M^4 be a homotopy 4-sphere. Then*

$$M^4 \times M^4 - \Delta(M^4) \approx S^4 \times S^4 - \Delta(S^4).$$

PROOF. From Theorem 6 (a) we see that there is a diffeomorphism
$f: M^4 \times M^4 \to S^4 \times S^4$. The proof is complete if we can show that

$$M^4 \times M^4 - \Delta(M^4) \approx M^4 \times M^4 - f^{-1}\Delta(S^4).$$

This is a consequence of the following theorem.

THEOREM 11. *Let $\varphi: M_0 \to M_1$ be a homotopy equivalence between
closed m-manifolds. For $i = 0$, 1 let $g_i: M_i \to N$ be diffeomorphic embeddings in an unbounded n-manifold N, such that $g_0 \simeq g_1\varphi$. Then*

$$N - g_0(M_0) \approx N - g_1(M_1),$$

*provided $2n > 3(m + 1)$. Moreover, the diffeomorphism is isotopic in N
to the inclusion $N - g_0(M_0) \to N$.*

PROOF. Let us identify M_i with the submanifolds $g_i(M_i)$ of N, so that
g_i is the inclusion $M_i \to N$. Let $X_1 \supset X_2 \supset \cdots$ be a decreasing sequence
of open tubular neighborhoods of M_0, such that $Cl(X_{j+1}) \subset X_j$ for
$j = 1$, 2, . . ., and $\cap X_j = M_0$, where Cl means closure. Let
$Y_1 \supset Y_2 \supset \cdots$ be a similar sequence of open tubular neighborhoods of
$M_1 = \cap Y_j$.

We shall use Haefliger's work [1] on embeddings and isotopy. Because
of the assumption on dimension, any map of M_i in an open subset of N
which is a homotopy equivalence is homotopic to an embedding; any two
homotopic embeddings of M_i in an open subset U of N are isotopic by
an isotopy of U which is fixed outside of a compact set.

Let $\xi_0 = \eta_0 = \eta_1 =$ the identity map of N.

Since $g_1\varphi: M_0 \to Y_1$ is a homotopy equivalence, there is an embedding
$h: M_0 \to Y_1$ with $h \simeq g_1\varphi$. Since $h \simeq g_0$ in N, there is an isotopy of N

carrying g_0 into h. Thus we obtain a diffeomorphism $\xi_1 \colon N \to N$ enjoying the following properties:

($P_{\xi 1}$) ξ_1 is isotopic to the identity (symbolized by $\xi_1 \cong 1$).

($Q_{\xi 1}$) $\xi_1(X_1) \subset Y_1$.

($R_{\xi 1}$) $\xi_1 \colon M_0 \to Y_1$ and $\varphi \colon M_0 \to Y_1$ are homotopic in Y_1.

Similar considerations show that there is a diffeomorphism $\eta_2 \colon N \to N$ such that:

($P_{\eta 2}$) $\eta_2 \cong 1$, the isotopy being fixed outside of Y_1.

($Q_{\eta 2}$) $\eta_2(Y_2) \subset \xi_1(X_2)$.

($R_{\eta 2}$) $\eta_2 \colon M_1 \to \xi_1(X_1)$ and $\xi_1 \varphi^{-1} \colon M_1 \to \xi_1(X_1)$ are homotopic in $\xi_1(X_1)$.

Continuing recursively in this manner, we obtain two sequences $\{\xi_k\}$, $\{\eta_k\}$ of diffeomorphisms of N, $k = 1, 2, \ldots$. These have the following properties. Put $\xi_k \cdots \xi_1 = \xi^k$ and $\eta_k \cdots \eta_1 = \eta^k$. Then for $k \geq 1$:

($P_{\xi k}$) $\xi_k \cong 1$, the isotopy being fixed outside of $\xi^{k-1}(X_k)$.

($P_{\eta k}$) $\eta_k \cong 1$, the isotopy being fixed outside of $\eta^{k-1}(Y_k)$.

($Q_{\xi k}$) $\xi^k(X_k) \subset \eta^k(Y_k)$.

($Q_{\eta k}$) $\eta^k(Y_k) \subset \xi^{k-1}(X_k)$.

($R_{\xi k}$) ξ^k and $\eta^k \varphi$ are homotopic as maps of M_0 in $\eta^k(Y_k)$.

($R_{\eta k}$) η^k and $\eta^{k-1}\varphi^{-1}$ are homotopic as maps of M_1 in $\xi^{k-1}(X_k)$.

From these properties it follows that $\xi^k = 1$ on $N - X_{k-1}$, and $\eta^k = 1$ on $N - Y_{k-1}$. Hence for $x \in N - M_0$ and $y \in N - M_1$, the sequences $\{\xi^k(x)\}$ and $\{\eta^k(x)\}$, $k = 1, 2, \ldots$, are constant for k sufficiently large. Define $\xi(x) = \lim_{k \to \infty} \xi^k(x)$ and $\eta(y) = \lim_{k \to \infty} \eta^k(y)$. Then $\xi \colon N - M_0 \to N$ and $\eta \colon N - M_1 \to N$ are diffeomorphic embeddings. It is easily proved that ξ and η have the same image, namely

$$\cup_k(N - \xi^k(X_k)) = \cup_k(N - \eta^k(Y_k)).$$

Thus $\eta^{-1}\xi \colon N - M_0 \to N - M_1$ is the desired diffeomorphism.

4. Combinatorial homotopy 5-spheres

Throughout this section, let M be a combinatorial homotopy 5-sphere. It is known that M is homeomorphic to S^5, but whether $M \equiv S^5$ is still unknown. In theorem 4 (see section 1) we present a sufficient (and trivially necessary) condition for this to occur, namely that M bound a compact orientable combinatorial 6-manifold V.

PROOF OF THEOREM 4. We may assume V is connected. We then make V simply connected, if necessary, by surgery [3]. (Those who feel queasy about surgery on combinatorial manifolds may wish to endow V with a compatible differential structure in a neighborhood of the 1-skeleton. This can easily be done directly, or [2] can be used.)

Assuming that V is simply connected, we proceed to build up a compatible differential structure in V over neighborhoods of successive skeletons. For this purpose the results of the author's paper [2] are used. Assuming that there is a compatible differential structure in a neighborhood of the k-skeleton, there exists one in a neighborhood of the $(k + 1)$-skeleton provided $H^{k+1}(V, \Gamma_k) = 0$. It is known that the group $\Gamma_k = 0$ for $k \leq 3$ and $k = 5$. The assumption that V is simply connected implies (by duality) that $H^5(V, \Gamma_4) = 0$. Therefore V has a compatible differential structure. Consequently M has one too. It follows from Smale [6] that $M \equiv S^5$, QED.

ADDED IN PROOF. The recent theorem $\Gamma_4 = 0$ of J. Cerf implies that always $M \equiv S^5$.

References

[1] A. HAEFLIGER, Plongements différentiables de variétés dans variétés, *Comm. Math. Helv.*, *36* (1961), p. 46–82.

[2] M. HIRSCH, Obstruction theories for smoothing manifolds and maps, *Bull. Amer. Math. Soc.*, *69* (1963), p. 352–356.

[3] M. KERVAIRE and J. MILNOR, Groups of homotopy spheres (to appear).

[4] B. MAZUR, Simple neighborhoods, *Bull. Amer. Math. Soc.*, *68* (1962), p. 87–92.

[5] R. S. PALAIS, Local triviality of the restriction map for embeddings, *Comm. Math. Helv.*, *34* (1960), p. 305–312.

[6] S. SMALE, Differentiable and combinatorial structures on manifolds, *Annals of Math.*, *73* (1961), p. 498–502.

[7] ———, Generalized Poincaré's conjecture in dimensions greater than 4, *Annals of Math.*, *73* (1961), p. 391–406.

[8] J. STALLINGS, Polyhedral homotopy spheres, *Bull. Amer. Math. Soc.*, *66* (1960), p. 485–488.

[9] E. C. ZEEMAN, The generalized Poincaré conjecture, *Bull. Amer. Math. Soc.*, *67* (1961), p. 270.

Local Properties of Analytic Varieties

HASSLER WHITNEY

1. Introduction

Algebraic and analytic varieties have become increasingly important in recent years, both in the complex and the real case. Their local structure has been intensively investigated, by algebraic and by analytic means. Local geometric properties are less well understood. Our principal purpose here is to study properties of tangent vectors and tangent planes in the neighborhood of singular points. We study stratifications of an analytic variety into analytic manifolds; in particular, we may require that a transversal to a stratum is also tranversal to the higher dimensional strata near a given point. A conjecture on possible fiberings of the variety (and of surrounding space) is stated; it is proved at points of strata of codimension 2 in the surrounding space. In the last sections, we see that a variety may have numbers or functions intrinsically attached at points or along strata; also an analytic variety may be locally unlike an algebraic variety.

The original purpose of the present study was to help solidify the theory of singularities of differentiable mappings; this field may be considered as a branch of differential topology. In this theory, a type of singularity is defined by means of a certain algebraic variety lying in a subsidiary space. A mapping has the given singularity at the point p if the corresponding mapping into the subsidiary space maps p into the variety; the mapping is generic at p if the corresponding mapping is transverse to the strata of the variety. It is here that the transversality mentioned above comes into play.

The varieties mentioned above are real algebraic; however, the properties discussed are of an analytic nature, so they might as well be studied in the more general analytic case. The splitting of a real variety into manifolds was studied in an elementary way in [14]; the splitting is in general not a stratification as we define it here; moreover, it has not certain further properties required. In order to carry the theory deeper, it was found most useful to go over to complex varieties, where powerful tools are available. This paper is concerned almost wholly with the complex

205

case; to apply the results to a real variety, one may use the complexification of this variety (see [16]).

In §2 we assemble some properties of analytic varieties which are
needed later. At a simple point of a variety there is a natural definition
of tangent vector. At a singular point, several different definitions are of
importance; we study them in §3. The definitions are given in terms of
the injection of the variety in C^n; yet they are intrinsic to the abstract
variety. We give the proof of this (essentially known result) in §4. In the
algebraic case, it is classical (although apparently only recently proved;
see [11]) that the tangent cone is defined by the vanishing of the initial
polynomials of the ideal of the variety at the given point. The theorem,
in the analytic case, is given in §5; the proof will be completed in a later
paper [15]. The connection with the algebraic theory is explained in §6; in
particular, we give a purely intrinsic characterization of the tangent cone,
which seems not to be in the literature.

To study transversality questions, we must consider not "tangent
vectors," but "tangent planes" at a singular point of the variety. In §7
we define such a plane to be the limiting position of a sequence of tangent
planes at simple points. We define a stratification of V in §8 to be an
expression of V as a union of analytic manifolds, the frontier of each
stratum being a union of lower dimensional strata. There is a natural way
of defining a primary stratification; this may be used as a starting point
for improved stratifications. In particular, we may require that as we
approach one stratum M from a higher dimensional stratum M', any
limiting position of tangent planes to M' contains the tangent plane to M
at the given point. The transversality property mentioned earlier then
follows. Moreover, we may require that if we approach a point p of M
along a given direction in M', a limiting position of tangent planes to M'
contains this direction. Such limiting positions were considered in §7.
These properties, in the real case, relate to the paper [13] of R. Thom in this
volume. Some of the proofs are deferred to [15].

Let M be a stratum in a stratification of V. It is natural to hope that
a neighborhood of any point $p \in M$ in V (in fact, a neighborhood in the
containing space) is expressible analytically as a product of an open
subset of M with a cross section through p. H. Rossi [10] has shown that this
is possible at p if and only if there are holomorphic vector fields tangent
to V at all simple points, near p, and forming a basis at p for the tangent
space to M at p (see Lemma 9.1). It is not possible in general, however, as
we shall see in §13. Instead, we look for a "semi-analytic" fibration of V
near p. We conjecture (§9) that every analytic variety has a stratification
such that there is a semi-analytic fibration near each point. For a related
result, we solve an interpolation problem for a set of analytic functions

over a simply connected region of the complex plane, these functions taking on distinct values at each point.

In the Weierstrass Preparation Theorem, there is a hypothesis that the given function does not vanish identically along a certain axis. We elucidate this in §10, showing that the degree of the equivalent pseudopolynomial is a minimum if that axis does not lie in the tangent cone of the corresponding variety, and is larger than the minimum otherwise. Let M be an analytic manifold in V (for instance, a stratum of a stratification), where V is a hypersurface. We show that except in a certain analytic subvariety of M, the tangent cone of V is a continuous function in M. If M is an $(n-2)$-dimensional stratum of the hypersurface $V \subset C^n$, from which we have cut out the above subvariety, then near any $p \in M$ we may express the branches of $V - M$ by holomorphic functions $x_n = \phi(x_1, \ldots, x_{n-1})$. Using this, we show in §12 that a hypersurface may be stratified so that the fibering conjecture holds throughout the $(n-2)$-dimensional strata. An interpolation procedure, described in §11, is used; it gives a semi-analytic fibration, whereas an analytic procedure would not have the required continuity properties.

In §13 we define some varieties for which there is no stratification with analytic fibrations at all points; the varieties are "non-homogeneous" along certain strata. The same type of construction gives (§14) analytic varieties that are not locally algebraic along certain strata. This shows that a certain theorem of N. Levinson [7] to the effect that a fairly general holomorphic function of two variables is, in a new coordinate system, a polynomial, cannot be extended to more variables. In constructing the examples, a basic property of cross ratios is used. In the final section we show that the same properties may be obtained by another method, using fewer sheets than before.

2. Preliminaries

2.1. Let C denote the set of complex numbers, and C^n, complex n-space. There is a natural coordinate system $(x_1, \ldots, x_n)$ in C^n. A (more general) "coordinate system" in the open set $U \subset C^n$ is a one–one holomorphic transformation of an open set $U' \subset C^n$ onto U, with nonvanishing Jacobian (hence the transformation is biholomorphic). If $(x, y, \ldots)$ is a coordinate system in U, then C_x denotes the x-axis, C_{xy} the (x, y)-plane, etc.

2.2. For a point set $Q \subset C^n$, clos $Q = \bar{Q}$ is its closure, and fron $Q = \bar{Q} - Q$ is its frontier. A set $\{Q_1, Q_2, \ldots\}$ of sets is *locally finite* if any compact set has points in but a finite number of the Q_i.

2.3. We use the hermitian metric in C^n. Then for $v = (v_1, \ldots, v_n) \in C^n$,

$|v| = \Sigma_i v_i \bar{v}_i$ ($\bar{v}_i$ = conjugate imaginary of v_i). $|q - p|$ is the distance from p to q. v is orthogonal to w if $\Sigma_i v_i \bar{w}_i = 0$.

2.4. A point set V in the open set $U \subset C^n$ is an *analytic variety* in U provided that V is closed in U, and for each $p \in V$ there is a neighborhood U' of p in C^n and a set $f_1, \ldots, f_s$ of holomorphic functions in U' such that $V \cap U'$ is the set of common zeros of the f_i in U'. Basic properties of analytic varieties may be found in [3], [9] and [6]. For a study of real C-analytic varieties in R^n (R = reals), see [4] and [16].

2.5. The point $p \in V \subset U \subset C^n$ is a *simple* (or *regular* or *ordinary*) point of V if there is a neighborhood U' of p and there are holomorphic functions $f_1, \ldots, f_m$ in U' such that the differentials $df_1(p), \ldots, df_m(p)$ are independent, and $V \cap U'$ is the set of common zeros of the f_i. We may then choose a new coordinate system in a neighborhood U'' of p such that $V \cap U''$ is an open subset of the $(x_1, \ldots, x_{n-m})$-plane. The *dimension* $\dim_p V$ of V at p is then $n - m$. The *tangent space* $T(V, p)$ of V at the simple point p is the set of vectors v expressible as $\lim a_i(q_i - p)$, where $q_i \in V$, $q_i \to p$, and the a_i are complex numbers. With $f_1, \ldots, f_m$ as above, $T(V, p)$ is the set of solutions of $df_i(p) \cdot v = 0$. A point of V which is not simple is *singular*.

2.6. An *analytic manifold* is an analytic variety all of whose points are simple; we require normally that its points all be of the same dimension. (Sometimes it is required to be connected.)

2.7. The *dimension* $\dim V$ of V is the highest dimension of V at simple points. The *dimension at* p of V, $\dim_p V$, is the dimension of $V \cap U'$ for small neighborhoods U' of p. V is of *constant dimension* if $\dim_p V$ is constant; it is of *constant dimension near* p if $V \cap U'$ is of constant dimension for some neighborhood U' of p. V is a *hypersurface* in C^n if it is of constant dimension $n - 1$. An irreducible variety is of constant dimension [9 Satz 5]. If $\dim_p V = d$ then there is an analytic manifold M of dimension $n - d$ containing p such that for some neighborhood U' of p, $V \cap M \cap U' = \{p\}$, and there is no such manifold of higher dimension (see [9]).

2.8. Any analytic variety may be expressed uniquely as the union of a set of irreducible analytic varieties, none of these being contained in the union of the others. This set of sets is locally finite. A proper subvariety of an irreducible variety (in particular, of a connected analytic manifold) is of lower dimension. Given a locally finite set of analytic varieties in an open set, their union is an analytic variety.

2.9. Given $p \in V \subset U \subset C^n$, let $I(V, p)$ denote the ring of germs of holomorphic functions in C^n near p which vanish on V. (In general, we need not distinguish between a function in some neighborhood of p and its germ at p; in §6 we take more care on this point.) The sheaf of all

$I(V, p)$ is *coherent* (see [3, Exposé XVI]); that is, for each $p \in U$ there is a neighborhood U' of p and a set $f_1, \ldots, f_s$ of holomorphic functions in U' which generate $I(V, q)$ for each $q \in U'$. This means that if $g_q \in I(V, q)$, g_q being the germ at q of the holomorphic function g, then there is a neighborhood U'' of q and there are holomorphic functions $\phi_1, \ldots, \phi_s$ in U'' such that $g = \Sigma_i \phi_i g_i$ in U''. (If $q \in U - V$, then $I(V, q)$ contains all holomorphic germs at q.) If V is a hypersurface, $I(V, p)$ is generated by a single function.

2.10. Suppose $V \subset U \subset C^n$. A function f defined in an open subset U^* of V is *holomorphic* in U^* if for each $p \in U^*$ there is a neighborhood U' of p in C^n and a holomorphic function F in U' such that its restriction $F|(V \cap U')$ to $V \cap U'$ equals f there. Let $O(V, p)$ denote the ring of germs of holomorphic functions in V at p. There is a natural isomorphism $O(V, p) \approx O(C^n, p)/I(V, p)$.

2.11. Suppose the space V is given, together with the set of functions on open subsets of V which are "holomorphic"; each $O(V, p)$ must come from an imbedding of a neighborhood of p in V into some C^n. Then we have an *abstract analytic variety*, or, an *analytic space*. See [12] or [6] for details.

2.12. Let V and W be analytic spaces, and let Φ be a mapping of V into W. Then Φ is *holomorphic* if, for each holomorphic function f in some open subset U of W, Φ^*f is holomorphic in $\Phi^{-1}(U)$. (By definition, $(\Phi^*f)(p) = f(\Phi(p))$.) Suppose Φ is one–one; then Φ is *biholomorphic* provided that both Φ and Φ^{-1} are holomorphic. In particular, if $V \subset U \subset C^n$, then the injection $V \to U$ is biholomorphic.

LEMMA 2.13. *Let Φ be a homeomorphism of V into C^n. Then*:

(a) *For Φ to be holomorphic, it is sufficient that each Φ^*x_i be holomorphic.*

(b) *For $\psi = \Phi^{-1}$ to be holomorphic, it is sufficient that for each holomorphic function g in an open set U in V, ψ^*g be, near each point of $\Phi(V)$, the restriction to $\Phi(V)$ of a holomorphic function in an open set in C^n.*

(c) *For (b) to hold, it is sufficient that the condition hold for holomorphic functions $f_1, \ldots, f_s$, such that each holomorphic function g in V is expressible as $\phi(f_1, \ldots, f_s)$, where ϕ is holomorphic.*

Part (a) above follows from the fact that each holomorphic function in C^n is expressible holomorphically in terms of $x_1, \ldots, x_n$; similarly, (c) follows from (b). Part (b) above follows from the definitions of holomorphic functions in V and of holomorphic mappings.

2.14. We give two examples. (1) Let $V = C_x \cup C_y \cup C_z \subset C^3$, and let W be given by $yx(y - x) = 0$ in C^2. Let Φ be the identity in $C_x \cup C_y$ and let Φ map C_z linearly into $y - x = 0$. Then Φ is holomorphic but not biholomorphic; the function z in V does not go into the restriction to W of a holomorphic function in C^2.

(2) Map $V = C^1 = C_t$ into C^2 by $x = t^2$, $y = t^3$; this is a homeomorphism. By Lemma 2.13, (a), the mapping is holomorphic. It is not biholomorphic, since the function t in the image is not the restriction to the image of V of a holomorphic function (near 0).

LEMMA 2.15.   *Let V and W be analytic varieties in $U \subset C^n$. Then $V^* = \text{clos}(V - W)$ and $V^{**} = V^* \cap W$ are analytic varieties, and $\dim_p V^{**} < \dim_p V^*$ for $p \in V^{**}$. Moreover, V^* is the union of the irreducible components of V which have points outside W.*

Express V in terms of its irreducible components:

$$V = (V_1 \cup V_2 \cup \cdots) \cup (X_1 \cup X_2 \cup \cdots), \quad X_i \subset W, \quad V_i \not\subset W;$$

each union is locally finite. Now $V^* = V_1 \cup V_2 \cup \cdots$. For if $p \in V^*$, then $p \in \text{clos}(V_1 \cup V_2 \cup \cdots)$, and hence $p \in \bar{V}_i = V_i$ for some i. Conversely, suppose $p \in V_i$ for some i. If $p \in V_i - W$, then $p \in V^*$. Suppose $p \in V_i \cap W = V_i'$. Since V_i is irreducible, $\dim_p V_i' < \dim_p V_i = \dim V_i$ (see 2.8); hence each neighborhood of p contains points of $V_i - W \subset V^*$, and $p \in V^*$. The rest of the lemma now follows.

LEMMA 2.16.   *Let M_1, M_2, . . . be the connected components of the set of simple points of the analytic variety V. Then the closures of the M_i are the irreducible components of V.*

Each M_i has an open subset contained in some irreducible component V_i of V; by 2.8, $M_i \subset V_i$ and hence $\bar{M}_i \subset V_i$. By [9, Satz 10], V_i contains no point of M_j for any other j. Let W_i be the union of the V_j with $j \neq i$; this is an analytic variety. By the last lemma, $\bar{M}_i = \text{clos}(V_i - W_i)$ is analytic; hence $\bar{M}_i = V_i$.

COROLLARY 2.17.   The set of simple points of V is dense in V.

LEMMA 2.18.   (a) *The set of singular points of an analytic variety (in C^n) is analytic or is void.* (b) *Let M_0 be the set of simple points of highest dimension of V, and set $V' = V - M_0$; then M_0 is an analytic manifold, and V' is an analytic variety of lower dimension or is void.*

First suppose V is irreducible. By the last lemma, the set M of simple points of V is a connected analytic manifold; it is of dimension $r = \dim V$. Take any $p \in V'$ (if V' is non-void). Let $f_1, \ldots, f_s$ generate $I(V, q)$ for each q in some neighborhood U of p. Let $D_1, \ldots, D_m$ be the set of all determinants of order $n - r$ from the matrix of partial derivatives of the f_i; let W be the analytic variety in U defined by the vanishing of the f_i and the D_j. For $q \in M \cap U$, some set of $n - r$ members of the f_i have independent differentials at q, hence, one of the $D_j(q)$ is $\neq 0$, and $q \notin W$. For $q \in V' \cap U$, all the $D_j(q)$ are 0, and $q \in W$. To show this, suppose some $D_j(q)$ is $\neq 0$. Then the corresponding f_i define a connected analytic manifold M' of dimension r in a neighborhood U' of q and containing q, and $V \cap U' \subset M'$. Since $q \in \bar{M}$, part of $\bar{M}$ lies in M'; hence (see 2.8) $V \cap U' = M'$. Thus q is a simple point of V, a contradiction. We have now proved that $W = V' \cap U$, which shows that V' is analytic. Moreover, $\dim V' < r$, by Lemma 2.15.

In the general case, the lemma follows easily on expressing V in terms of its irreducible components (see Lemma 2.16).

LEMMA 2.19. *Let* $W \subset U \subset C^n$ *be an analytic variety of dimension* $<r$, *and let* $V \subset U - W$ *be an analytic variety with* $\dim_p V \geq r$ *for all* $p \in V$. *Then* $\bar{V} \cap U$ *is an analytic variety in* U.

For the proof, see [9, Satz 13] or [2, p. 679].

2.20. Let the analytic manifolds M, M' in an open subset of C^n intersect at p (and perhaps at further points). We say M' is *transversal* to M at p if $T(M, p)$ and $T(M', p)$ together span C^n. In particular, we must have $k = \dim M + \dim M' \geq n$. Then $M \cap M'$, near p, is an analytic manifold of dimension $k - n$.

2.21. A *cone* $Q \subset C^n$ with *vertex* p is a subset of C^n such that for any $q \in Q$ and any complex number a, $p + a(q - p) \in Q$. We call $v = q - p$ a *vector* of Q; the condition is then that av also be a vector of Q. (In the real case, one might require $a > 0$.)

3. Possible definitions of tangent cones

At a singular point of the analytic variety $V \subset C^n$ there are a number of possible definitions of tangency of vectors, several of which are useful for different purposes. Corresponding to each definition we obtain a set of vectors, which in each case is a cone (see 2.21). In later sections, "the tangent cone" will always refer to the cone $C(V, p) = C_3(V, p)$. Each cone is easily seen to be identical with the tangent space $T(V, p)$ at any simple point p.

$C_1(V, p)$: $v \in C_1(V, p)$ if and only if the following is true. There is a neighborhood U of p in C^n and there is a holomorphic vector field $v(q)$ in U such that $v(p) = v$, and $v(q) \in T(V, q)$ at all simple points q of V in U. This criterion appears on Rossi, [10, §3]; compare Lemma 9.1 below.

$C_2(V, p)$: For each sequence $\{q_i\} \to p$ of simple points there is a sequence $\{v_i\} \to v$ of vectors, with $v_i \in T(V, q_i)$. A basic requirement of good stratifications of a variety is expressible in terms of this definition; see §8, (a'). The definition is related to that of C_1; see the proof that $C_2 \subset C_3$ below.

$C_3(V, p) = C(V, p)$: There is a sequence $\{q_i\} \to p$ of points of V and a sequence $\{a_i\}$ of complex numbers such that $a_i(q_i - p) \to v$. In other words, v is in the direction of a limit of secants from p. This is the commonly designated "tangent cone." See also Remark 5.11.

$C_4(V, p)$: There is a sequence $\{q_i\} \to p$ of simple points and a sequence $\{v_i\} \to v$ with $v_i \in T(V, q_i)$.

$C_5(V, p)$: There are sequences $\{q_i\} \to p$ and $\{q_i'\} \to p$ in V and a sequence $\{a_i\}$ such that $a_i(q_i' - q_i) \to v$. This definition seems to be of lesser interest.

$C_6(V, p)$: For every germ $f \in I(V, p)$ we have $df(p) \cdot v = 0$. This is sometimes called the "tangent space" of V at p.

The cones C_1, C_2 and C_6 are vector spaces; the others are not, in general.

If V is a cone with vertex at the origin 0, then $C_3(V, 0) = V$; this is false in general for the other cones.

In the real domain, one might choose somewhat different definitions; for instance, for the curve $y^2 - x^3 = 0$ in C^2, one might wish the cone at 0 to contain the non-negative points of the x-axis only.

We give some examples. Let the varieties $V_1, \ldots, V_4$ be hypersurfaces, defined by the following functions:

In C^2: $f_1 = xy,$ $f_2 = y^2 - x^3;$

In C^3: $f_3 = z^2 - xy,$ $f_4 = y^2 - zx^2.$

The corresponding cones at the origin (except for C_5) are as shown in the table. (Recall that C_x denotes the x-axis, etc.)

	V_1	V_2	V_3	V_4
C_1	$\{0\}$	$\{0\}$	$\{0\}$	$\{0\}$
C_2	$\{0\}$	C_x	$\{0\}$	C_x
C_3	V_1	C_x	V_3	C_{x_2}
C_4	V_1	C_x	C^3	C^3
C_6	C^2	C^2	C^3	C^3

For another example concerning C_1, see Remark 13.3.

In common cases, the vector space spanned by C_5 will be C_6; however, this is not always so. Note that if $V \subset C^3$ is the union of the three axes, then $C_5 = C_{xy} \cup C_{xz} \cup C_{yz}$, $C_6 = C^3$. On the other hand, let $W \subset C^3$ be the union of three lines in C_{xy}: $x = 0$, $x - y = 0$, $x + y = 0$, and the curve $y = z - x^2 = 0$; then $C_5 = C_{xy}$ while $C_6 = C^3$.

We now show that the above cones form an increasing sequence:

(3.1) $C_1 \subset C_2 \subset C_3 \subset C_4 \subset C_5 \subset C_6.$

$C_1 \subset C_2$: Trivial, since holomorphic functions are continuous.

$C_2 \subset C_3$: Let $v \in C_2$ be given; we may suppose $|v| = 1$. Given $\varepsilon > 0$, choose a neighborhood U of p such that for each simple point $q \in V \cap U$ there is a vector $v' \in T(V, q)$ with $|v' - v| < \varepsilon$. Set $\phi(q) = $ projection of v into $T(V, q)$; then ϕ is holomorphic in the set M of simple points of V in U, and $|\phi(q) - v| < \varepsilon$ in M.

Say U contains the η-neighborhood of p. Choose a point q of M within $\eta\varepsilon$ of p. Considering M as a real manifold and ϕ as a real vector field in M, construct the curve Γ through q so as to have $\phi(q')$ as tangent vector at each point q'. Suppose we can follow Γ till we reach a point q_1 distant η from q. Set $a = 1/\eta$. Now

$$|a(q_1 - p) - v| \leqq |a(q_1 - q) - v| + a|q - p| < 2\varepsilon,$$

and since $q_1 \in V$, this proves $v \in C_3(V, p)$. If Γ runs into a singular point q' of V, then we may start from a point on the opposite side of q' (note that if $C_3(V, q')$ contains a vector u, it contains $-u$ also, by Remark 5.11 below), and start a new arc Γ'; we may in fact let Γ' start from q'. Continue till we find q_1 distant η from q. We shall not go into details here.

$C_3 \subset C_4$: Let V' be the variety of singular points of V. Take any

$$v \in C_3(V, p) = C(V, p).$$

By (3.6) there is an irreducible component V_1 of V with $v \in C(V_1, p)$. Let V_1' be the union of the set of singular points of V_1 and the intersection of V_1 with the other components of V. By Lemmas 5.13 and 2.18,

$$\dim C(V_1', p) = \dim_p V_1' < \dim_p V_1 = \dim C(V_1, p),$$

and $C(V_1, p)$ is of constant dimension. Hence arbitrarily near v we may find a vector v' in $C(V_1, p)$ which is not in $C(V_1', p)$. By Lemma 3.8 there is a 1-dimensional variety $W \subset V_1$ containing p, such that $v' \in C(W, p)$. It is elementary that W contains a sequence $\{q_i\} \to p$ and a sequence $\{v_i\} \to v'$, v_i being tangent to W at q_i. Near p, W contains only simple points of V (except for p); hence $v_i \in T(V, q_i)$ (i large), proving that $v' \in C_4(V, p)$ and hence $v \in C_4(V, p)$.

$C_4 \subset C_5$: Take $v \subset C_4(V, p)$ and corresponding sequences $\{q_i\}$, $\{v_i\}$. We may take q_i'' in V very near q_i and take a_i so that $a_i(q_i'' - q_i)$ is near v_i. Now $a_i(q_i'' - q_i) \to v$, proving $v \subset C_5(V, p)$.

$C_5 \subset C_6$: This is trivial.

LEMMA 3.2. *Suppose* $p \in W \subset V$. *Then*

(3.3) $$C_i(W, p) \subset C_i(V, p) \qquad i = 3, 4, 5, 6.$$

This is evident for $i = 3, 5, 6$. We shall not go into the proof for $i = 4$. (See [15].) As a consequence, if $p \in V \cap W$,

(3.4) $$C_i(V \cap W, p) \subset C_i(V, p) \cap C_i(W, p), \qquad i = 3, 4, 5, 6.$$

The lemma fails for $i = 1, 2$, as is shown by taking $V = V_1$ as above, $W = C_x$, $p = 0$. For an example with V irreducible, take $V = V_3$ as above, $W = C_x$, $p = 0$. For the variety V of Example 13.2, taking $W = C_t$, (3.3) fails with $i = 1$ at all points of W.

We cannot expect equality in (3.4); this is shown by taking V and W in C^2, defined by $y = 0$ and by $y - x^2 = 0$ respectively.

LEMMA 3.5. *Suppose $p \in V \cap W$. Then*

$$(3.6) \qquad C_i(V \cup W, p) = C_i(V, p) \cup C_i(W, p), \qquad\qquad i = 3, 4.$$

This is clear. For $i = 5, 6$, $\supset$ holds, by Lemma 3.2; however, $=$ does not, as is seen by letting V and W be the irreducible components of the variety $C_x \cup C_y \subset C^2$.

In contrast with this, it is easily seen that

$$(3.7) \qquad C_i(V \cap W, p) \subset C_i(W, p) \qquad\qquad (i = 1, 2)$$
$$\text{if } \dim_p (W \cap V) < \dim_p (W).$$

Given a tangent vector v at a simple point V, there is of course an analytic arc through p with v as tangent at p. At singular points, the following is true:

LEMMA 3.8. *Given $p \in V \subset U \subset C^n$ and $v \in C(V, p)$, there is a 1-dimensional variety W with $p \in W \subset V$ such that $v \in C(W, p)$.*

The proof is not difficult. It will be given in [15].

PROBLEM 3.9. Given the analytic variety V and $p \in V$, show that there is a neighborhood U of p with the following property. For any $q \in V \cap U$ there is a connected 1-dimensional variety $W \subset V \cap U$ containing p and q, which has no singular points other than possibly at p.

This problem is probably of great difficulty. If we ask only for a real analytic arc from p to q, the problem is much simpler; see [16], Proposition 2, and the reference to Bruhat-Cartan given there.

LEMMA 3.10. *Given $p \in V \subset C^n$ and $\varepsilon > 0$, there is a neighborhood U of p such that for each simple point $q \neq p$ of $V \cap U$ there is a vector $v \in T(V, q)$ pointing nearly away from p:*

$$\left| \frac{v}{|v|} - \frac{q - p}{|q - p|} \right| < \varepsilon.$$

This is equally true in the real case. For the proof, see [15]. Note that the size of U cannot be taken uniformly as a function of p; this is shown by several of the varieties defined above.

4. Intrinsic character of tangent cones

Let V be an abstract analytic variety, with the ring $O(V, p)$ of germs of holomorphic functions at p. We give an intrinsic characterization of the tangent cone $C_6(V, p)$ in Lemma 4.1, of importance in studying the effect on cones of holomorphic mappings. (For C_3, see the next section.)

Suppose we have two biholomorphic imbeddings of an abstract variety V_0 into open subsets of complex spaces C^n, C'^m; then there is a biholomorphic homeomorphism ϕ of one imbedded variety onto the other, and this may be extended to a holomorphic mapping Φ of some U^n into C'^m. Now Φ is necessarily biholomorphic over some analytic manifold M containing $V \cap U^n$, and $d\Phi$ carries each tangent cone in C^n onto that in C'^m (Theorem 4.7). Most of the results of this section may be found in Rossi [10, §2].

Recall that a *derivation* δ on a ring O of germs of functions about p is a linear function on O such that

$$\delta(fg) = g(p)\delta(f) + f(p)\delta(g).$$

Let $\Delta(V, p)$ denote the linear space of derivations of $O(V, p)$.

LEMMA 4.1. *Suppose $p \in V \subset U \subset C^n$. Then there is a natural isomorphism θ of $C_6(V, p)$ onto $\Delta(V, p)$, defined as follows: Given $v \in C_6(V, p)$ and $f \in O(V, p)$, choose a holomorphic extension F of f through a neighborhood of p in C^n, and set*

(4.2) $$[\theta(v)](f) = dF(p) \cdot v.$$

First, θ is well defined. For if $F_1|V = F_2|V$, set $G = F_2 - F_1$; then $G \in I(V, p)$, $dG(p) \cdot v = 0$ since $v \in C_6(V, p)$, $dF_1(p) \cdot v = dF_2(p) \cdot v$. We see at once that $\theta(v) \in \Delta(V, p)$.

Clearly θ is linear. To show that it is one–one, suppose $\theta(v) = 0$. Then $dF(p) \cdot v = 0$ for all holomorphic F, and hence $v = 0$.

To show that θ is onto $\Delta(V, p)$, let δ be any derivation in $O(V, p)$. Taking p as origin 0 of coordinates, set

$$\bar{x}_i = x_i|V, \qquad v_i = \delta(\bar{x}_i), \qquad v = (v_i, \ldots, v_n).$$

Take any $f \in O(V, p)$; say $F|V = f$. Expand F at 0:

(4.3) $$F(x_1, \ldots, x_n) = a + \Sigma b_i x_i + \Sigma R_i(x_1, \ldots, x_n)x_i, \qquad R_i(0) = 0.$$

Then

$$\delta(f) = \Sigma b_i \delta(\bar{x}_i) = \Sigma v_i \partial F(0)/\partial x_i = dF(0) \cdot v,$$

and hence $\theta(v) = \delta$, if $v \in C_6(V, p)$. This holds; for taking any $F \in I(V, p)$ gives (by the same reasoning) $f = 0$, $dF(p) \cdot v = \delta(0) = 0$.

REMARK 4.4. For $V = C^n$, we have $C^n \approx \Delta(C^n, p)$.

Let ϕ be a holomorphic mapping of V into V'_r, with $\phi(p) = p'$. Then there is a naturally defined linear function

(4.5) $$\phi_\Delta : \Delta(V, p) \to \Delta(V', p'),$$

defined as follows: Given $\delta \in \Delta(V, p)$ and $f' \in O(V', p')$, set

(4.6) $(\phi_\Delta \delta)(f') = \delta(\phi^* f')$.

ϕ_Δ behaves in the natural manner with regard to mappings.

Part of the next theorem requires the analytic character of the $C_i(V, p)$; see Theorem 5.6 below.

THEOREM 4.7. *Suppose* $p \in V \subset U \subset C^n$, $p' \in V' \subset U' \subset C'^{n'}$, *and* ϕ *is a holomorphic mapping of* V *into* V' *with* $\phi(p) = p'$. *Then there is a holomorphic mapping* Φ *of a neighborhood* U_1 *of* p *in* C^n *into* $C'^{n'}$ *such that* $\Phi|(V \cap U_1) = \phi|(V \cap U_1)$. *For any such* Φ, *we have (letting* θ, θ' *be as in* (4.2))

(4.8) $in\ C_6(V, p),\qquad d\Phi(p) = \theta'^{-1} \circ \phi_\Delta \circ \theta,$

(4.9) $d\Phi(p)$ *maps* $C_i(V, p)$ *holomorphically into* $C_i(V', p')$
$$(i = 3, 4, 5, 6).$$

Suppose, furthermore, that ϕ *is a biholomorphic homeomorphism onto* V'. *Then*

(4.10) $d\Phi(p)|C_i(V, p)$ *is one–one biholomorphic onto* $C_i(V', p')$
$$(i = 1, \ldots, 6).$$

Also, if $n \leq n'$, *we may make* Φ *a biholomorphism in* U_1. *If* $n > n'$, *we may choose an analytic manifold* $M^{n'} \subset C^n$ *with* $V \cap U_1 \subset M^{n'}$, *and make* Φ *a biholomorphism in* $M^{n'}$.

First, since each coordinate ϕ_i $(i = 1, \ldots, n')$ of ϕ is holomorphic in V, it has a holomorphic extension Φ_i; these functions give Φ.

To prove (4.8), take any $v \in C_6(V, p)$. Say

$$v \xrightarrow{\ \theta\ } \delta \xrightarrow{\ \phi_\Delta\ } \delta' \xleftarrow{\ \theta'\ } v'.$$

Now take any holomorphic function F' in a neighborhood of p', and set

$$F = \Phi^* F', \qquad f' = F'|V', \qquad f = F|V.$$

Then, using (4.6) and (4.2),

$$dF'(p') \cdot v' = \delta'(f') = \delta(f) = dF(p) \cdot v$$
$$= d(F' \circ \Phi)(p) \cdot v = dF'(p') \cdot [d\Phi(p) \cdot v];$$

hence $v' = d\Phi(p) \cdot v$, and (4.8) follows.

(4.9) for $i = 6$ is an immediate consequence of (4.8). Since $d\Phi(p)$ is linear in $C_6(V, p)$, it is holomorphic in each $C_i(V, p)$. Suppose $v \in C_5(V, p)$. Choose sequences $\{q_j\}$, $\{r_j\} \to p$ in V, and $\{a_j\}$, $a_j(r_j - q_j) \to v$. Given $\varepsilon > 0$,

$$|\Phi(r_j) - \Phi(q_j) - d\Phi(p) \cdot (r_j - q_j)| \leq \varepsilon |r_j - q_j|$$

for j large enough; hence

$$d\Phi(p) \cdot v = \lim a_j[\Phi(r_j) - \Phi(q_j)] \in C_5(V', p').$$

Replacing q_j by p in the above proof gives (4.9) with $i = 3$.

Now take $v \in C_4(V, p)$; say $\{q_j\} \to p, q_j$ simple, $v_j \in T(V, q_j)$, $v_j \to v$. Then (4.9) with $i = 3$ gives

$$v_j' = d\Phi(q_j) \cdot v_j \in C_3(V', q_j') \subset C_4(V', q_j');$$

hence there is a simple point q_j'' and a vector v_j'' such that

$$v_j'' \in T(V', q_j''), \quad |q_j'' - q_j'| < 1/j, \quad |v_j'' - v_j'| < 1/j.$$

Hence

$$d\Phi(p) \cdot v = \lim v_j'' \in C_4(V', p').$$

If ϕ is a biholomorphism, then clearly ϕ_Δ is an isomorphism onto, and (4.10) with $i = 6$ follows from (4.8). By (3.1), $d\Phi(p)$ is one–one in each $C_i(V, p)$; by symmetry, (4.10) for each i will follow from (4.9) for the same i. Thus we now need only prove (4.9) for $i = 1, 2$. For $i = 1$, note that if $v(q)$ is holomorphic in U_1, then $v'(\Phi(q)) = d\Phi(q) \cdot v(q)$ is holomorphic in $\Phi(U_1)$. The proof for $i = 2$ is simple also.

Choose an analytic manifold M as in Lemma 4.12 below. Because of (4.10) and (4.13), Φ is a biholomorphism from $M \cap U_1$ (for U_1 small enough) onto $\Phi(M \cap U_1)$. Set $m = \min (n, n')$. Leaving Φ fixed in $M \cap U_1$, we may clearly alter it in a chosen $M^m \supset M$ so it is biholomorphism there. This completes the proof.

REMARK 4.11. Taking $V = C_x$, $V' = C_x \cup C_y$ in C^2, ϕ = identity in V, shows that (4.9) may fail for $i = 1, 2$.

LEMMA 4.12. *Suppose $p \in V \subset U \subset C^n$. Then there is an analytic manifold M containing the part of V near p, such that*

$$(4.13) \qquad C_6(V, p) = T(M, p).$$

For any analytic manifold M' containing V near p, $C_6(V, p) \subset T(M', p)$.

Let $F_1, \ldots, F_s$ be a maximal set of elements of $I(V, p)$ with independent differentials at p; then for some U, $F_1 = \cdots = F_s = 0$ defines an analytic manifold M in U, and $V \cap U \subset M$. If (4.13) is false, there is a vector v in $T(M, p)$ which is not in $C_6(V, p)$. We may then choose $F \in I(V, p)$ with $dF(p) \cdot v \neq 0$. But this shows that $dF(p)$ is independent of the $dF_i(p)$, a contradiction. Thus (4.13) holds. The last part of the lemma is clear.

COROLLARY 4.14. *Given $p \in V \subset U < C^n$, there is a coordinate system with origin at p (analytically related to the original coordinates) such that the part of V near p is in the $(x_1, \ldots, x_d)$-plane, where $d = \dim C_6(V, p)$.*

5. Algebraic character of tangent cones

For any V and p, the cones C_1, C_2, and C_6 are vector spaces. We shall show that the remaining cones are algebraic varieties; moreover, for $C = C_3$, we give the representation in terms of initial polynomials of functions in $I(V, p)$. First we show that for $i = 4, 5, 6$, the set of cones $C_i(V, p)$ for all $p \in V$ forms an analytic variety.

THEOREM 5.1. *Let V be an analytic variety in the open set $U \subset C^n$. Set*

$$(5.2) \qquad C_i(V) = \{(p, v) \in U \times C^n : p \in V, v \in C_i(V, p)\}, \qquad i = 1, \ldots, 6.$$

Then for $i = 4, 5, 6$, $C_i(V)$ is an analytic variety in $U \times C^n$. Moreover, $C_4(V)$ is the smallest analytic variety containing all (p, v) with p simple, $v \in T(V, p)$.

First take the case $i = 6$ (Rossi, [10, Lemma 4.1]). Take any $p \in U$; by coherence, there are functions $f_1, \ldots, f_s$, holomorphic in a neighborhood U_1 of p, which generate $I(V, q)$ for each $q \in U_1$. Set

$$A = \{(q, v): q \in U_1, df_i(q) \cdot v = 0 \ (i = 1, \ldots, s)\};$$

then A is analytic in $U_1 \times C^n$. So is $(V \cap U_1) \times C^n$. Also

$$C_6(V) \cap (U_1 \times C^n) = [(V \cap U_1) \times C^n] \cap A,$$

showing that $C_6(V)$ is analytic.

For the case $i = 4$, we need merely note that, if V' is the set of singular points of V, then

$$(5.3) \qquad C_4(V) = \text{clos}\,[C_6(V) - V' \times C^n] \cap (U \times C^n);$$

now apply Lemma 2.15. The last statement of the theorem is clear.

Now consider the case $i = 5$. Using the coordinates in C^n, define the holomorphic functions in $C^n \times C^n \times C^n$

$$(5.4) \qquad \alpha_{jk}(p, q, v) = \begin{vmatrix} q_j - p_j & q_k - p_k \\ v_j & v_k \end{vmatrix};$$

these all vanish if and only if $q = p$ or v is a multiple of $q - p$. Set

$$B = \{(p, q, v): p, q \in U; \alpha_{jk}(p, q, v) = 0 \quad (\text{all } j, k)\}.$$

This is an analytic variety, and hence so is

$$B' = B \cap (V \times V \times C^n).$$

Set $D = \{(p, p): p \in V\}$ and

$$B'' = \text{clos}\,[B' - D \times C^n] \cap (U \times U \times C^n)$$

this also is analytic, as is

$$C_5' = B'' \cap (D \times C^n).$$

Now clearly

$$(p, v) \in C_5(V) \cap (U \times C^n) \text{ if and only if } (p, p, v) \in C_5',$$

showing that $C_5(V)$ is analytic. (If C_5' is defined near (p_0, p_0, v_0) by functions f_i, then the functions $f_i'(p, v) = f_i(p, p, v)$ define $C_5(V)$ near (p_0, v_0).)

REMARK 5.5. The sets $C_i(V)$ $(i = 1, 2, 3)$ are not closed, and hence are not analytic, in general. (See for instance, Example 7.8.)

THEOREM 5.6. *Given* $p \in V \subset U \subset C^n$, *each cone* $C_i(V, p)$ *is an algebraic variety.*

By a theorem of Chow (see for instance [9, Satz 14]), it is sufficient to show that the cone is analytic. This is trivial for $i = 1, 2, 6$, since the cone is then a vector space. For $i = 4, 5$, it follows from the last theorem. We must still consider the case $i = 3$. Set

$$E_p = \{(q, v) \colon q \in U, \; \alpha_{jk}(p, q, v) = 0 \; (\text{all } j, k)\};$$

this is analytic in $U \times C^n$. So is $E_p' = E_p \cap (V \times C^n)$, and so is

$$C_p' = \text{clos} \, [E_p' - \{p\} \times C^n] \cap (U \times C^n).$$

Noting that $v \in C(V, p)$ if and only if $(p, v) \in C_p'$, the result follows. (It follows also from Theorem 5.8 below.)

We shall now find polynomials defining $C(V, p)$. Suppose f is a holomorphic function in an open set U containing $p = (a_1, \ldots, a_n)$. Expanding about p and collecting terms of the same degree gives

(5.7) $$f = f^{[m]} + f^{[m+1]} + \ldots, \qquad f^{[m]} \not\equiv 0,$$

where each $f^{[k]}$ is a homogeneous polynomial of degree k in the $x_i - a_i$. We then say that f is of *order* m at p, and call $f^{[m]}$ the *initial polynomial* of f at p. The number m is characterized as the order to which f first fails to vanish at p, and $f^{[m]}$ is the function defining $C(V_f, p)$, where V_f is defined by f (see Lemma 10.6).

THEOREM 5.8. *Given* $p \in V \subset U \subset C^n$, $C(V, p)$ *is defined by the vanishing of all initial polynomials at p of functions in $I(V, p)$.*

One part of the theorem is easy to prove: Taking p as origin of coordinates, let f be any function in $I(V, p)$; we shall show that for each $v \in C(V, p), f^{[m]}(v) = 0$ if ord $f = m$. For any complex number λ, we have

(5.9) $$f(\lambda v) = \lambda^m [f^{[m]}(v) + \lambda R(v, \lambda)],$$

where R is holomorphic. Take $\{q_i\} \to 0$ in V and $\{a_i\}$ so that $a_i q_i \to v$. Set $\lambda_i = 1/a_i$ (we may suppose $v \neq 0$). Now

$$0 = f(q_i) = \lambda_i^m [f^{[m]}(a_i q_i) + \lambda_i R(a_i q_i, \lambda_i)].$$

Since $a_i q_i \to v$, $\lambda_i \to 0$ and R is bounded, we must have $f^{[m]}(v) = 0$.

The other half of the theorem is more difficult to prove; see [15].

REMARK 5.10.   In general, $I(C(V, p), p)$ is not generated by the initial parts of a given set of generators of $I(V, p)$. For an example, let $V^1 \subset C^3$ be defined by the vanishing of

$$f = xy - y^3, \qquad g = xz - z^3;$$

then f and g generate $I(V, 0)$, but $f^{[2]}$ and $g^{[2]}$ do not generate $I(C(V, 0), 0)$. The latter ideal is generated by $f^{[2]} = xy$, $g^{[2]} = xz$, and

$$(zf - yg)^{[4]} = yz(z^2 - y^2).$$

REMARK 5.11.   In the definition of $C = C_3$, we could require that the a_i be real and positive; for Theorem 5.8 may be proved with this definition, and it then follows that $av \in C$ if and only if $v \in C$ (a complex).

How near is V to $C(V, p)$ near p? We give an answer in terms of the Hausdorff distance between two sets: Let $S_\rho(p) = \{q : |q - p| = \rho\}$ be sphere of radius ρ about p. Let $U_\rho(Q)$ denote the ρ-neighborhood of the point set Q, i.e., the set of points, each within ρ of some point of Q. Set

$$\text{dist } (P, Q) = \inf \{\rho : P \subset U_\rho(Q) \text{ and } Q \subset U_\rho(P)\}.$$

Then

(5.12) $\rho^{-1} \text{dist } [V \cap S_\rho(p), C(V, p) \cap S_\rho(p)] \to 0$ as $\rho \to 0$.

To show this, call the two sets V_ρ, C_ρ. That $V_\rho \subset V_{\rho\varepsilon}(C_\rho)$ for small ρ follows at once from the definition of $C(V, p)$. With the help of Lemma 3.8 it is easy to see that $C_\rho \subset U_{\rho\varepsilon}(V_\rho)$ for small ρ. (Use a finite set of vectors in $(C(V, p)$.)

LEMMA 5.13.   For $p \in V \subset U \subset C^n$,

$$\dim C(V, p) = \dim_p V.$$

If V is of constant dimension near p, so is $C(V, p)$.

The truth of the equality follows from the proof concerning $C(V, p)$ in Theorem 5.6. The last statement will be proved in [15]; it makes use of (5.12).

REMARK 5.14. $C(V, p)$ may be reducible even if V is irreducible, as is shown by the variety $z^3 - xy = 0$, at the origin.

6. Intrinsic study of $C(V, p)$

We wish to give an intrinsic characterization of the tangent cone of V at p as a set of derivations on $O(V, p)$. We need some definitions.

Let $\mathfrak{m}$ be the maximal ideal of $O(V, p)$; it consists of those elements of $O(V, p)$ which vanish at p. The kth power $\mathfrak{m}^k$ of $\mathfrak{m}$ consists of those elements expressible as a product of k elements of $\mathfrak{m}$, together with finite sums of such elements.

Example 6.1.   Let $y^2 - x^3$ define V in C^2, and set $\bar{x} = x|V$, $\bar{y} = y|V$. Then the element $\bar{y}^2$ of $\mathfrak{m}^2$ equals $\bar{x}^3$ and hence lies also in $\mathfrak{m}^3$.

Let $C_\Delta(V, p)$ denote the set of those derivations δ of $O(V, p)$ with the following property: given any s, k, and elements $u_{ij}(i = 1, \ldots, s; j = 1, \ldots, k)$ of $\mathfrak{m}$,

(6.2) $\qquad$ if $\sum_i u_{i1} \cdots u_{ik} \in \mathfrak{m}^{k+1}$ then $\sum_i \delta(u_{i1}) \cdots \delta(u_{ik}) = 0$.

THEOREM 6.3.   *Suppose $p \in V \subset U \subset C^n$. Then the isomorphism θ of Lemma 4.1, restricted to $C(V, p)$, is one–one onto $C_\Delta(V, p)$.*

First, take any $\delta \in C_\Delta(V, p)$. Say $\theta(v) = \delta$; then $v_i = \delta(\bar{x}_i)$. Take any $f = f^{[\mu]} + f' \in I(V, p)$ (f' of order $> \mu$). Now $f^{[\mu]}|V = -f'|V$ is of order $> \mu$, and hence is in $\mathfrak{m}^{\mu+1}$; applying (6.2) with $k = \mu$ to the expression of $f^{[\mu]}$ as a polynomial, we find $f^{[\mu]}(v) = 0$. By Theorem 5.8, $v \in C(V, p)$.

Conversely, take any $v \in C(V, p)$ and corresponding δ. Suppose

$$\sum_{i=1}^s u_{i1} \cdots u_{i\mu} = \sum_{j=1}^t w_{j1} \cdots w_{j\mu'}, \quad \mu' = \mu + 1,$$

with $u_{ik}, w_{ik} \in \mathfrak{m}$. Expand each u_{ij}:

$$u_{ij} = \sum_h a_{ijh}\bar{x}_h + g_{ij}(\bar{x}_1, \ldots, \bar{x}_n), \text{ ord } g_{ij} > 1,$$

and expand each w_{ij} similarly. Now if

$$F(x_1, \ldots, x_n) = \sum_{i=1}^s \left(\sum_{h=1}^n a_{i1h}x_h \right) \cdots \left(\sum_{h=1}^n a_{i\mu h}x_h \right),$$

we have

$$\sum_i u_{i1} \cdots u_{i\mu} - \sum_j w_{j1} \cdots w_{j\mu'} = (F + G)|V, \quad \text{ord } G > \mu.$$

Since $F + G = 0$ in V and $v \in C(V, p)$, $F(v) = 0$. Using $v_i = \delta(\bar{x}_i)$ and $\delta(u_{ij}) = \Sigma_h a_{ijh}\delta(\bar{x}_h)$ gives $\Sigma_i \delta(u_{i1}) \cdots \delta(u_{i\mu}) = 0$, proving $\delta \in C_\Delta(V, p)$.

We next connect $C_\Delta(V, p)$ with the graded ring G of $\mathfrak{m}$; see Samuel [11, pp. 68–69] and Zariski-Samuel [17, pp. 248–250].

Set $\mathfrak{m}^0 = O(V, p)$,

$$(6.4) \qquad\qquad L_i = \mathfrak{m}^i/\mathfrak{m}^{i+1}, \quad G = \sum_{i=0}^{\infty} L_i;$$

the elements of G are the finite sums $\alpha_0 + \cdots + \alpha_k$, $\alpha_i \in L_i$. The multiplication in $\mathfrak{m}$ defines a multiplication in G, making it into a graded ring.

LEMMA 6.5.   *Let γ be a linear function on $L_1 = \mathfrak{m}/\mathfrak{m}^2$. Then there is an extension Γ of γ over G which is a ring homomorphism into C if and only if the following condition is satisfied: for any s, μ, and set $\{\alpha_{ij}\}(i = 1, \ldots, s; j = 1, \ldots, \mu)$ of elements of L_1,*

$$(6.6) \qquad \text{if } \sum_i \alpha_{i1} \cdots \alpha_{i\mu} = 0, \text{ then } \sum_i \gamma(\alpha_{i1}) \cdots \gamma(\alpha_{i\mu}) = 0.$$

If Γ exists, it must be given as follows: in L_0, Γ is the natural isomorphism onto C. For any element β of any L_μ ($\mu > 0$), choose a representation $\beta = \sum_i \alpha_{i1} \cdots \alpha_{i\mu}$; set $\Gamma(\beta) = \sum_i \gamma(\alpha_{i1}) \cdots \gamma(\alpha_{i\mu})$. That the result is independent of the representation follows at once from (6.6). Clearly Γ has the required properties.

Any derivation δ on $O(V, p)$ is defined in $\mathfrak{m}$ and vanishes in $\mathfrak{m}^2$; hence it gives rise to a linear function $\bar\delta$ on L_1.

THEOREM 6.7.   *A derivation δ on $O(V, p)$ is in $C_\Delta(V, p)$ if and only if the corresponding linear function $\bar\delta$ on L_1 can be extended to be a ring homomorphism of the graded ring G into C.*

This is an immediate consequence of the definition of C_Δ and of the last lemma.

We have been working in V directly. Let us now return to the situation $p \in V \subset U \subset C^n$. Choose coordinates as in Corollary 4.14; the part of V near p lies in $(x_1, \ldots, x_d)$-space, and $d = \dim C_6(V, p)$. Let J be the injection of V in C^n. For a function f in V, let $\pi_p f$ denote the germ of f at p. For a germ u lying in $\mathfrak{m}^\mu$, let $\rho_\mu u$ denote the corresponding element of $L_\mu = \mathfrak{m}^\mu/\mathfrak{m}^{\mu+1}$. Set

$$\bar{x}_i = x_i | V = J^* x_i, \quad \pi_p \bar{x}_i = u_i, \quad \rho_1 u_i = \alpha_i.$$

It is easily seen that $\alpha_1, \ldots, \alpha_d$ form a base in L_1; hence

(6.8) $C_6(V, p)$ or $\Delta(V, p)$ may be considered as the dual of L_1.

Consider the polynomial ring $C[x_1, \ldots, x_d]$. We shall define a homomorphism ϕ of this ring into the graded ring G as follows: for any homogeneous polynomial f of degree μ, set

$$(6.9) \qquad\qquad \phi(f) = \rho_\mu \pi_p J^* f = f(\alpha_1, \ldots, \alpha_d) \in L_\mu.$$

For any polynomial $f = f^{[0]} + \cdots + f^{[k]}$, set $\phi(f) = \Sigma_i \phi(f^{[i]})$. Let K_ϕ denote the kernel of ϕ.

LEMMA 6.10. *With the above notations, the following are equivalent for homogeneous polynomials f*:

(a) $f \in K_\phi$.

(b) $f(\alpha_1, \ldots, \alpha_d) = 0$.

(c) f *is the initial polynomial of a function F in $I(V, p)$.*

This is easy to verify; it is practically implicit in results above.

As a consequence, we have the following characterization of $C(V, p)$:

THEOREM 6.11. *Suppose $p \in V \subset U \subset C^n$, and coordinates are chosen as above. Then with the above notations, $v \in C(V, p)$ if and only if for all homogeneous polynomials f in K_ϕ we have $f(v) = 0$.*

REMARK 6.12. One may give an intrinsic definition of an analytic manifold as follows: it is an analytic variety M such that for each $p \in M$, $O(M, p)$ is a regular ring, that is, is isomorphic with $C[x_1, \ldots, x_d]$ for some d. If we have $M \subset C^n$, then with coordinates as above, M near p is an open subset of $(x_1, \ldots, x_d)$-space, $K_\phi = 0$, and $O(M, p)$ is regular; conversely, if $O(M, p)$ is regular, say isomorphic with $C[x_1, \ldots, x_d]$, then considering $x_1, \ldots, x_d$ as coordinates near p imbeds M near p biholomorphically onto an open subset of C^d. Note that p is a simple point of the analytic variety V if and only if $C(V, p) = C_6(V, p)$.

Example 6.13. For $V: y^2 - x^3 = 0$ in C^2, 0 is a singular point. In V add the new holomorphic function t, with $t^2 = x$, $t^3 = y$; V becomes an analytic manifold, holomorphically but not biholomorphically imbedded in C^2.

7. Tangent spaces

So far we have considered vectors at a singular point p of an analytic variety V, relating them to vectors at nearby simple points. We now take up similar questions, studying tangent planes $T(V, q)$ (q simple) as elements of a Grassmann space, instead of the individual vectors in these spaces.

Let $P^{n-1, r-1}$ be the space of projective alternating contravariant $(r - 1)$-vectors in projective $(n - 1)$-space P^{n-1}. An element α of $P^{n-1, r-1}$ has components $\alpha_{\lambda_1 \ldots \lambda_r}$, each λ_i running from 1 to n. Certain $(r - 1)$-vectors (the simple ones) are the $(r - 1)$-directions of (unoriented) r-planes in C^n; these form the Grassmann space $G^{n-1, r-1}$.

Suppose we have $V \subset U \subset C^n$, V *being of constant dimension* r. For each simple point q of V, let $T_0(V, q)$ denote the $(r - 1)$-direction of $T(V, q)$. Consider the set of all pairs $(q, T_0(V, q))$ in $U \times G^{n-1, r-1}$. Let $\tau(V)$ denote the closure of this set in $U \times G^{n-1, r-1}$; we call it the *tangent space* of V.

(Using individual vectors in place of tangent planes gives $C_4(V)$, except that
the affine case was used previously; see Theorem 5.1.) If V is an analytic
manifold, the set of pairs shown above is already closed.

Set $\tau(V, p) = \{\alpha\colon (p, \alpha) \in \tau(V)\}$; we may call this the *tangent space set*
of V at p. For q simple, $\tau(V, p)$ has the single element $\dot{T}_0(V, p)$. For an
example, consider the variety V_4 of §3, defined by $y^2 - zx^2 = 0$. For
$p = (0, 0, z)$ with $z \neq 0$, $\tau(V, p)$ has two elements, corresponding to the
tangent planes of the two sheets of V there. At 0, $\tau(V, 0)$ is the set of
1-directions of all planes through the x-axis, as we see by considering the
parabolas in which the planes $x = x_0$ cut V.

THEOREM 7.1. *Let V be an analytic variety of constant dimension r in
the open set $U \subset C^n$. Then $\tau(V)$ is an analytic variety in $U \times G^{n-1,r-1}$, and
for each $p \in V$, $\tau(V, p)$ is an algebraic variety in $G^{n-1,r-1}$.*

The last statement is a consequence of the first and of the Theorem
of Chow. To prove the first, take any $p \in V$. There are functions $f_1, \ldots, f_s$,
holomorphic in a neighborhood U_1 of p, which generate $I(V, q)$ for each
$q \in U_1$. We shall sketch the proof that $\tau(V) \cap (U_1 \times G^{n-1,r-1})$ is analytic.
For full details, see [15].

Given $q \in U_1$, $\lambda = (\lambda_1, \ldots, \lambda_{n-r})$, $\nu = (\nu_1, \ldots, \nu_{n-r})$, $(\lambda_i \leq s, \nu_i \leq n)$,
let $D_{\lambda\nu}(q)$ be the determinant with elements $\partial f_{\lambda_i}(q)/\partial x_{\nu_j}$. Given any
$\mu = (\mu_1, \ldots, \mu_{n-r+1})$ $(\mu_i \leq n)$ and λ, define the vector function $v_{\lambda\mu}(q)$
by means of its components: letting $\mu^{(i)}$ denote μ with the ith component
omitted, set

(7.2) $$v_{\lambda\mu}^{\mu_i}(q) = (-1)^{i-1}D_{\lambda\mu^{(i)}}(q), \text{ other } v_{\lambda\mu}^j(q) = 0.$$

Take any simple point q of $V \cap U_1$, and any λ and μ. If the $df_{\lambda_i}(q)$
are dependent, then $v_{\lambda\mu}(q) = 0$. Otherwise, the f_{λ_i} define V near q, and
$df_{\lambda_i}(q) \cdot v_{\lambda\mu}(q) = 0$ for each i, proving $v_{\lambda\mu}(q) \in T(V, q)$. It is easy to see in
fact that the set of all $v_{\lambda\mu}(q)$ span $T(V, q)$.

Given $\alpha \in G^{n-1,r-1}$, let us write down the condition that α be $T_0(V, q)$
at the simple point q. Geometrically, the exterior product of any vector
of $T(V, q)$ with α must be 0. It is sufficient to use a spanning set of
vectors. Analytically, this is expressed as follows: for any λ, μ and $\sigma = (\sigma_1, \ldots, \sigma_{r+1})$, letting $\hat{\imath}$ denote the omission of the corresponding symbol,

(7.3) $$\sum_{i=1}^{r+1}(-1)^{i-1}v_{\lambda\mu}^{\sigma_i}(q)\alpha^{\sigma_1\cdots\hat{\imath}\cdots\sigma_{r+1}} = 0.$$

Let W_0 consist of all pairs $(q, \alpha) \in U_0 \times G^{n-1,r-1}$ such that $q \in V$ and

(7.3) holds for all λ, μ and σ; then W_0 is analytic. Let V' be the singular variety of V. Clearly

(7.4) $\quad \tau(V) \cap (U_1 \times G^{n-1,r-1})$

$$= \mathrm{clos}\,(W_0 - V' \times G^{n-1,r-1}) \cap (U_1 \times G^{n-1,r-1}),$$

and just as in §5, this shows that $\tau(V)$ is analytic.

REMARK 7.5. The natural projection of $\tau(V)$ onto V is holomorphic, and is one–one except over V'. Thus $\tau(V)$ is a modification, or "blowing-up," of V (see [5]).

We shall need to study not only what limits of tangent planes we obtain on approaching a singular point of V, but also what limits are obtained on the approach through a given direction. This will be carried out along the points of an analytic manifold M lying in V (in practice, lying in the singular set of V).

A tangent cone relative to M will be useful; we define it as follows:

Let $C(V, M, p)$ $(p \in M)$ denote the set of all vectors v with the following property: there are sequences $\{p_i\} \to p$ in M, $\{q_i\} \to p$ in V, and $\{a_i\}$, such that $a_i(q_i - p_i) \to v$. Clearly

(7.6) $\qquad C(V, p) \subset C(V, M, p) \subset C_5(V, p),$

(7.7) $\qquad C(V, \{p\}, p) = C(V, p), \quad C(V, V, p) = C_5(V, p).$

Example 7.8. Note that $y^2 = x^2(1 - x)$ defines a curve with a crossing point at the origin, and no other singularity. Now in (t, x, y)-space, form such a curve through each point $\rho_t = (t, 0, 0)$, contracting it by the factor t^2; this gives the variety defined by $t^2y^2 - t^2x^2 + x^3 = 0$. For later purposes, we wish to get rid of the singular line that coincides with the y-axis. To this end, we add the term $-y^4$, giving the variety V defined by

$$f(t, x, y) = t^2y^2 - t^2x^2 + x^3 - y^4.$$

It is easy to see that the singular variety (defined by $f = df = 0$) of V consists of the t-axis C_t only. For $t \neq 0$, $C(V, \rho_t)$ is the pair of planes $y = \pm x$, while $C(V, 0)$ is the plane $x = 0$. Also

$$C(V, C_t, \rho_t) = C(V, \rho_t)\ (t \neq 0), \quad C(V, C_t, 0) = C^3.$$

Note that the sequence $a_i(q_i - p_i)$ with

$$p_i = \rho_{1/i}, \quad q_i = (1/i, 1/i^2, 0), \quad a_i = i^2,$$

defines the vector $e_x = (0, 1, 0)$ in $C(V, C_t, 0)$, and that $T(V, q_i)$ is nearly orthogonal to e_x for i large. We are interested in the set of points of M where there is such an occurrence.

We shall form a modification of V in which the points of M are blown up. Choose a holomorphic function $N(p)$ in M which, at each p, is an analytic plane of maximum dimension transverse to M at p; supposing that M is small enough, this function will exist. Let U_0 be a neighborhood of M such that the connected components of the $N(p)$ in U_0 and containing p fill out U_0 in a one–one holomorphic way; then setting $\gamma(q) = p$ for q in the component of $N(p)$ gives a holomorphic retraction γ of U_0 onto M. Let η denote the natural projection of $C^n - \{0\}$ onto P^{n-1}. Let V_0 denote the set of simple points of V. Consider the set of pairs

$$(q, \eta(q - \gamma(q))), \quad q \in V_0 \cap U_0 - M;$$

let $V^* \subset U_0 \times P^n$ denote the closure of the set of these pairs. We see easily that V^* is analytic (compare the proof of Theorem 5.1, $i = 5$). If π is the natural projection onto $V \cap U_0$, π is one–one in $V_0 \cap U_0 - M$, and the points over $p \in M$ correspond to the vectors in

$$C_N(V, M, p) = C(V, M, p) \cap N(p).$$

Now consider the set of triples

$$\phi(q) = (q, \eta(q - \gamma(q))), \ T_0(V, q)), \ q \in V_0 \cap U_0 - M;$$
set

$$(7.9) \qquad \tau^*(V, M) = \mathrm{clos}\, \{\phi(q)\} \cap (M \times P^{n-1} \times G^{n-1, r-1}).$$

(The points away from M do not interest us.) By the usual methods one may show that this set is analytic. Set

$$(7.10) \quad \tau^*(V, M, p, \beta) = \{\alpha \colon (p, \beta, \alpha) \in \tau^*(V, M)\}, \ p \in M, \ \beta \in P^{n-1};$$

this is the set of limits of r-directions $T_0(V, q)$ as $q \to p$ in such a manner that the direction from $\gamma(q)$ to q approaches β. (It is void if β is not parallel to $N(p)$.)

Recall that for the V_4 considered in §3, setting $M = C_z$, some elements of $\tau(V, 0)$ do not contain M; on the other hand, for $p \in M$, each α in $\tau^*(V, C_z, p, \beta)$ contains β. In contrast with this, take the variety V of Example 7.8, and set $M = C_t$. For $p \in M$, each element of $\tau(V, p)$ contains the 0-direction of C_t; on the other hand, $\tau^*(V, C_t, 0, \eta(e_x))$ contains the 1-direction of C_{ty}, which does not contain $\eta(e_x)$. In the next section we look further into these phenomena.

REMARK 7.11. Changes of coordinates cause linear transformations of differentials, and hence do not alter the structure of the tangent spaces.

8. Stratifications

If V is an analytic variety of dimension r, then $V = V_0 \cup V'$, where V_0 is the set of simple points of dimension r of V and hence is an analytic manifold, and V' is an analytic variety of lower dimension (Lemma 2.18). We may therefore split V' similarly, and continue until we have expressed V as a union of analytic manifolds. This suggests the following definition:

A *stratification* of the analytic variety V is an expression of V as the disjoint union of a locally finite set of analytic manifolds, each of constant dimension, called the *strata*, such that the frontier of each stratum is the union of a set of lower dimensional strata. (We may require the strata to be connected.)

Example 8.1. Let W be the variety V_3 of §3 (defined by $z^2 - xy = 0$), together with the z-axis. Then with the splitting $W = W_0 \cup W'$ as above, $W' = C_z$, an analytic manifold. Note that fron $(W_0) = \{0\} \neq C_z$; the splitting is not a stratification.

LEMMA 8.2. *The closure of each stratum of a stratification is an analytic variety whose dimension is that of the stratum. The frontier of a stratum is an analytic variety of lower dimension.*

We prove this by induction on the dimension of the stratum. Given the stratum M, of dimension d, note that fron (M) is a closed set; hence we may write

$$\text{fron } (M) = \bar{M} - M = M_1 \cup M_2 \cup \cdots = \bar{M}_1 \cup \bar{M}_2 \cup \cdots = A,$$

where dim $M_i < d$. By induction, each $\bar{M}_i$, and hence A, is an analytic variety; dim $A < d$. That $\bar{M}$ is analytic now follows from Lemma 2.19.

Take any analytic variety $V \subset U \subset C^n$. We prove the *existence* of a stratification by defining the *primary stratification*: The highest dimensional strata are the connected components of the set V_0; the complement V' is analytic. Now suppose the strata of dimension $> d$ have been defined, the closure of each is analytic, and the complement in V of the union of these strata is an analytic variety V^* of dimension d. Let $M_1^*, M_2^*, \ldots$ be the (locally finite) set of connected components of the set M^* of simple points of V^* of dimension d; by Lemma 2.16, each set $\bar{M}_i^*$ is analytic.

Consider any M_i^*, and any previously defined stratum M_j. Set

$$A_j = \bar{M}_j \cap V^*, \quad A_{ij} = A_j \cap \bar{M}_i^*;$$

these are analytic. The set of sets A_{ij} is locally finite; hence the union B_i of those A_{ij} of dimension $<d$ is analytic. Set

$$M_i = M_i^* - B_i;$$

this is a connected analytic manifold. The M_i form new strata; the $\bar{M}_i = \bar{M}_i^*$ are analytic. The complement in V of the union of all the strata so far is $(V^* - M^*) \cup (B_1 \cup B_2 \cup \cdot \cdot \cdot)$, which is analytic. Hence we may continue defining the strata.

We must show that the frontier K of any stratum M_j is a union of strata of lower dimension. It is clearly contained in such a union; hence we need merely show that if K contains a point p of a stratum M_i, then $M_i \subset K$. With the notations as above, $p \notin B_i$; hence (since $p \in A_{ij}$) $\dim A_{ij} = d$. Therefore, by 2.8, $M_i^* \subset \bar{M}_j$ and hence $M_i \subset K$. Thus we have a stratification.

In this connection, see [15, Theorem 18.11].

REMARK 8.3.   Applying the definition of a stratification directly in the real case leads to difficulties. For instance, take V_4 as in §3, in the real domain. The highest dimensional stratum M^2 should consist naturally of the simple points of V_4; now fron (M^2) consists of half the z-axis, and this is not an analytic variety. For C-analytic sets V (see [16]), one may take the complexification V^*, stratify it, and let the strata of V be the real parts of the strata of V^*, in spite of the failure of certain properties.

We now look into the question of improving a given stratification.

Example 8.4.   The primary stratification of V_4 is $V_4 = M^2 \cup M^1$, where $M^1 = C_z$. As noted at the end of the last section, the point 0 of C_z has an unpleasant property; we may remove it by taking 0 out of M^1 and making it into a new stratum M^0. A suggestion for what should be considered a "complete stratification" will be given in the next section.

We shall say that a stratification is *regular with respect to tangent planes* if the following is true: suppose $p \in M_i \subset \bar{M}_j$. Then (recalling that $\bar{M}_j$ is an analytic variety of constant dimension)

(a) Each plane T corresponding to an element of $\tau(\bar{M}_j, p)$ contains $T(M_i, p)$.

(b) Each plane T corresponding to an element of $\tau(\bar{M}_j, M_i, p, \beta)$ contains β, for any 1-direction β.

In simpler language, the following must hold: with the retraction γ of a neighborhood of M_i onto M_i as in §7, take any simple point q of $\bar{M}_j$ sufficiently near p; then $T(\bar{M}_j, q)$ must nearly contain both $T(M_i, p)$ and the vector $q - \gamma(q)$. Note that (a) may be phrased as follows:

(a′) $T(M_i, p) \subset C_2(\bar{M}_j, p)$,

Some examples of failure of these properties were given at the end of §7.

THEOREM 8.5.   *Any analytic variety $V \subset U \subset C^n$ has a stratification that is regular with respect to tangent planes.*

We shall give the method of proof only; see [15] for details.

Starting with the primary stratification, examine first each stratum M of next highest dimension relative to the strata of highest dimension. The points of M of bad behavior form an analytic subvariety S; we remove these from M (they will go into lower dimensional strata). With the original highest dimensional strata and the new strata of next highest dimension, reform a stratification. Now examine the strata of third highest dimension, and remove the points of bad behavior relative to higher dimensional strata. Continuing in this manner gives the required stratification.

At any given stage, we are examining a stratum M relative to a higher dimensional stratum M', such that $M \subset \bar{M}'$. Let S_a be the subset of M where (a) fails for this pair. We find S_a as follows: for each $p \in M$ let $G(p) \subset G^{n-1,d-1}$ ($d = \dim M'$) be the set of $(d-1)$-directions whose planes contain $T(M, p)$; we say p is "good" if $\tau(M', p) \subset G(p)$, and p is "bad" otherwise. The sets

$$W_0 = \{(p, \alpha): p \in M, \ \alpha \in G(p)\},$$
$$W_1 = \{(p, \alpha): p \in M, \ \alpha \in \tau(\bar{M}', p)\}$$

are analytic varieties in $M \times G^{n-1,d-1}$ (the first is a manifold). By Lemma 2.15, clos $(W_1 - W_0)$ is an analytic variety; it projects onto an analytic variety $S_a \subset M$, clearly containing all bad points. We must show that $\dim S_a < \dim M$. If not, then a neighborhood of some $q \in W_1$ projects onto a neighborhood of $p \in M$, with maximum rank. Let Γ be an arc in M through p in the direction of a vector v not in the plane corresponding to some element of $\tau(\bar{M}', p)$. We may take a section in $U \times G^{n-1,r-1}$ (U being a neighborhood of p in C^n) to replace $\bar{M}'$ by a 2-dimensional variety containing Γ, with tangent 2-planes not containing v; this leads at once to a contradiction (as suggested to me by R. Thom).

By a similar process, find a bad set S_b, analytic, of dimension $< \dim M$. Now $S = S_a \cup S_b$ is the set we remove from M.

COROLLARY 8.6. $V \subset U \subset C^n$ may be stratified so that the following is true: given p in the stratum M of dimension d and given a transversal plane P^k to M through p (then $k \geq n - d$), there is a neighborhood U' of p in C^n such that P^k is transversal to $M' \cap U'$ for each stratum M'.

This holds for the stratification of the last theorem; only (a) is used.

Consider now a *real C-analytic variety* $V \subset U \subset R^n$. Take the complexification V^* (see [16]) and stratify it by the last theorem. Let the strata of V be the real parts of the strata of V^*. Then properties corresponding to (a) and (b) hold for the real strata. One may show therefore that the stratification is of the type required by R. Thom in his paper [13] in this volume.

9. The fibering conjecture

Suppose we have a stratification of the variety $V \subset U \subset C^n$ that we consider to be "good." Then it is reasonable to suppose that a neighborhood of any point p_0 of V is expressible as a product, as follows. Suppose p_0 is in the stratum M. Let N be the analytic plane orthogonal to M at p_0. Then a neighborhood U_0 of p_0 is expressible as the disjoint union of fibers $F(q)$, as follows. Set $M_0 = M \cap U_0$, $N_0 = N \cap U_0$. Then $F(p_0) = M_0$, and for each $q \in N_0$, $F(q)$ is a manifold biholomorphically homeomorphic with M_0; the fibration is *consistent* with the stratification, in that each fiber is either disjoint from or lies in each stratum. Moreover the fibration is expressible through a function $\phi(p, q)$ ($p \in M_0$, $q \in N_0$) such that

$$\phi(p, p_0) = p \ (p \in M_0), \quad \phi(p_0, q) = q \ (q \in N_0),$$
$$F(q) = \{q' = \phi(p, q) \colon p \in M_0\};$$

$\phi(p, q)$ is analytic in p and continuous in q. We call this a *semi-analytic fibration* of a neighborhood of p_0 in C^n. It is *analytic* if ϕ is analytic in both variables.

In general there is no analytic fibration: see Remark 13.3 below.

LEMMA 9.1. *Suppose $p \in M$, M being a stratum of dimension d. Then there is an analytic fibration of a neighborhood of p in C^n consistent with the fibration if and only if there are holomorphic vector fields $v_1(q), \ldots, v_d(q)$ in a neighborhood of p in C^n, consistent with the fibration, such that $v_1(p), \ldots, v_d(p)$ span $T(M, p)$.*

This is essentially contained in Rossi, [10, Corollary 3.4].

In the particular case that $d = 1$, the essential condition is simply that $T(M, p) \subset C_1(V, p)$.

CONJECTURE 9.2. *Any analytic variety $V \subset U \subset C^n$ has a stratification such that each point has a neighborhood with a semi-analytic fibration.*

We shall prove a special case of the conjecture in §12.

A stratification satisfying the conjecture (possibly with further conditions on the functions ϕ) would probably be sufficient for all needs. For instance, condition (a) of the last section follows at once. To see this, note that any fiber $F(q)$ with $q \subset M_j$ sufficiently near p_0 is near $F(p_0) = M_0$. Supposing coordinates chosen so that M_0 is part of the $(x_1, \ldots, x_d)$-plane ($d = \dim M$), $F(q)$ is expressed by holomorphic functions $x_i = f_i(x_1, \ldots, x_d)$, $i = 1, \ldots, n - d$. These functions are small throughout M_0; hence their partial derivatives are small in a smaller neighborhood of p_0. Since $F(q) \subset M_j$ if $q \in M_j$, this clearly implies the condition (a).

To obtain condition (b) in a simple manner, one should probably require more than just continuity of ϕ in the second variable.

In the case of a *real analytic variety*, one might look for real analytic fibers. This is a much simpler problem. Probably by continuing the method begun in §12 one may carry out a proof, with relatively mild conditions on the stratification.

PROBLEM 9.3. With a good stratification, may one fiber a complete neighborhood of any stratum?

PROBLEM 9.4. Given $p \in V$, can one express a neighborhood of p as the union of a set of 1-dimensional analytic varieties, each without singularities except at p, and disjoint except at p?

This would be a generalization of Problem 3.8.

We give one rather trivial case in which a complete region may be fibered:

LEMMA 9.5. *Let U be a simply connected region of the plane C, and let $f_1, \ldots, f_s$ be holomorphic functions in U such that*

$$(9.6) \qquad f_i(x) \neq f_j(x) \quad \text{if } i \neq j, \, x \in U.$$

Then there is a consistent analytic fibration of $U \times C$, defined by means of a holomorphic function ϕ.

Say $0 \in U$. We wish to define $\phi(x, y)$ $(x \in U, y \in C)$ such that

$$(9.7) \qquad \phi(0, y) = y, \quad \phi(x, f_i(0)) = f_i(x);$$

we require also that for each fixed $x \in U$, ϕ is a homeomorphism of C with itself. Then the fibers

$$F(y) = \{(x, y'): x \in U, \, y' = \phi(x, y)\} \qquad\qquad (y \in C)$$

have the required properties.

We defines the fibers as the solutions of a differential equation in $U \times C$. We need merely define $\partial\phi/\partial x$ at each point. We do this by means of the usual interpolation formula:

$$(9.8) \quad \frac{\partial\phi(x, y)}{\partial x} = \sum_{i=1}^{s} \frac{[y - f_1(x)] \cdots \hat{\imath} \cdots [y - f_s(x)]}{[f_i(x) - f_1(x)] \cdots \hat{\imath} \cdots [f_i(x) - f_s(x)]} \frac{df_i(x)}{dx}.$$

The given fibers are solutions; analyticity is clear.

10. Tangent cones to hypersurfaces

Given the holomorphic function f defined near $p_0 \in C^n$, let $f^{[*]}(p_0; p)$ denote the initial polynomial of f, when expanded about p_0 (see §5). Note that

$$(10.1) \qquad f^{[*]}(p_0; p) = f(p_0) \quad \text{if } f(p_0) \neq 0.$$

Clearly

$$(10.2) \qquad (fg)^{[*]}(p_0; p) = f^{[*]}(p_0; p)g^{[*]}(p_0; p).$$

We first relate the tangent cones of a hypersurface to the Weierstrass Preparation Theorem. This theorem reads as follows: Let f be analytic in a neighborhood of 0 in C^n, and suppose $f \not\equiv 0$ on the x_n-axis. Then there is a pseudopolynomial ω:

$$(10.3) \qquad \omega(x_1, \ldots, x_n) = x_n^k + \sum_{i=1}^{k} A_i(x_1, \ldots, x_{n-1})x_n^{k-i},$$

where the A_i are holomorphic and vanish at the origin in C^{n-1}, and there is a holomorphic function Φ near 0, such that

$$(10.4) \qquad f(x) = \Phi(x)\omega(x), \quad \Phi(0) \neq 0.$$

Hence

$$(10.5) \qquad f^{[*]}(0; x) = \Phi(0)\omega^{[*]}(0; x).$$

LEMMA 10.6. *Let V be a hypersurface in C^n, and suppose $0 \in V$. Let f be a holomorphic function near 0 generating $I(V, 0)$; see 2.9. Define ω as above. Then $v \in C(V, 0)$ if and only if $f^{[*]}(0; v) = 0$, or, $\omega^{[*]}(0; v) = 0$.*

Moreover:

(a) *If the unit vector e_n in the x_n-direction is not in $C(V, 0)$, then the degree of ω equals the order of f at 0, and each A_i is of order at least i.*

(b) *Otherwise, the degree of ω is greater than the order of f at 0, and some A_i is of order $<i$.*

First, take any vector v satisfying $f^{[*]}(0, v) = 0$. For any $g \in I(V, p)$, we may write $g = \phi f$ for some holomorphic ϕ; by (10.2), $g^{[*]}(0, v) = 0$ also. Now Theorem 5.8 and (10.5) show that $C(V, p)$ is defined both by $f^{[*]}$ and by $\omega^{[*]}$.

Say the order of f and hence of ω at 0 is m. In Case (a), $e_n \notin C(V, 0)$, we have $\omega^{[*]}(0; e_n) = \omega^{[m]}(e_n) \neq 0$; since $\omega(\lambda e_n) = \lambda^k$, this shows that $m = k$. No A_i is of order $<i$, for otherwise ω would be of order $<k = m$. The reasoning in Case (b) is similar.

LEMMA 10.7. *Let M be an analytic manifold in an open subset of the analytic hypersurface V, and let f generate $I(V, p)$ for each $p \in M$. Let m be the lowest order of f at points of M. Then: (a) the set S_c of points of M where the order of f is $>m$ is an analytic subvariety of M. (b) $C(V, p)$ is continuous in $M - S_c$.*

Take any $p_0 \in M$. Choose new axes $(t_1, \ldots, t_d, x_1, \ldots, x_{n-d})$ about p_0 (which does not affect the order of f) so that the part of M near p_0 is an open subset of the d-plane C_t; take the origin at p_0. Since f is of order at least m at each $(t, 0)$, we may write

$$(10.8) \qquad f(t, x) = \sum_{|\mu|=m} a_\mu(t)x_1^{\mu_1} \cdots x_{n-d}^{\mu_{n-d}} + R_t(x),$$

where the a_μ and R are holomorphic, and R_t is of order $> m$ for each t. (For $\mu = (\mu_1, \ldots, \mu_{n-d})$, we write $|\mu| = \mu_1 + \cdots + \mu_{n-d}$.) Clearly f is of order $> m$ at $\rho_t = (t, 0)$ if and only if all the $a_\mu(t)$ are 0; this defines the analytic variety S_c in M near p_0.

For $\rho_t \in M - S_c$, set

$$(10.9) \qquad g_t(x) = f^{[*]}(\rho_t; t', x) = \sum_{|\mu|=m} a_\mu(t) x_1^{\mu_1} \cdots x_{n-d}^{\mu_{n-d}}$$

(which is independent of t'); the elements of $C(V, \rho_t)$ are the solutions of $g_t(x) = 0$, and these are continuous functions of the $a_\mu(t)$ (where the latter do not all vanish). This proves (b).

Let us set (with coordinates as above)

$$\sigma_x = (0, x), \quad \sigma_x' = (0, x/|x|) \text{ if } x \neq 0.$$

We strengthen (b) above as follows:

LEMMA 10.10. *With the hypotheses of the last lemma and with the above notations, suppose $\rho_{t_0} \in M - S_c$ and $\varepsilon > 0$. Then there is a $\delta > 0$ such that if*

$$(t, x) \in V, \quad |t - t_0| < \delta, \quad |t' - t_0| < \delta, \quad 0 < |x| < \delta,$$

we have

$$(10.11) \qquad \text{dist } (\sigma_x', C(V, \rho_{t'})) < \varepsilon.$$

Because of (b) above, we may take $t' = t_0$. By compactness, we may find $\gamma > 0$ so that if $|x| = 1$ and $|g_{t_0}(x)| < \gamma$ then $\text{dist}(\sigma_x, C(V, \rho_{t_0})) < \varepsilon$. As in (5.9), we may write

$$f(t, \lambda x) = \lambda^m [g_t(x) + \lambda R'(t, x, \lambda)],$$

where R' is holomorphic. Say $|R'| < N$ if $|x| = 1$, $|t| < \delta_0$, $|\lambda| < \delta_0$. Choose $\delta < \min (\delta_0, \gamma/2N)$ so that

$$\text{if } |t - t_0| < \delta \text{ then } |a_\mu(t) - a_\mu(t_0)| < \lambda/2(n - d + 1)^m, \text{ all } \mu.$$

Now if (t, x) satisfies the required conditions, then $f(t, x) = 0$, and hence, setting $y = x/|x|$, $x = \lambda y$,

$$-g_{t_0}(y) = \Sigma[a_\mu(t) - a_\mu(t_0)]y_1^{\mu_1} \cdots y_{n-d}^{\mu_{n-d}} + \lambda R'(t, y, \lambda).$$

Hence $|g_{t_0}(y)| < \gamma$ and (10.11) with $t' = t_0$ follows.

We now give a particular result, which will be used in §12.

Let V be a hypersurface in an open subset of C^n; choose a stratification. If M_1 is a stratum of dimension $n - 2$, remove the analytic subsets S_a and S_b as in the proof of Theorem 8.5. Remove also the subset S_c defined in Lemma 10.7. This leaves an analytic manifold M. We may thus form a stratification of V such that no $(n - 2)$-dimensional stratum has points of type S_a, S_b or S_c.

REMARK 10.12. It seems quite possible that (in the present case) $S_c \subset (S_a \cup S_b)$.

LEMMA 10.13. *Let M be an $(n-2)$-dimensional stratum of the hypersurface V as above. Take any $p_0 \in M$ and any $v_0 \notin C(V, p_0)$. Then there is a neighborhood U of p_0 in C^n such that if q is any point of $(V - M) \cap U$, then q is simple and $v_0 \notin T(V, q)$.*

We may choose coordinates $(t_1, \ldots, t_{n-2}, x, y)$ with p_0 as origin so that for some U_0 about p_0, $M \cap U_0$ is an open subset of C_t, and so that v_0 is the unit vector e_y (see Remark 7.11). Let $e_1, \ldots, e_{n-2}$ be the unit vectors in C_t. Let C' be the set of unit vectors in $C(V, 0) \cap C_{xy}$. Since C' is compact we may find $\varepsilon > 0$ such that if

$$\left| w^{(i)} - e_i \right| \leq \varepsilon \ (i \leq n-2), \ \operatorname{dist}(w^{(n-1)}, C') \leq 2\varepsilon,$$

then $w^{(1)}, \ldots, w^{(n-1)}$, e_y are independent.

By the choice of stratification, there is a $\delta > 0$ with the following property. Take any $q = (t, x, y) \in V - M$ within δ of 0. Set $\gamma(q) = (t, 0, 0)$ (see §7). Now $q - \gamma(q) = (0, x, y) = v$ say. Set $v' = v/|v|$. Because of the stratification, q must be simple. Now:

(a') Each e_i (which is in $T(M, 0)$) is within ε of a vector $w^{(i)}$ of $T(V, q)$.

(b') v' is within ε of a vector $w^{(n-1)}$ of $T(V, q)$.

(c') v' is within ε of a vector w of $C(V, 0)$ (see Lemma 10.10).

Since (see (10.9)) $C(V, 0)$ is the set of solutions of an equation $\sum a_i x^i y^{m-i} = 0$, we may take $w \in C_{xy}$; we may clearly also take $|w| = 1$. Thus $w \in C'$.

By the choice of ε, the vectors $w^{(1)}, \ldots, w^{(n-1)}$, e_y are independent. Since all but the last are in $T(V, q)$, a vector space of dimension $n - 1$, $e_y \notin T(V, q)$. This proves the lemma.

COROLLARY 10.14. With the conditions of the last lemma and the coordinates chosen there, a neighborhood of any point q of $V - M$ in V with q sufficiently near p_0 may be represented in the form $y = f(t_1, \ldots, t_{n-2}, x)$, f being holomorphic.

11. An interpolation formula

We describe a method of interpolation between functions that will be used in the proof of the fibering theorem in the next section.

Let T be a set, and let Z be a finite dimensional affine metric space. Let functions $\phi_1, \ldots, \phi_m \colon T \to Z$ be given and have distinct values at each t. Let t_0 be a fixed point of T. Set

$$a_i = \phi_i(t_0), \quad \Delta_i(t) = \phi_i(t) - a_i \qquad (i = 1, \ldots, m).$$

Suppose that

(11.1) $$\gamma = \sup \frac{|\Delta_k(t) - \Delta_j(t)|}{|a_k - a_j|}$$

is finite. We shall then define a function $\psi \colon T \times Z \to Z$, with the following properties:

(a) For all z, $z' \in Z$ and $t \in T$,

(11.2)
$$\psi(t_0, z) = z \qquad\qquad (z \in Z)$$

(11.3)
$$\psi(t, a_i) = \phi_i(t) \qquad\qquad (i = 1, \ldots, m),$$

(11.4)
$$|[\psi(t, z') - \psi(t, z)] - [z' - z]| \leq 4(m - 1)\gamma|z' - z|.$$

(b_0) If T is a topological space and the ϕ_i are continuous, then ψ is continuous.

(b_1) If T is an affine space and the ϕ_i are differentiable to a certain order, or are real analytic, then so is $\psi(t, z)$, except perhaps at $z = a_i$.

(b_2) If T is an open subset of C^k, $Z = C^\ell$, and the ϕ_i are holomorphic, then so is each $\psi_z'(t) = \psi(t, z)$.

(c) If $\gamma < 1/4(m - 1)$, then for each t, $\psi_t(z) = \psi(t, z)$ is a homeomorphism of Z onto Z.

REMARK 11.5. Let $F(z) = \psi_z'(T)$ be the set of all $\psi(t, z)$ for $t \in T$. Then with the condition of (c), these form a fibering of $T \times Z$. With the conditions of (b_2) also, the fibering is semi-analytic (§9).

We first define weighting functions σ_i as follows. Set

$$\sigma_k(a_k) = 1, \quad \sigma_j(a_k) = 0 \quad (j \neq k).$$

If $z \neq a_k$ for all k, set

$$\rho_i(z) = |z - a_i|, \quad \mu_i(z) = 1/\rho_i(z), \quad \sigma_i(z) = \mu_i(z)/\Sigma_j\mu_j(z).$$

We let the change in $\psi(t, z)$ from its initial value at t_0 be a weighted average of the changes Δ_i in the ϕ_i:

(11.6)
$$\psi(t, z) = z + \sum_{i=1}^{m} \sigma_i(z)\Delta_i(t).$$

Then (11.2) and (11.3) hold.

We need an inequality on the rate of change of the σ_i. Take any $z \in Z$ and any unit vector v; consider the functions ρ_i, μ_i, σ_i at $z + \lambda v$ as functions of the real variable λ. Since $|v| = 1$, we have

$$|\partial\rho_i/\partial\lambda| \leq 1.$$

Also

$$\frac{\partial\mu_i}{\partial\lambda} = -\frac{1}{\rho_i^2}\frac{\partial\rho_i}{\partial\lambda}, \quad \left|\frac{\partial\mu_i}{\partial\lambda}\right| \leq \mu_i^2.$$

Moreover,

$$\frac{\partial \sigma_i}{\partial \lambda} = \frac{1}{\Sigma \mu_k} \frac{\partial \mu_i}{\partial \lambda} - \frac{\mu_i}{(\Sigma \mu_k)^2} \Sigma \frac{\partial \mu_k}{\partial \lambda},$$

and hence

$$(11.7) \qquad \left| \rho_i \frac{\partial \sigma_i}{\partial \lambda} \right| \leq \frac{\mu_i}{\Sigma \mu_k} + \frac{\Sigma \mu_k^2}{(\Sigma \mu_k)^2} \leq 2.$$

We now prove (11.4). Given z, z', t, we may write

$$z' = z + av, \quad |v| = 1, \quad a \geq 0.$$

Set

$$\theta(\lambda) = \psi(t, z + \lambda v).$$

Now

$$[\psi(t, z') - \psi(t, z)] - [z' - z] = \theta(a) - \theta(0) - av = \int_0^a \left[\frac{\partial \theta}{\partial \lambda} - v \right] d\lambda.$$

If we prove

$$(11.8) \qquad \left| \frac{\partial \theta}{\partial \lambda} - v \right| \leq 4(m - 1)\gamma,$$

then (11.4) will follow, since $a = |z' - z|$.

Take any fixed λ, $0 \leq \lambda \leq a$. Choose s so that

$$(11.9) \qquad \rho_s(z + \lambda v) \leq \rho_i(z + \lambda v), \quad \text{all } i.$$

Set $z_\lambda = z + \lambda v$. Since $\Sigma \sigma_i = 1$, (11.6) gives

$$\theta(\lambda) = z + \lambda v + \Delta_s(t) + \sum_{i \neq s} \sigma_i(z_\lambda)[\Delta_i(t) - \Delta_s(t)],$$

$$\frac{\partial \theta}{\partial \lambda} - v = \sum_{i \neq s} \frac{\partial \sigma_i(z_\lambda)}{\partial \lambda} [\Delta_i(t) - \Delta_s(t)].$$

By (11.1) and (11.9),

$$|\Delta_i(t) - \Delta_s(t)| \leq \gamma |a_i - a_s| \leq \gamma[\rho_i(z_\lambda) + \rho_s(z_\lambda)] \leq 2\gamma \rho_i(z_\lambda);$$

now (11.8) follows with the help of (11.7). Thus (11.4) is proved.

Properties (b) are clear. Under the condition of (c), it is clear from (11.4) that ψ is one–one; we must still show that, for t fixed, $\psi_t(z) = \psi(t, z)$ maps Z onto Z. Set $N = \Sigma |\Delta_i(t)| + 1$. Take any $z_0 \in Z$, and let S be the sphere about z_0 of radius N. Now

$$|\psi_t(z) - z| = |\Sigma \sigma_i(z) \Delta_i(t)| < N.$$

Therefore no line segment from $\psi_t(z)$ to z ($z \in S$) touches z_0. We may deform ψ_t along these line segments into the identity, showing that the degree of ψ_t in S about z_0 is 1. By a standard theorem of algebraic topology, ψ_t maps some point of Z inside S onto z_0. This completes the proof.

12. A fibering theorem

Recalling the definition of §9, we prove the following theorem:

THEOREM 12.1. *An analytic hypersurface V in an open subset of C^n may be stratified so that a neighborhood of each point of each stratum of dimension $n - 2$ has a semi-analytic fibration.*

We use the stratification employed in Lemma 10.13. Take $p_0 \in M$ as there, and choose coordinates about p_0 as in the proof of the lemma. Then in a neighborhood U_0 of p_0, the points of $V - M$ may be represented locally in the form $y = f(t, x)$, where $t = (t_1, \ldots, t_{n-2})$ (see Corollary 10.14). If we take a fixed $x_0 \neq 0$, the points above (t, x_0) in U_0 are all simple, and are given by holomorphic functions $\phi_1(t, x_0), \ldots, \phi_m(t, x_0)$ (for some m), these m roots being distinct for each t.

In order to apply §11, we need the following lemma.

LEMMA 12.2. *With the above notations, let $\varepsilon > 0$ be given. Then there is a $\delta > 0$ with the following property: take any x with $0 < |x| < \delta$. Then the functions ϕ_i are defined above for $|t| < \delta$. Take any j and k, and set*

$$\alpha(t, x) = \phi_k(t, x) - \phi_j(t, x).$$

Then

(12.3) $$\frac{|\alpha(t, x) - \alpha(0, x)|}{|\alpha(0, x)|} < \varepsilon \quad \text{if } |t| < \delta, \, 0 < |x| < \delta.$$

If we keep t fixed and let x make m circuits about 0, α comes back to its original value; hence we may define a holomorphic function β near 0 such that

$$\beta(t, \xi) = \alpha(t, \xi^m).$$

Since the ϕ_i are distinct for $x \neq 0$, we have $\beta \neq 0$ for $\xi \neq 0$. Hence if we let ξ make a circuit about 0, $\beta(t, \xi)$ will make a number h of circuits about 0, where h is independent of the choice of circuit and of t. Therefore, as a function of ξ, β is of order h at $\xi = 0$ for each t, and we may write

$$\beta(t, \xi) = \xi^h[a(t) + \xi R(t, \xi)], \quad a(t) \neq 0.$$

Take $\delta_0 > 0$ so that $|a(t) - a(0)| < |a(0)|\varepsilon/3$ if $|t| < \delta_0$. Take δ_1 and N so that $|R(t, \xi)| < N$, $2\delta_1 N < |a(0)|\varepsilon/3$ if $|t| < \delta_0$, $|\xi| < \delta_1$. For such (t, ξ),

$$\frac{|\beta(t, \xi) - \beta(0, \xi)|}{|\beta(0, \xi)|} \leq \frac{|a(t) - a(0)| + |\xi||R(t, \xi) - R(0, \xi)|}{|a(0)| - |\xi||R(0, \xi)|}$$

which is $< \varepsilon$ (if $\varepsilon < 1$). Set $\delta = \min(\delta_0, \delta_1^m)$; then (12.3) follows.

Set $\varepsilon = 1/4m$, and choose δ accordingly. Let U be the set of all (t, x, y) with $|t|, |x| < \delta$; we shall fiber U. Let U_x be the part of U with this x; we fiber each U_x separately.

First take $x \neq 0$. Set $t_0 = 0$. Then the conditions of §11 are satisfied, including (b$_2$) and (c); (11.1) holds, with $\gamma \leq \varepsilon$, by (12.3). We may therefore form a semi-analytic fibering of U_x by the formula (11.6); see Remark 11.5. It is clear that the resulting fibering of the part of U over all $x \neq 0$ is continuous.

For $x = 0$, we have at the start the single fiber $M : y = 0$; let $y =$ constant give the remaining fibers. We must show that the fibering is continuous in a neighborhood of $x = 0$. Because of the continuity of the ϕ_i, we may, given $\varepsilon > 0$, find $\eta > 0$ so that

$$|\phi_k(t, x)| < \varepsilon \quad \text{if} \quad |t| < \delta, |x| < \eta.$$

Using (11.6) and $\Sigma \sigma_i(y) = 1$ gives (for each x)

$$|\psi_x(t, y) - y| \leq \Sigma \sigma_i(y)|\Delta_i(t)| < 2\varepsilon, \quad |x| < \eta.$$

Thus the fibers defined by the $\psi_x(t, y)$ converge to the fibers $\psi_0(t, y) = y$. This completes the proof.

REMARK 12.4.   If we used Lemma 9.5 in place of (11.6) for the fibering of the $U_x (x \neq 0)$, an analytic instead of semi-analytic fibration would result. However, we could not then in general fiber U_0 to obtain a continuous fibering. The impossibility in general is shown by Example 13.2 below. In the present case, letting $V \subset C^3$ be defined by

$$y(y - x)(y - (2 + t)x) = 0,$$

fibering by means of Lemma 9.5 gives fibers which do not converge as $x \to 0$.

13. Examples of non-homogeneity

First we show that with certain analytic varieties there may be a complex number intrinsically attached.

Example 13.1.   Let $V \subset C^2$ be defined by the vanishing of

$$f = xy(y - x)(y - ax).$$

V consists of four intersecting analytic lines. Taking them in the order of the factors of f, they have a cross ratio, which is $\sigma_a = a$. Taking them without regard to order, we have a set σ_a^* of six cross ratios; these are distinct if $|a| > 2$, and $|a|$ is then the largest.

Now consider V as an abstract analytic variety. Take any neighborhood of the intersection point, and any imbedding of it into an open set in C'^2.

By Theorem 4.7 there is a biholomorphism Φ of a neighborhood of 0 in C^2 into C'^2 which extends the biholomorphism between the varieties; moreover, $d\Phi(0)$ is linear in $C_6(V, 0) = C^2$, and is one–one between the tangent cones. Hence the four tangent lines of the newly imbedded variety have the same set of cross ratios as before.

Thus the set σ_a^* is an invariant of V itself. In particular, taking a near 3, *the number a is an invariant.*

Next we define a variety with a naturally defined function along the singular locus.

Example 13.2. Let $V \subset U \subset C^3$ be defined by the vanishing of

$$f(t, x, y) = xy(y - x)(y - (3 + t)x);$$

require $|t| < 1$ in U. Near 0, the singular locus V' is the t-axis C_t. Consider any point $\rho_t = (t, 0, 0)$ of C_t. The tangent cone $C(V, \rho_t)$ consists of four analytic planes, intersecting in C_t. These four planes have a set of cross ratios, which equals that of the four lines in which $C(V, \rho_t)$ intersects any transverse plane, for instance, one orthogonal to C_t. One of these cross ratios is $\sigma_t = 3 + t$. Again by Theorem 4.7, this number is intrinsically associated with the point ρ_t, for t small. Thus, considering V as an abstract analytic variety, the function σ_t is invariantly defined on V'.

Because of this, we may say that V is *non-homogeneous along V'*. This means the following: take two distinct points p_1, p_2 of V'. Then it is not true that there are neighborhoods U_1, U_2 of these points in V and there is a biholomorphism Φ of U_1 onto U_2.

REMARK 13.3. For the above V, there is a semi-analytic fibration of a neighborhood U_1 of 0, by Theorem 12.1. There is no analytic fibration. For if there were, then we could form a biholomorphic transformation in U_1 simply by changing t along the fibers, contrary to the non-homogeneity proved above. (In particular, $C_1(V, p) = \{0\}$, $p \in C_t$; compare Rossi, [10, Theorem 3.2].) Note that with the chosen semi-analytic fibration, the fibering of each individual sheet of V is analytic.

Example 13.4. Taking f as in Example 13.2, define V by the vanishing of

$$g(t, x, y, z) = z^2 - [f(t, x, y)]^2.$$

(We could use $g = z^2 - tf^2$, making V irreducible; it would still be reducible at other points of the singular variety V'.) Now V consists of two sheets, intersecting along the singular locus V', defined by $z = f = 0$; thus V' is biholomorphic with the variety of Example 13.2. The present variety has the following property, not shared by the previous one: If W is an analytic variety and Φ is a holomorphic homeomorphism onto a neighborhood of 0 in V, then W consists similarly of two intersecting sheets, and is therefore similarly non-homogeneous along the intersection of the four sheets of the singular variety W'. (Φ need not be biholomorphic.)

The property obtained above may hold for a normal variety, though it takes more theory to prove it:

Example 13.5.   With f as in Example 13.2 again, define V by the vanishing of

$$g(t, x, y, z) = z^5 - f(t, x, y).$$

V is clearly irreducible at all points. The singular variety V' of V is again C_t (near 0). Since V' is of codimension 2 in V, it follows that V is normal (see for instance [1]). Hence (see [6, Satz 22]) any continuous function in V near 0 which is holomorphic at all simple points is holomorphic in V near 0. Moreover [6, Satz 23] any holomorphic homeomorphism of an analytic variety onto a neighborhood of 0 in V is biholomorphic.

By Lemma 10.6, $C(V, p)$ is defined by the vanishing of the initial polynomial of g, expanded about p. For $p = \rho_{t_0} = (t_0, 0, 0)$, this polynomial is $-f(t_0, x, y)$, which is independent of t. The cone consists of four planes through C_t, with a largest cross ratio $3 + t_0$; again we have non-homogeneity along V'.

I am indebted to D. B. Mumford for pointing out the properties of this example to me.

14. Varieties not locally algebraic

We say the analytic variety V is *locally algebraic* at the point p if there is an algebraic variety W with a point q such that there is a biholomorphic homeomorphism of some neighborhood of q in W onto a neighborhood of p in V.

Example 14.1.   Define V in a neighborhood of 0 in C^3 by the vanishing of

$$f(t, x, y) = xy(y - x)(y - (3 + t)x)(y - \gamma(t)x),$$

where γ is a transcendental function, and $\gamma(0) = 4$. V has five sheets, intersecting along C_t. The largest cross ratio of the first four sheets at $\rho_t = (t, 0, 0)$ is $3 + t$; the largest cross ratio of the first three and the last sheet is $\gamma(t)$. As in the last section, each cross ratio is intrinsically related to the variety at the given point. Hence the set of pairs $(3 + t, \gamma(t))$, and hence the function γ, is intrinsic to the variety. We show that the variety is not locally algebraic at any point of C_t.

Suppose then that $W \subset C^n$ is an algebraic variety, and ϕ is a biholomorphic homeomorphism of a neighborhood $W \cap U_0$ of 0 in W onto a neighborhood of 0 in V. By Theorem 4. dim 7, $C_6(W, 0) = \dim C_6(V, 0) = 3$; hence, by Lemma 4.12, there is an analytic manifold M of dimension 3 about $0 \subset C^n$ containing W near 0. Since dim $W \cap U_0 =$ dim $V = 2$, we may suppose dim $W = 2$. Let P be the tangent plane to M at 0. We may choose an analytic line L through 0 which avoids $W - \{0\}$, so that if π is the projection along L of C^n onto some $C^{n-1} \supset P$, then for some U_1 about 0, $\pi(W) \cap U_1 = \pi(W \cap U_0) \cap U_1$. It is a standard fact that $\pi(W)$ is an algebraic variety. Moreover, π is a biholomorphism in $M \cap U_1$; hence we may use $\pi(W) \subset C^{n-1}$ in place of $W \subset C^n$. Continuing, we may suppose $W \subset C^3$.

Now W is an algebraic hypersurface in C^3; hence it is defined by a polynomial g. Let W' be the singular variety of W. With ϕ and U_0 as above, ϕ extends to a biholomorphism Φ of some $U \subset U_1$ about $p_0 \in W'$ with $\phi(p_0) = 0$. Now Φ^{-1} carries each sheet in V into an analytic sheet in W. Hence g may be factored analytically, and hence algebraically, into five factors $g_1, \ldots, g_5$, which may clearly be supposed irreducible. Now g_i generates $I(W_i, p)$ for the corresponding sheet; hence g generates $I(W, p)$, for each $p \in W' \cap U$. By Lemma 10.6, for each such p, the vectors $v \in C(W, p)$ are the solutions of $g^{[*]}(p; v) = 0$. The solutions are algebraic in terms of the coefficients, which in turn are algebraic in terms of the value of a parameter t defining $p \in W'$; hence both cross ratios under discussion are algebraic functions of t, and the pair of them determines an algebraic function. But this function is γ, and we have a contradiction.

Example 14.2. With f as above, set $g = z^6 - f$. Then (compare Example 13.5) V, defined by $g = 0$, is normal, and not locally algebraic at any singular point near 0.

REMARK 14.3. Any analytic curve is locally algebraic. N. Levinson [7] has proved the following stronger result: Let F be any holomorphic function of the form

$$F(x, y) = y^k \Phi(x, y)\omega(x, y), \quad \Phi(0, 0) \neq 0,$$

$$\omega(x, y) = y^m + \sum_{i=1}^{m} a_i(x)y^{m-1}, \quad a_i(0) = 0 \quad (i = 1, \ldots, m),$$

the discriminant of ω not being identically 0. Then there is an analytic change of coordinates under which F becomes a polynomial.

For a function $F(x_1, \ldots, x_n, y)$ of more variables, of a similar form, Levinson [8] has shown that it may be transformed into a polynomial in y with coefficients analytic in the x_i. However, it cannot in general (say with $n = 2$) be transformed into a polynomial. For if it could, then it would define an algebraic variety, biholomorphic to the variety defined by the given function, which may not be possible. Thus the functions of Examples 14.1 and 14.2 cannot be transformed through analytic changes of coordinates into polynomials.

15. Some further examples

First we study certain 1-dimensional varieties with just two sheets; they turn out to be biholomorphic with one of the varieties V_μ^* of (15.2). For certain 1-dimensional varieties with three sheets, there is an intrinsic number attached. (In Example 13.1 we needed four sheets.) We then show that the phenomena of Examples 13.2 and 14.1, and hence of non-homogeneity and non-algebraic character, are obtainable through varieties with fewer sheets than used there.

15.1. We suppose given an analytic variety V expressible as $V_1 \cup V_2$, each V_i being an analytic 1-dimensional manifold (compare Remark 6.12), these manifolds intersecting in a single point p. We shall show that V is (near p) biholomorphically homeomorphic with one of the varieties

$$(15.2) \qquad V_\mu^*: y(y - x^\mu) = 0 \text{ in } C^2 \ (\mu \text{ an integer} \geq 1).$$

Note that $V_1^*: y(y - x) = 0$ is biholomorphic with $V_1': yx = 0$.

To start, we may suppose V imbedded in C^n. Since V_1 is an analytic manifold, we may take new axes near p, with origin at p, so that V_1 is on the x_1-axis.

We wish the function $x_1 | V_2$ to generate $O_2 = O(V_2, 0)$. If this is not so, then some $x_i | V_2$ generates O_2. Set $x_1' = x_1 + x_i$. With the coordinates $(x_1', x_2, \ldots, x_n)$, $x_1' | V_2$ generates O_2. Take this coordinate system, dropping primes. V_1 (near 0) is still on the x_1-axis.

Now V_2 near 0 is given by equations $x_k = \phi_k(x_1)$ $(k \geq 2)$. Let μ be the lowest order occurring among the ϕ_k; we may suppose it occurs for $k = 2$. Then the equations for V_2 have the form

$$x_2 = x_1^\mu(a + x_1 R(x_1)), \quad a \neq 0,$$
$$x_k = x_1^\mu R_k(x_1), \qquad\quad k > 2.$$

Set

$$a' = 1/a, \quad S(x_1) = \frac{-a' R(x_1)}{a + x_1 R(x_1)} \text{ near } x_1 = 0,$$

$$x_2' = [a' + x_1 S(x_1)]x_2.$$

With the new coordinates $(x_1, x_2', \ldots, x_n)$, V_1 is again the x_1-axis, and (as we see by insertion) $x_2' = x_1^\mu$ on V_2. Drop primes again; let Φ denote the resulting biholomorphic imbedding of V (near p) into C^n.

Taking the functions $x_1 = x$ and $x_2 = y$ only in V gives a holomorphic mapping Ψ of V into C^2, which is clearly a homeomorphism. We show that Ψ is biholomorphic. By Lemma 2.13, it is sufficient to show that the functions $x_3, \ldots, x_n$ in $\Phi(V)$ are expressible in terms of x_1 and x_2. The relations $x_k = x_1^\mu R_k(x_1)(k > 2)$ hold in V_2 in the new coordinates; hence

$x_k = x_2 R_k(x_1)$ for $k > 2$ in both V_1 and V_2, as required. Thus $\Psi'(V) = V_\mu$ near 0, completing the proof.

We shall say that the two sheets of V_μ^* have μ-*contact* at p.

15.3. We now study a variety $V = V_1 \cup V_2 \cup V_3$, each V_i being a 1-dimensional analytic manifold, with p in each, with no other intersections, and each pair of sheets having 2-contact; moreover, we assume $\dim C_6(V, p) = 2$. There is then a biholomorphic imbedding (near p) into C^2; by the considerations above, we may find an imbedding so that two of the sheets go into the variety $y(y - x^2) = 0$. Because of the invariance of μ-contact, we see that the imbedded V is given by the vanishing of

$$f(x, y) = y(y - x^2)(y - x^2\phi(x)), \quad \phi(0) = c \neq 0, 1.$$

We shall show that c *is an invariant of* V (taking the sheets in a fixed order).

Consider any other imbedding into C^2 such that the first two sheets go into $y = 0$ and $y - x^2 = 0$. By Theorem 4.7 the biholomorphism from one imbedding into the other is the restriction of a biholomorphism from C^2 into C^2. Taking coordinates (x, y) and (u, v), write this as

$$u = ax + a'y + \ldots, \quad v = bx + b'y + b''x^2 + \ldots.$$

Since V_1 is carried into itself, we must have $v = 0$ if $y = 0$; hence $b = b'' = 0$. If $y = x^2$, we must have $v = u^2$; hence (with $y = x^2$)

$$u = ax + a'x^2 + \ldots, \qquad u^2 = a^2x^2 + \ldots,$$
$$v = b'x^2 + \ldots, \qquad v - u^2 = (b' - a^2)x^2 + \ldots;$$

hence $b' = a^2$. Now on the image V_3' of V_3: $y = cx^2 + \cdots$ we have

$$u = ax + \ldots, \quad u^2 = a^2x^2 + \ldots, \quad v = a^2cx^2 + \ldots;$$

hence V_3' is given by $v = cu^2 + \ldots$, with the same c.

REMARK 15.4. We may find c intrinsically as follows: choose generators f, g of $O(V, p)$ (for instance, the functions x, y above) such that $f|V_1$ generates $O(V_1, p)$ (and hence each $O(V_i, p)$), and $g|V_1 = 0$. For any $\varepsilon \neq 0$, let $p_{i\varepsilon}$ be the point of V_i where f has the value ε. Then

$$c = \lim_{\varepsilon \to 0} g(p_{3\varepsilon})/g(p_{2\varepsilon}).$$

Example 15.5. Let $V \subset C^3$ near 0 be defined by the vanishing of

$$f(t, x, y) = y(y - x^2)(y - (2 + t)x^2);$$

then at $\rho_t = (t, 0, 0)$, the number $2 + t$ is intrinsically associated. Therefore the variety is non-homogeneous along C_t.

Example 15.6. Let $V \subset C^3$ near 0 be defined by the vanishing of

$$f(t, x, y) = y(y - x^2)(y - (2 + t)x^2)(y - \gamma(t)x^2),$$

where γ is transcendental and $\gamma(0) = 3$. Then the pair $(2 + t, \gamma(t))$ for each t and hence the function γ is intrinsically associated with V. For an algebraic variety, γ is algebraic: hence V is not locally algebraic along C_t.

INSTITUTE FOR ADVANCED STUDY

REFERENCES

[1] S. ABHYANKAR, Concepts of order and rank on a complex space, and a condition for normality, *Math. Annalen, 141* (1960), p. 171–192.

[2] E. BISHOP, Partially analytic spaces, *Am. Journal of Math., 83* (1961), p. 669–692.

[3] H. CARTAN, Séminaire 1951–52, École Normal Sup., Paris.

[4] ———, Variétés analytiques-réelles et variétés analytiques-complexes, *Bull. Soc. Math. France, 85* (1957), p. 77–100.

[5] H. GRAUERT and R. REMMERT, Zur Theorie der Modifikationen. I. Stetige und eigentliche Modifikationen komplexer Räume., *Math. Annalen, 129* (1955), p. 274–296.

[6] ———, Komplexe Räume, *Math. Annalen, 136* (1958), p. 245–318.

[7] N. LEVINSON, A polynomial canonical form for certain analytic functions of two variables at a critical point, *Bull. Am. Math. Soc., 66* (1960), p. 366–368.

[8] ———, Transformation of an analytic function of several complex variables to a canonical form, *Duke Math. Journal, 28* (1961), p. 345–354.

[9] R. REMMERT and K. STEIN, Über die wesentlichen Singularitäten analytischer Mengen, *Math. Annalen, 126* (1953), p. 263–306.

[10] H. ROSSI, Vector fields on analytic spaces, *Annals of Math., 78* (1963), p. 455–467.

[11] P. SAMUEL, Méthodes d'algèbre abstraite en géométrie algébrique, *Ergebnisse der Math.*, (N. F.) Heft 4, Springer, Berlin, 1955.

[12] J.-P. SERRE, Géométrie algébrique et géométrie analytique, *Annales de l'Institut Fourier, VI* (1955), p. 1–42.

[13] R. THOM, Sur l'homologie des variétés algébriques réelles, this volume.

[14] H. WHITNEY, Elementary structure of real algebraic varieties, *Annals of Math., 66* (1957), p. 545–556.

[15] ———, Tangents to an analytic variety (to appear in *Annals of Math.*).

[16] ———, and F. BRUHAT, Quelques propriétés fondamentales des ensembles analytiques-réels, *Comm. Math. Helvetici, 33* (1959), p. 132–160.

[17] O. ZARISKI and P. SAMUEL, *Commutative Algebra*, vol. II. Princeton, N.J.: D. van Nostrand Co., 1960.

On Infinite Processes Leading to Differentiability in the Complement of a Point

JOHN R. STALLINGS[1]

---

0. The infinite product technique

Let us recall a technique essentially due to Mazur [6] for proving results about the embedding of spheres.

G will denote a Brandt groupoid; it is a set with a binary law of composition defined for some pairs a, $b \in G$, giving $a \cdot b \in G$. This law of composition is associative when possible; certain elements $\{e\}$ are identities, such that $e \cdot e = e$ is always defined and whenever $e \cdot a$ or $a \cdot e$ is defined that product is equal to a; for every a there are identities ℓ_a and r_a such that $\ell_a \cdot a = a \cdot r_a = a$; and for every a there is a^{-1} such that $a \cdot a^{-1} = \ell_a$. It follows that $(a^{-1})^{-1} = a$, since

$$(a^{-1})^{-1} = \ell_a \cdot (a^{-1})^{-1} = a \cdot a^{-1} \cdot (a^{-1})^{-1} = a \cdot \ell_{a^{-1}} = a;$$

and hence $a^{-1} \cdot a = \ell_{a^{-1}} = r_a$.

We consider some infinite product $a_1 \cdot a_2 \cdot a_3 \cdots$ defined on all sequences of elements of G for which $a_n \cdot a_{n+1}$ is always defined, with values in a set H, such that this product is associative (with respect to the law of composition in G). Then we notice the following formula:

$$
\begin{aligned}
& a_1 \cdot a_2 \cdot a_3 \cdots \\
&= (a_1 a_1^{-1} a_1) \cdot (a_2 a_2^{-1} a_1^{-1} a_1 a_2) \cdot (a_3 \cdots) \cdots \\
&= (a_1 a_1^{-1}) \cdot (a_1 a_2 a_1^{-1} a_1^{-1}) \cdot (a_1 a_2 a_3 \cdots) \cdots \\
&= \ell \cdot \ell \cdot \ell \cdots
\end{aligned}
$$

where ℓ is the left identity of a_1.

Thus, the value of an infinite product is a function of only the left identity of the first term in the product.

We now describe a few applications of this observation.

---

[1] Sloan Foundation Fellow.

245

1. Spheres with a wild point

Let R^n denote the n-dimensional vector space of n-tuples $(x_1, x_2, x_3, \ldots)$ of real numbers, for some fixed $n \geq 3$. R^n_+ will denote the subset with $x_1 \geq 0$; R^{n-1} the subset with $x_2 = 0$; and $R^{n-1}_+ = R^{n-1} \cap R^n_+$.

We consider the set A defined thus: an element of A is a function $f \colon R^{n-1} \to R^n$ such that:

(1) f is infinitely differentiable and the rank of the tangent map at each point of R^{n-1} is $n - 1$.

(2) f is an embedding of R^{n-1} as a closed subset of R^n.

(3) $f \vert R^{n-1}_+$ is the identity map on R^{n-1}_+.

(4) $f(R^{n-1}) \cap R^n_+ = R^{n-1}_+$.

That is, f is a diffeomorphic embedding of R^{n-1} into R^n, which is (by virtue of (3) and (4)) half-nice at infinity.

Define two elements of A to be equivalent, $f \sim g$, if there is a C^∞ diffeomorphism of R^n onto itself, $h \colon R^n \to R^n$, such that $hf = g$. Since the image of an element of A in R^n has a tubular neighborhood and since any orientation-preserving diffeomorphism of R^{n-1} on itself is diffeotopic to the identity, this is equivalent to asserting $f \sim g$ if there is a diffeomorphism $h \colon R^n \to R^n$, which maps R^{n-1}_+ on itself in an orientation-preserving way, such that $h(f(R^{n-1})) = g(R^{n-1})$.

Now, there is a diffeomorphism of the plane $\{(x_1, x_3)\}$ which maps the half-plane $\{x_1 < 0\}$ onto a subset of the half-strip $\{x_1 < 0, 0 < x_3 < 1\}$. And hence there is a diffeomorphism $h \colon R^n \to R^n$ mapping the half-space $\{(x_1, x_2, \ldots) \vert x_1 < 0\}$ into the half-slab $\{x_1 < 0, 0 < x_3 < 1\}$.

Let $f \in A$. Then $hfh^{-1} \vert R^{n-1}$ is, one easily sees, equivalent to f; and it has the additional property that it is the identity outside the half-slab.

Let f, $g \in A$. Then $f \sim f_1$ with f_1 the identity outside the slab $\{0 < x_3 < 1\}$, and $g \sim g_1$ with g_1 the identity outside the slab $\{2 < x_3 < 3\}$. Define $e \in A$ as follows:

$$a(x_1, x_2, \ldots) = (x_1, x_2, \ldots) \text{ if } x_3 \leq 0,\ 1 \leq x_3 \leq 2,\ 3 \leq x_3;$$
$$= f_1(x_1, x_2, \ldots) \text{ if } 0 < x_3 < 1;$$
$$= g_1(x_1, x_2, \ldots) \text{ if } 2 < x_3 < 3.$$

The equivalence class of e is seen easily to depend only on the equivalence classes of f and g; denoting the equivalence class of α by $[\alpha]$, we define

$$[f] \cdot [g] = [e].$$

Denote the set of equivalence classes of A and G. The above defined multiplication is clearly associative, and there is a two-sided identity element, namely, the class containing the identity embedding $R^{n-1} \subset R^n$.

If $f_1, f_2, \ldots$, are elements of A such that f_n is the identity outside the slab $\{2n < x_3 < 2n + 1\}$, we can extend the definition of multiplication in the obvious way to define an infinite product $[f_1] \cdot [f_2] \cdots \in G$.

If we can apply the result of section 0, it will show that there is only one element in G; in other words, every such embedding as we are considering will be equivalent to the standard one. All that needs to be done is to show that G is a group; that is the same as to show that every element has an inverse.

Let $\varphi \colon R^n \to R^n$ be defined thus:

$$\varphi(x_1, x_2, x_3, x_4, \ldots) = (x_1, -x_2, -x_3, x_4, \ldots).$$

φ is the $180°$ rotation parallel to the (x_2, x_3)-plane. If $f \in A$, define $f^* = \varphi f \varphi^{-1} | R^{n-1}$. Clearly $f^* \in A$ and $f^*(R^{n-1}) = \varphi(f(R^{n-1}))$. It is claimed that $[f] \cdot [f^*]$ is the identity element of G; i.e., $[f^*]$ is the inverse of $[f]$.

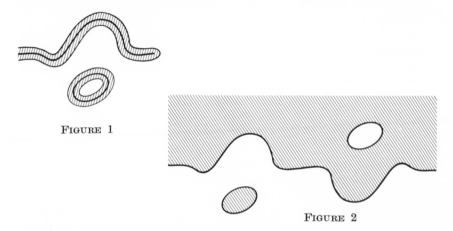

FIGURE 1

FIGURE 2

First we suppose f is the identity outside the half-slab $\{x_1 \leq 0, 0 < x_3 < 1\}$. Consider a tubular neighborhood of $f(R^{n-1})$ in R^n; it is diffeomorphic to $R^{n-1} \times (-1, 1)$. In this tubular neighborhood, consider a very nice neighborhood U of R_+^{n-1}; U is also a very nice neighborhood of R_+^{n-1} in R^n; therefore $R^n - U$ is diffeomorphic to a closed half-space R_+^n. On the other hand, since n is large enough, within the tubular neighborhood, U may be moved around to a very nice neighborhood of any other half of $f(R^{n-1})$; let T be the set of points of R^{n-1} with $x_3 \leq 1$; then U is moveable to a nice neighborhood V of $f(T)$ by a diffeomorphism of R^n; hence $R^n - V$ is diffeomorphic to a closed half-space.

The image of f^* is obtained by rotating parallel to the (x_2, x_3)-plane; and an equivalent embedding is obtained by shifting a bit in the x_3 direction. Take the product of f and f^*; rather than writing down a formula, a picture is sufficient to suggest a proof that the closure of either component of $R^n - e(R^{n-1})$, where e is this product, is diffeomorphic to $R^n - V$ and hence to a half-plane. Figures 1 and 2 represent cross-sections parallel to the (x_2, x_3)-plane, the x_2-coordinate being vertical and the x_3-coordinate horizontal. Figure 1 represents f with V drawn in and shaded, while Figure 2 represents the product e in which the shaded region is the intersection of one component of $R^n - e(R^{n-1})$ with the cross-section. The shaded region of Figure 2 is diffeomorphic to the complement of V in Figure 1. To be more accurate, the cross-section of V may not be so nice as that shown here; this construction actually shows that a component of R^n minus a tubular neighborhood of $e(R^{n-1})$ is diffeomorphic to the complement of V; and of course one must define the "unfolding" diffeomorphism in a uniform way throughout all cross-sections.

And so, since both halves of the e-situation are diffeomorphic to half-spaces, it follows that e is equivalent to the trivial embedding.

Therefore:

THEOREM 1. *Any diffeomorphic embedding of R^{n-1} as a closed subset of R^n, if it is half-nice, is equivalent differentiably to the standard embedding.*

And now, a rather surprising corollary.[1]

COROLLARY. *If $n \geq 4$, any diffeomorphic embedding of R^{n-1} as a closed subset of R^n is differentiably equivalent to the standard embedding.*

To prove this, it is enough to show any embedding $f: R^{n-1} \to R^n$ is equivalent to a half-nice one. Let L be a straight half-line in R^{n-1}; then $f(L)$ is a differentiable arc going to infinity in R^n. *Since $n \geq 4$, $f(L)$ can be straightened out in R^n*; that is, $f(L)$ can be moved to coincide with L and then adjusted so that the equivalent embedding is the identity on L. Then on a tubular neighborhood of L the embedding can be untwisted, beginning at the finite end and untwisting out toward infinity; this equivalent embedding is the identity on a neighborhood of L; we then push outward a little to make the embedding the identity on a tube of constant width about L; and then make a rather large expansion of this tube into a full half-space. The resultant embedding equivalent to f is now half-nice.

We remark that the corollary is false for $n = 3$, as shown by examples of Fox and Artin [2]. The above proof makes it evident that this happens because a differentiable arc knots in R^3 but in no other R^n.

By taking one-point compactifications, the reader may obtain results about spheres differentially embedded except at one point.

---

[1] [Added in proof.] A similar result is due to J. C. Cantrell. Almost locally flat embedding of S^{n-1} in S^n, *Bull. Amer. Math. Soc.*, *69* (1963), p. 716–718.

These results are analogous to certain of Mazur's and Morse and Huebsch's theorems [6, 10].

2. One attack at h-cobordism (Smale-Mazur)

A cobordism of dimension n is a triple $(M; A, B)$ where M is a compact n-manifold with boundary, whose boundary is the disjoint union of the closed $(n-1)$-manifolds A and B. We generally wish to require M, A, and B to be oriented differentiable manifolds with the orientation of the boundary of M compatible with that of A and incompatible with that of B, and to identify two cobordisms if there is an orientation-preserving diffeomorphism between them.

If $(M; A, B)$ and $(N; B, C)$ are two cobordisms with a common boundary part B (oriented oppositely in the two cases), we define $(M; A, B) \circ (N; B, C)$ to be $(M \cup N; A, C)$, where $M \cup N$ is the union of M and N pasted together along B.

Let C^n denote the class of all cobordisms of dimension n. With the above defined law of composition, C^n is almost a Brandt groupoid; the left identity of $(M; A, B)$, for example, is $(A \times I; A \times 0, A \times 1)$.

Define G^n as the set of all cobordisms of dimension n having both a left and a right inverse; that is, $\alpha \in G^n$ if there are β and $\gamma \in C^n$ such that $\beta \circ \alpha$ and $\alpha \circ \gamma$ are defined and equal to identity cobordisms of the form $(A \times I; A \times 0, A \times 1)$. G^n is a Brandt groupoid; what must be shown is the existence of a right inverse to each element of G^n. Let $\alpha \in G^n$, so that $\beta \circ \alpha$ and $\alpha \circ \gamma$ are identities; it will be shown that $\gamma \in G^n$; clearly γ has a left inverse, namely α; but α is also a right inverse to γ, because $\gamma \circ \alpha$ is defined, and $\gamma \circ \alpha = (\beta \circ \alpha) \circ (\gamma \circ \alpha) = \beta \circ (\alpha \circ \gamma) \circ \alpha = \beta \circ \alpha$, which is an identity.

The elements of G^n will be called *invertible cobordisms*.

Let $(M_n; A_n, A_{n+1})$, $n = 1, 2, \ldots$, be a sequence of invertible cobordisms; we may form an infinite product by pasting together the M_n into a chain; the result is a manifold, no longer compact, with one boundary part A_1.

The result of section 0 shows this, in particular:

$$(M; A, B) \circ (B \times I; B \times 0, B \times 1) \circ (B \times I; B \times 0, B \times 1) \circ \cdots$$
$$= (A \times I; A \times 0, A \times 1) \circ (A \times I; A \times 0, A \times 1) \circ \cdots$$

These manifolds are (diffeomorphically) equivalent to $M - B$ and $A \times [0, 1)$ respectively. Hence:

THEOREM 2: *Let $(M; A, B)$ be an invertible cobordism. Then $M - B$ is equivalent to $A \times [0, 1)$.*

Now, invertible cobordisms are closely related to h-cobordisms. An h-cobordism is a differentiable cobordism $(M; A, B)$ such that both the inclusions $A \subset M$ and $B \subset M$ are homotopy equivalences.

To each h-cobordism $(M; A, B)$ one associates an element $\tau(M; A, B) \in W(\Pi)$, where $\Pi = \pi_1(A)$ and $W(\Pi)$ is the Whitehead torsion group [15] of the group Π; namely, $\tau(M; A, B)$ is the torsion of the homotopy equivalence $A \to M$. The function τ is additive in this sense:

$$\tau((M; A, B) \circ (N; B, C)) = \tau(M; A, B) + \tau(N; B, C),$$

where we identify $\pi_1(A)$ and $\pi_1(B)$ under an isomorphism

$$\pi_1(A) \approx \pi_1(M) \approx \pi_1(B).$$

A theorem of Mazur states [8]: *Let $(N; A, B)$ be an h-cobordism of dimension $n \geq 6$; let $\tau(M; A, B) = 0$. Then $(M; A, B)$ is equivalent to the trivial cobordism $(A \times I; A \times 0, A \times 1)$.* The proof of this is an application of Smale's handlebody theory [12]; it implies that $(M; A, B)$ can be presented in the form $A \times I$, plus handles of degrees k and $k + 1$, where $k = \left[\dfrac{n}{2}\right]$. The hypothesis $\tau(M; A, B) = 0$ implies that by adding on some trivial pairs of handles of degrees k and $k + 1$ and sliding them around, one can get all the handles to cancel out. This leaves $(M; A, B)$ presented as $A \times I$. Certain delicate points in the geometry insist that for this proof to be valid one must assume the dimension n is at least six.

Another result can be proved: *If $\alpha \in W(\Pi)$ where $\Pi = \pi_1(A)$, and dimension $A = n - 1 \geq 5$, then there is an h-cobordism $(M; A, B)$ with $\tau(M; A, B) = \alpha$.* To see this, represent α by a matrix over the integral group ring of Π and attach to $A \times I$ handles of degrees 2 and 3 so that the incidence relations between these handles form the given matrix.

THEOREM 3. *If $(M; A, B)$ is an h-cobordism of dimension $n \geq 6$, then it is invertible, and hence Theorem 2 applies.*

PROOF. Construct an h-cobordism $(N; B, C)$ such that

$$\tau(N; B, C) = -\tau(M; A, B).$$

Then by the theorem of Mazur quoted above, since

$$\tau((M; A, B) \circ (N; B, C)) = 0,$$

it follows that $(M; A, B) \circ (N; B, C)$ is trivial. The existence of a left inverse is similarly proved, and so $(M; A, B)$ is invertible.

3. Another attack at h-cobordism (Engulfing Theory)

In fact, Theorem 3 is valid for $n = 5$. The proof which will be given now does not involve Smale's theory or Whitehead torsion, but instead involves the Engulfing Theorem [13].

Suppose $(M; A, B)$ to be an h-cobordism of dimension $n \geq 5$; we also suppose the manifolds involved are combinatorial manifolds; any differentiable results desired here can be obtained from the combinatorial ones by means of techniques of Hirsch [4].

Let U and V be regular neighborhoods of A and B in M; and let T be a sufficiently fine combinatorial triangulation of M. It is well known that U and V are combinatorially equivalent to $A \times I$ and $B \times I$.

K will denote the union of all closed simplexes Δ of T such that either $\Delta \subset A$ or both $\Delta \cap B = \emptyset$ and dimension $\Delta \leq 2$. L will denote the maximum subcomplex of the barycentric subdivision of T which is disjoint from K.

Then, $A \subset K$ and $B \subset L$; dimension $K - A \leq 2$; dimension $(L$ minus a small neighborhood of $B) \leq n - 3$; every simplex of the barycentric subdivision of T is the join uniquely of a face in K and a face in L.

It follows from the Engulfing Theorem that there is a polyhedral equivalence $\alpha: M \to M$ which is the identity on $A \cup B$, such that $L \subset \alpha(V)$; and from the same theorem, since $2 \leq n - 3$, that there is a polyhedral equivalence $\beta: M \to M$ which is the identity on $A \cup B$, such that $K \subset \beta(U)$. Then, since K and L almost fill up M, there is a polyhedral equivalence $\gamma: M \to M$, such that $M = \alpha(V) \cup \gamma\beta(U)$. By a small adjustment, if necessary, we can arrange $\alpha(V)$ and $\gamma\beta(U)$ to overlap properly so that their boundaries do not intersect.

Behold! $\gamma\beta(U)$ is a trivial cobordism between two copies of A. It has been cleft into two cobordisms, one given by M — interior $\alpha(V)$ and the second by $\alpha(V) \cap \gamma\beta(U)$. The first one, M — interior $\alpha(V)$, since V is a regular neighborhood of B, is equivalent to the original cobordism $(M; A, B)$. Thus $(M; A, B)$ has a right inverse, and similarly a left inverse.

THEOREM 4. *Every h-cobordism $(M; A, B)$ of dimension $n \geq 5$ is invertible. Therefore $M - B$ is equivalent to $A \times [0, 1)$.*

COROLLARY. *If $(M; A, B)$ is an h-cobordism of dimension $n \geq 5$, then the following two polyhedra are homeomorphic:*

(a) *The closed cone on A.*

(b) *M plus a cone on B.*

The corollary follows from the theorem because case (a) is the one-point compactification of $A \times [0, 1)$, and case (b) is the one-point compactification of $M - B$.

4. The falsity of the Hauptvermutung in dimension 5

This corollary leads easily to examples of homeomorphic polyhedra which are not polyhedrally equivalent.

Here is the simplest example. Let K denote the cell complex consisting of a 1-sphere S to which a 2-cell D has been attached by a map of degree five along its boundary. Then $\pi_1(K) = \Pi$ is the group of five elements; its group ring may be considered the integral polynomial ring in the symbol t, with a relation $t^5 = 1$. This ring has non-trivial units, for example $\xi = 1 - t + t^2$, since $(1 - t + t^2)(t + t^2 - t^4) = 1$.

There is a map $f: K \to K$ such that $f|S$ is the identity and such that the chain map defined by f in dimension 2 is multiplication by ξ. f is a homotopy equivalence with non-zero Whitehead torsion.

K, being 2-dimensional, may be polyhedrally embedded in R^5 by a map $g: K \to R^5$. Let U be a regular neighborhood of $g(K)$ in R^5. The map $gf: K \to U$ may be approximated by an embedding $h: K \to U$. Let V be a regular neighborhood of $h(K)$ in the interior of U.

Let A, B denote the boundaries of U and V, and $M = U -$ interior V. It is easy to prove that $\pi_1(A) \approx \pi_1(M) \approx \pi_1(B)$ is a group of order five. From this and the homological situation in the universal covering spaces we can prove:

(a) $A \subset M$ and $B \subset M$ are homotopy equivalences. Thus $(M; A, B)$ is a 5-dimensional h-cobordism.

(b) The Whitehead torsion of the inclusion $B \subset M$ is the same as for $V \subset U$, which is the same as that of the map f, and thus non-zero;

$$\tau(M; B, A) \neq 0.$$

Now, by the corollary to Theorem 4, the following two polyhedra are homeomorphic:

$$X = \text{the cone on } A$$

$$Y = M \text{ plus the cone on } B$$

But X and Y cannot be polyhedrally equivalent. If $\varphi: X \to Y$ were a polyhedral equivalence, for local homological reasons φ would map the conical point $x_0 \in X$ to the conical point $y_0 \in Y$. Hence, triangulating φ finely, and removing the stars of x_0 and y_0, there would be a polyhedral equivalence of the pair $(A \times I, A \times 0)$ onto (M, B); these pairs happen to be homotopically trivial, and thus their Whitehead torsion is defined. The Whitehead torsion of $(A \times I, A \times 0)$ is zero, but that of (M, B) is not zero; hence no polyhedral equivalence of these pairs exists, and so no such φ exists.

THEOREM 5.   *The five-dimensional polyhedra X and Y described above are homeomorphic but not polyhedrally equivalent.*

This is, of course, the same sort of example as Milnor's [9], but of a smaller dimension.

5. Other applications

Another sort of theorem which can be proved using the infinite product technique is the fact that in quite general circumstances a union of cones or mapping cylinders is—topologically or differentiably—a cone or mapping cylinder. It is pointless to go into detail about this here, since there is no dearth of literature in this subject. We mention in particular Brown [1], Kwun [5], Mazur [7], and Stallings [14].

6. Remarks

The recent developments in polyhedral and differential topology have come so rapidly that a mysterious bipolarity seems to exist. The knotting and unknotting results of Haefliger [3] and Zeeman [16] appear to have little in common; our "engulfing" theory [13] and the "handlebody" theory of Smale [12] give similar-sounding results but seem quite different as techniques.

We have tried in sections 2 and 3 to sketch proofs of nearly the same thing using two different methods. To sum up:

The Smale-Mazur h-cobordism theory is strong and takes into account a subtle matter involving the Whitehead torsion. Its techniques are really rather direct. The defect of the theory is its lack of results in dimensions ≤ 5.

The other h-cobordism theory is less constructive and more geometrical. A central role is played by the infinite product technique. The Engulfing Theorem is proved geometrically by a roundabout method that seems to involve the vanishing of higher and higher obstructions. And this theory lacks results in dimensions ≤ 4.

We should now seek a handlebody method applicable to dimension five. Also, especially for inductive proofs, there is a great necessity to understand manifolds of dimensions three and four; as far as I know these problems have been attacked most hopefully by an intricate study of geometry and group theory [11].

PRINCETON UNIVERSITY

References

[1] M. Brown, The monotone union of open n-cells is an open n-cell, *Proc. Amer. Math. Soc.*, *12* (1961), p. 812–814.

[2] R. H. Fox and E. Artin, Some wild cells and spheres in three-dimensional space, *Ann. of Math.*, *49* (1948), p. 979–990.

[3] A. Haefliger, Knotted $(4k − 1)$-spheres in $6k$-space, *Ann. of Math.*, *75* (1962), p. 452–466.

[4] M. Hirsch, Smooth regular neighborhoods, *Ann. of Math.*, *76* (1962), p. 524–530.

[5] K. W. Kwun, Uniqueness of the open cone neighborhood, to appear.

[6] B. Mazur, On embeddings of spheres, *Bull. Amer. Math. Soc.*, *65* (1959), p. 59–65.

[7] ———, The method of infinite repetition in pure topology, to appear.

[8] ———, Relative neighborhoods and the theorems of Smale, *Ann. of Math.*, *77* (1963), p. 232–249.

[9] J. Milnor, Two complexes which are homeomorphic but combinatorially distinct, *Ann. of Math.*, *74* (1961), p. 575–590.

[10] M. Morse and W. Huebsch, Schoenflies extensions without interior differential singularities, *Ann. of Math.*, *76* (1962), p. 18–54.

[11] C. D. Papakyriakopoulos, A reduction of the Poincaré conjecture to group theoretic conjectures, *Ann. of Math.*, *77* (1963), p. 250–305.

[12] S. Smale, Generalized Poincaré's conjecture in dimensions greater than four, *Ann. of Math.*, *74* (1961), p. 391–406.

[13] J. Stallings, The piecewise-linear structure of Euclidean space, *Proc. Cambridge Philos. Soc.*, *58* (1962), p. 481–488.

[14] ———, Groups with infinite products, *Bull. Amer. Math. Soc.*, *68* (1962), p. 388–389.

[15] J. H. C. Whitehead, Simple homotopy types, *Amer. Journal of Math.*, *72* (1950), p. 1–57.

[16] E. C. Zeeman, Unknotting combinatorial balls, to appear.

Sur L'Homologie des Variétés Algébriques Réelles

RENÉ THOM

Résumé

On montre, à l'aide de la théorie de Morse sur les variétés à bord, que si A est l'ensemble des zéros dans $\mathbf{R}^n$ d'un polynôme de degré p, alors la somme des nombres de Betti de A est majorée par $(p)^n$; on donne une borne analogue pour les ensembles algébriques réels projectifs.

Soit A un ensemble algébrique réel *affine*; c'est, par définition, l'ensemble des points de l'espace euclidien de dimension n, $\mathbf{R}^n$, dont les coordonnées $(x_1, x_2, \ldots, x_n)$ vérifient un système fini d'équations polynomiales à coefficients réels:

$$P_1(x_1, x_2, \ldots, x_n) = 0,$$
$$P_2(x_1, x_2, \ldots, x_n) = 0, \ldots, P_r(x_1, x_2, \ldots, x_n) = 0.$$

Il est bien connu que tout ensemble algébrique réel tel que A peut se définir à l'aide d'une seule équation, par exemple:

$$G(x_1, x_2, \ldots, x_n) = 0, \quad \text{où } G(x_1, x_2, \ldots, x_n) = \sum_i P_i^2(x_1, x, \ldots, x_n).$$

On ne considérera par la suite que des ensembles A définis par une seule équation $G = 0$; pour éviter toute redite, on adoptera la convention suivante: quand on dira que l'ensemble A est défini par l'équation $G = 0$, *on supposera que le polynôme G est positif*, ou, si G peut changer de signe, *que l'ensemble défini par $G = 0$ est une hypersurface régulière sans singularités.*

Avec cette convention, on se propose d'établir le théorème suivant:

THÉORÈME 1. *Soit A l'ensemble algébrique de $\mathbf{R}^n$ défini par une équation $G(x_i) = 0$, où le polynôme G est de degré p. Alors la somme des nombres de Betti de A (pris par rapport au corps $\mathbf{Z}_p$ ou $\mathbf{R}$ comme coefficients) est majorée par: (p^n).*

En raison du caractère localement compact et localement contractile de tout ensemble algébrique réel, il est indifférent de préciser la théorie de l'homologie utilisée; on pourra admettre, par exemple, qu'il s'agit de l'homologie singulière.

On établira le théorème 1 d'abord dans le cas où A est compact; deux lemmes nous seront nécessaires, ainsi qu'une propriété due à Lojasiewcz.

LEMME 1. *Soit K un ensemble algébrique compact de $\mathbf{R}^n$ défini par l'équation $F = 0$; il existe un nombre positif a tel que K soit rétracte par déformation d'une ou plusieurs composantes connexes compactes de la variété à bord définie par $F \leq a$.*

Soit (C) l'ensembles des points critiques du polynôme F (ensemble des zéros de la différentielle dF); C est un sous-ensemble algébrique de $\mathbf{R}^n$; par suite, en raison du théorème de Seidenberg-Tarski [1], l'image $F(C)$ est un ensemble "semi-algébrique," c'est-à-dire un ensemble défini à l'aide d'inéquations et d'équations polynomiales; un tel ensemble, sur la droite réelle $\mathbf{R}$, ne comprend que des points isolés et des intervalles, éventuellement fermés ou semi-fermés; or, d'après le théorème d'A. P. Morse sur l'ensemble des valeurs singulières d'une fonction différentiable, l'ensemble $F(C)$ ne peut comporter aucun intervalle, et se compose seulement de points isolés. Dans ces conditions, il existe un nombre a positif tel que dans $[-a, +a]$, il n'existe aucune valeur critique de F, sauf éventuellement zéro. Alors le système d'équations $F = \pm a$ définit une hypersurface (H) de $\mathbf{R}^n$, qui divise l'espace $\mathbf{R}^n$ en un certain nombre de composantes connexes (V_j); je dis que, si a est assez petit, celles des V_j qui contiennent des points de K sont relativement compactes dans R^n. Soit en effet, d un nombre positif; on sait [2]—c'est l'inégalité de Lojasie-wicz—que, pour d assez petit, en tout point situé à la distance euclidienne d de K, on a l'inégalité $|F| > d^\alpha$, α exposant positif; soit dés lors U l'ensemble compact des points situés à une distance de K inférieure à d; si l'on prend $a < d^\alpha$, tout point du bord ∂U est séparé de K par l'hypersurface (H); les composantes connexes (V_j) contenant K sont donc toutes contenues dans U, ce qui montre qu'elles sont relativement compactes.

Si l'on forme les trajectoires du champ grad F, on sait, également d'après Lojasiewicz, qu'elles permettent de définir une rétraction par déformation des (V_j) sur K [3]. Ceci achève par suite la démonstration du Lemme 1.

Disons, pour abréger, qu'une fonction u est *correcte* sur une hypersurface (H) d'équation $F = a$, si la fonction u ne présente sur (H) que des points critiques quadratiques non dégénérés. Alors, on a le:

LEMME 2. *Soit $u = \Sigma x_i^2$, et F un polynôme tel que l'équation $F = a$ définisse une hypersurface sans singularités; étant donné un compact $K \subset \mathbf{R}^n$, le polynôme F peut être approché par un polynôme G de même degré, tel que l'équation $G = a$ définisse dans un voisinage de K une hypersurface sans singularités sur laquelle la fonction (u) est correcte dans K.*

Ceci se démontre par un argument standard de transversalité, que nous reproduisons intégralement ci-dessous. Les points critiques de (u) sur l'hypersurface $F^{-1}(a)$ sont donnés par le système:

$$(S) \qquad F = a \qquad \frac{x_1}{F_{x_1}} = \frac{x_2}{F_{x_2}} = \cdots = \frac{x_i}{F_{x_i}} = \cdots = \frac{x_n}{F_{x_n}}.$$

Supposons, pour fixer les idées, que, sur le compact K considéré, l'une au moins des fonctions coordonnées (x_i) ne s'annule pas sur K: ceci suppose seulement que l'origine 0 n'est pas dans K; on pourra alors subdiviser K en compacts K_i sur lesquels (x_i) ne s'annule pas.

On peut alors écrire, sur K_1, le système (S) sous la forme:

$$F = a \qquad H_i(F) = F_{x_i} - \frac{x_i}{x_l} F_{x_l} = 0, \qquad i = 2, 3 \cdots n.$$

Dire qu'un point critique de u sur $F^{-1}(a)$ est non dégénéré, équivaut à dire que les hypersurfaces $H_i(F) = 0$ et $F^{-1}(a)$ se coupent transversalement en ce point.

Posons alors $G = F - \Sigma_j c_j x_j, j = 2, 3, \ldots, n$; les points critiques de (u) sur $G^{-1}(a)$ sont donnés par le système:

$$G = a; H_i(G) = H_i(F) - c_i = 0.$$

Considérons l'application auxiliaire $H: \mathbf{R}^n \to \mathbf{R}^{n-1}$ définie par:

$$c_j = H_j(F), j = 2, 2, \ldots, n.$$

Soit $(c_j = m_j)$ une valeur régulière de l'application H restreinte à l'hypersurface $F^{-1}(a)$; c'est dire qu' en tout point de $F^{-1}(a) \cap H^{-1}(m)$, la $(n-1)$ forme induite par $(H): H^*(dc_2 \wedge \cdots \wedge dc_n)$ n'est pas nulle dans $F^{-1}(a) \cap K_1$.

Or, si l'on fait $c_j = m_j$, l'application $H(G)$ ne diffère de l'application $H(F)$ que par une translation constante; par suite, en tout point de $H(F)^{-1}(m_j) = H(G)^{-1}(0)$, la $(n-1)$ forme $H^*(dc_2 \wedge \cdots \wedge dc_n)$ est non-nulle sur $F^{-1}(a)$, donc aussi sur $G^{-1}(a) \cap K_1$, pourvu que les coefficients (m_j) soient pris assez petits; il en résulte que les hypersurfaces $H_i(G) = 0$ et $G = a$ se coupent transversalement dans K_1; c'est dire que la fonction u est correcte dans: $G^{-1}(a) \cap K_1$.

Théorie de Morse pour les variétés à bord [4]

Soit M^{n+1} une variété à bord compacte, de bord $W = \partial M^{n+1}$; soit f une fonction "correcte" sur M^{n+1}: les points critiques de f sur l'intérieur de M, ainsi que ceux de la restriction de f au bord W de M sont quadratiques non dégénérés; désignons par i_k le nombre des points critiques de type k

dans l'intérieur de M, par j_k le nombre des points critiques de la restriction de f à W, tels que le gradient soit *rentrant* dans M, alors on a l'inégalité:

$$i_k + j_k \geqq b_k(M^{n+1}).$$

Dans le cas qui nous intéresse, la fonction f n'est autre que $u = x_i^2$, et la variété à bord est le voisinage de K constitué des V_j. En ce cas, si l'origine 0 est prise extérieure aux V_j, u n'a aucun point critique dans l'intérieur des $V_j(i_k = 0)$; il suffira donc de compter le nombre des points critiques de la restriction de u au bord de V_j; dans ce but, on remplace le polynôme F par un polynôme G tel que u soit correcte sur $G^{-1}(a) \cap K$, et que, par ailleurs, dans le voisinage U de K, les hypersurfaces $F = a$, $G = a$ soient isotopes: on sait, en effet, que cette condition est réalisée dés que G est assez voisin de F dans la C^1 topologie. Dans cette situation, le nombre total des points critiques de (u) sur $G = a$ est majoré par le nombre total des solutions du système (S):

$$G = a, \; x_1/G_{x_1} = x_2/G_{x_2} = \cdots = x_n/G_{x_n}.$$

Il y a donc en tout (n) équations de degré (p), et, par suite, d'après le théorème de Bezout, au plus $(p)^n$ solutions. Ceci établit donc le théorème 1 dans le cas où K est compact et F est un polynôme positif.

REMARQUE. On pourrait même observer que parmi les points critiques de u sur $G^{-1}(a) \cap K_1$, il en est certainement un au moins à gradient sortant, à savoir le maximum de u sur cette hypersurface; on pourrait donc, en ce cas, diminuer la borne d'une unité.

Dans le cas où le polynôme F prend des signes opposés, mais où néanmoins $F^{-1}(0)$ est une hypersurface W compacte sans singularités, on observe que les équations $F = \pm\, a$ définissent deux hypersurfaces isotopes à W, pour a assez petit; la fonction u présente sur ces hypersurfaces des points critiques qui se répartissent par couples, l'un à gradient rentrant, l'autre à gradient sortant; il en résulte qu'on obtient une majoration de $\Sigma_k j_k$ en prenant $(p)^n$, où p est le degré de F.

Toujours dans le cas où l'ensemble algébrique K est compact, il est possible toutefois d'obtenir une majoration un peu meilleure; soit K défini par le polynôme F positif, de degré p; on désignera par U le voisinage de K limité par des composantes de $F^{-1}(a)$. Remplaçons alors le polynôme F par un polynôme G voisin de F tel que la variété de niveau $G^{-1}(a)$ présente des composantes connexes isotopes à celles qui forment ∂U; le nouveau voisinage U_1 contenant K et limité par $G = a$, est de ce fait homéomorphe à U; de plus, on peut supposer que les points critiques du polynôme G sont génériques; comme ils sont définis par le système:

$$G_{x_1} = G_{x_2} = \cdots = G_{x_n} = 0,$$

il y en a au plus $(p - 1)^n$, dont une fraction seulement sera contenue dans U_1; il en résulte bien que la somme des nombres de Betti de U_1, donc de K, est majorée par $(p - 1)^n$. On a donc le:

THÉORÈME 2'. *Si K est un ensemble algébrique affine compact, défini par l'équation $F = 0$ où F est un polynôme positif de degré p, alors*:

$$\Sigma b_j(k) \leq (p - 1)^n$$

REMARQUE. Supposons de plus que le polynôme positif F soit une fonction *propre* sur $\mathbf{R}^n$; alors les hypersurfaces de niveau $F = m$, pour m grand, limitent un système fondamental de voisinages du point à l'infini de $\mathbf{R}^n$; ce sont donc des sphères d'homotopie; comme, par la dualité d'Alexander-Pontrjagin, on a:

$$b_j(K) = b_{n-j-1}(\mathbf{R}^n - U),$$

il en résulte que la somme $\Sigma b_j(K)$ est également majorée par le nombre des points critiques de F augmenté d'une unité tenant compte de la valeur $F = \infty$ obtenu au point infini de $\mathbf{R}^n$). Dans le cas donc où F est positif et *propre*, on a la majoration plus fine:

$$(2) \qquad\qquad \Sigma b_j(K) \leq 1 + (p - 1)^n.$$

De manière plus générale, supposons que l'ensemble algébrique A de $\mathbf{R}^n$ soit une variété compacte sans singularités, définie par le système d'équations:

$$f_1 = f_2 = \cdots = f_m = 0,$$

où les polynômes f_j sont de degré r; supposons de plus qu'en tout point de a, les vecteurs grad f_j engendrent le fibré normal à A; posons alors $g = \Sigma f_j^2$, et appliquons la théorie précédente à la variété à bord $g \leq a$. Ici, encore on constate que les points critiques de la fonction u se répartissent par couples (gradient entrant, gradient sortant) chaque couple étant associé à un point critique de (u) sur la variété A. Dans ces conditions on peut affirmer:

THÉORÈME 2. *La somme des nombres de Betti de la variété compacte A est majorée par*: $(2r)^{n-1}/2$.

REMARQUE. Si l'on définit, comme Chern-Lashof [5], la courbure totale de l'ensemble $A = F^{-1}(0)$ comme la courbure de Gauss des hypersurfaces $F = a$, pour a petit, alors il est clair que toutes les majorations obtenues plus haut pour la somme des nombres de Betti de A sont également valables pour la courbure totale de ces ensembles.

Le théorème 1 étant ainsi établi pour A compact, il reste à examiner le cas où A est non compact ; le lemme suivant permet de se ramener au cas compact.

LEMME 3. *Soit A un ensemble algébrique réel affine, B_r la boule de centre 0 de rayon r ; il existe une valeur r_0 de r, telle que A admet pour rétracte par déformation, l'intersection $A \cap B_{r_0}$.*

La démonstration de ce lemme fait appel à des propriétés topologiques des ensembles algébriques réels, qui n'ont pas encore été établies dans la littérature ; on trouvera dans [6] un exposé préliminaire des propriétés utilisées, que nous rappelons brièvement ci-dessous :

On sait que tout ensemble algébrique réel A peut-être décomposé en une réunion de variétés plongées (Manifold Collection), que nous appellerons les *strates* de A. Cette décomposition, mise en évidence par H. Whitney dans [7], admet un raffinement ayant les propriétés suivantes (dites d'incidence régulière) :

(1) La frontière de toute strate U de (A) est réunion finie de strates de dimension inférieure.

(2) Appelons étoile d'une strate (U) la réunion finie des strates V telles que la frontière de V contient U ; alors toute application $f \colon \mathbf{R}^k \Rightarrow \mathbf{R}^n$ transversale sur la strate U est également transversale sur les strates de l'étoile de U au voisinage de U.

(3) De manière plus précise : à toute strate U on peut associer une fonction polynomiale par morceaux φ_u, nulle sur U, positive à l'extérieur de U, telle que la différentielle $d\varphi_u$ soit non nulle dans les strates de l'étoile de U, au voisinage de U, alors toute application $f \colon \mathbf{R}^k \Rightarrow \mathbf{R}^n$ transversale sur U est transversale aux hypersurfaces de niveau de la fonction φ_u dans l'intersection d'une strate V de l'étoile et d'un voisinage de U.

Ceci étant admis, supposons qu'on ait muni l'ensemble A d'une "stratification" ayant les propriétés ci-dessus ; appelons valeur critique de la fonction $u = r^2$:

(1°) Les valeurs de u aux points qui sont strates de dimension zéro de A ; il n'y en a qu'un nombre fini.

(2°) Les valeurs critiques de la restriction de u aux différentes strates de A ; ici encore, il n'y en a qu'un nombre fini, car on peut reprendre mot pour mot ce qui a été dit de l'ensemble des valeurs singulières d'un polynôme sur une variété algébrique au début de la démonstration du Lemme 1. Dans ces conditions, on prendra pour valeur r_0 une valeur plus grande que toutes les valeurs critiques de $\sqrt{u}$ sur A.

On construit alors un champ de vecteurs Y, qui, dans chaque strate U coïncide avec le gradient de la restriction de (u) à (U), sauf dans un voisinage du bord de (U) ; la construction de (Y) se fait par induction sur la dimension des strates ; sur les strates de dimension un, le champ Y est tangent à la strate; supposant (Y) construit sur les strates de dimension $<p$, soit (U^p) une strate de dimension p; on construit dans un voisinage de bord ∂U de U une fonction φ_u, nulle sur ∂U, de différentielle non nulle dans ce voisinage; on prolonge Y de ∂U à U comme suit: soit x un point de U, y le point de U où aboutit la trajectoire du champ grad φ_u dans U sur une strate de ∂U; si la fonction est analytique, alors l'application $x \Rightarrow y$ est continue; on prendra pour valeur de Y en x la projection orthogonale du vecteur $Y(y)$ sur le plan tangent à la variété de niveau de la fonction $\varphi_u = (y)$; puis on prolongera Y à l'intérieur de (U) de telle manière que le champ reste transverse aux hypersurfaces $u = c^{\text{ste}}$, dans les sens u (ou r) croissant; c'est possible, car en chaque point, l'espace de ces directions transverses est contractile.

Intégrons alors le champ Y ainsi construit: sur chaque strate (u), (Y) est différentiable (et globalement continu); il y a donc existence et unicité locale de la trajectoire du champ (Y) en tout point de A où $\{\varphi_r > r_0$, et le groupe à un paramètre ainsi défini, permet de rétracter A sur $A \cap B_{r_0}$ par déformation continue le long des trajectoires de (Y).

Pour achever dés lors la démonstration du théorème 1 dans le cas non compact, il suffit de remarquer que $A \cap B_{r_0}$ est également rétracte par déformation de l'ensemble compact $F^{-1}(a) \cap B_{r_0}$; on utilise dans ce but les trajectoires du champ grad F légèrement modifié au voisinage du bord de la boule B_{r_0} de manière à admettre la sphère B_{r_0} comme variété invariante: ou encore, on pourrait modifier la métrique de manière que la sphère $S = \partial B_{r_0}$ coupe orthogonalement les strates de A. Alors la démonstration s'achève comme dans le cas compact.

REMARQUE. Ici encore, si l'on observe que les ensembles A et $\mathbf{R}^n - A$ ont même somme pour leurs nombres de Betti, et que $\Sigma b_j(R^n - A)$ est majoré par le nombre des points critiques de u à gradient sortant, on en déduit: $2\Sigma b_j(A) < 1 + p^n$, comme au théorème 2′.

Ensembles algébriques réels projectifs

Soit A un ensemble algébrique de l'espace projectif $P_n(\mathbf{R})$; soit $B = A \cap H$ une section hyperplane; la suite exacte de cohomologie donne:

$$(S) \qquad \to H^{r-1}(A) \to H^{r-1}(B) \xrightarrow{\delta} H^r(A, B) \to H^r(A) \to.$$

La cohomologie relative s'identifie, ainsi qu'il est bien connu, à la cohomologie à support compacts du complémentaire affine

$$A - B: H^r(A, B) \simeq H^r_k(A - B).$$

Désignons, comme au Lemme 3, par A_1 l'intersection $A - B \cap B_{r_0}$, et par C l'intersection de $A - B$ avec la sphère-bord S de la boule B_{r_0}; alors l'espace différence $A_1 - C$ est homéomorphe à $A - B$ (homéomorphisme réalisé grâce au groupe à un paramètre défini par le champ (Y) du Lemme 3, et par suite tout revient à calculer la cohomologie relative $H(A_1, 0)$; or, la paire d'espaces (A_1, C) est rétracte par déformation de la paire $(F^{-1}[0, a] \cap B_{r_0}, F^{-1}[0, a] \cap S_{r_0})$; on aura donc à calculer, pour la variété à bord $F^{-1}[0, a]$, la cohomologie relative de l'ensemble $u \leq r_0^2$ modulo la variété de niveau $u = r_0^2$.

Il reste donc à étudier, dans la théorie de Morse pour les variétés à bord, comment varie la cohomologie relative $H^*(f \leq b, f = b)$ lorsqu'on franchit un point critique de la fonction f sur le bord, or une étude locale montre immédiatement ce qui suit:

Lorsqu'on franchit un point critique de (f) d'indice k, à *gradient entrant*, l'effet homotopique de la transformation équivaut à l'adjonction d'une k-cellule à la fois à $f \leq b$ et à $f = b$; il en résulte que la cohomologie relative $H^*(f \leq b, f = b)$ ne varie pas; en effet, soit c la valeur critique associée:

Par déformation descendante le long des trajectoires de grad f, le couple $[f \leq c + \varepsilon, f = c + \varepsilon]$ peut se déformer en le couple $[(f \leq c - \varepsilon) \cup B_k, (f = c - \varepsilon) \cap B_k]$, et la cohomologie relative ne dépend que de l'espace différence, soit $f < c - \varepsilon$; par suite

$$H^*(f < c + \varepsilon, f = c + \varepsilon) \simeq H^*(f \leq c - \varepsilon, f = c - \varepsilon).$$

Par contre, si l'on franchit un point critique d'indice k du bord à *gradient sortant*, il n'y a aucun effet sur la cohomologie $H^*(f \leq b)$ alors que la cohomologie de $f = b$ est modifiée; plus précisément, le long des trajectoires de grad f, la paire $(f \leq c + \varepsilon, f = c + \varepsilon)$ est rétractée par déformation sur la paire: $(f \leq c - \varepsilon) \cup D_{k+1}, (f = c - \varepsilon) \cup b_k$, où b_k est l'hémisphère supérieur bord de la demi-boule D_{k+1}; il en résulte que l'espace différence $f < c + \varepsilon$ diffère de $f < c - \varepsilon$ par l'adjonction d'une $(k + 1)$-boule ouverte; ceci entraîne un saut d'une unité décroissant pour le $k^{\text{ème}}$, ou croissant pour le $(k + 1)^{\text{ème}}$ nombre de Betti relatif. Il en résulte finalement que la cohomologie relative $H^*(A, B)$ a sa somme des nombres de Betti majorée par $(p)^n$, si p est le degré du polynôme F. On pourrait même (pour F positif) abaisser cette majoration d'une unité, puisque il existe certainement un point critique (le minimum) où le gradient de (u) est entrant.

Pour obtenir finalement une majoration de $\Sigma_k b_k(A)$, il y a lieu de calculer une borne supérieure du nombre des points présentés par l'intersection de (A) avec un plan de dimension complémentaire. On peut prendre dans ce but le degré algébrique de la variété (A), soit (d). Si le degré (d) n'est pas connu (car, semble-t-il, il n'existe pas de procédure explicite permettant de le déterminer à partir des équations de (A)) on obtiendra une majoration en considérant le nombre des points singuliers de la variété $F = 0$ dans le plan de section, de dimension $(n - r)$, où r est la dimension de A; on doit alors résoudre le système:

$$F_{x_1} = F_{x_2} = \cdots = F_{x_{n-r}},$$

système qui admet au plus $(p - 1)^{n-r}$ solutions "génériques."

Finalement on obtient la majoration suivante:

THÉORÈME 3. *Soit A un ensemble algébrique de dimension $r \leq n - 2$ défini dans l'espace projectif $P_n(\mathbf{R})$ par une équation $F = 0$, où F est une polynôme homogène positif de degré p; alors la somme des nombres de Betti est majorée par:*

$$(p - 1)^{n-r} + (p)^{n-r+1} + \cdots + (p)^{n-r}.$$

Si d est le degré algébrique de la variété (A), cette borne peut s'écrire, sous les mêmes hypothèses:

$$d + (p)^{n-r+1} + \cdots + (p)^{n-r}.$$

Dans le cas où l'ensemble (A) est une *variété sans singularités*, on peut faire usage de la majoration, du théorème 2 ce qui conduit à:

$$d + 1/2[(p)^{n-r+1} + \cdots + (p)^{n-1}].$$

Enfin, dans le cas où A est une hypersurface partout régulière, définie par une équation $G = 0$ de degré p dans $P_n(R)$, alors on obtient la borne:

$$p + p^2 + \cdots (p)^n = p \cdot \frac{p^n - 1}{p - 1}.$$

Dans le cas de l'hyperplan projectif $(p = 1)$, cette majoration est effectivement atteinte.

Il y a intérêt à comparer les bornes ainsi obtenues avec celles données par O. A. Oleinik dans [8]; dans le cas, seul considéré par cet auteur, des variétés projectives sans singularités, les majorations obtenues sont incontestablement bien meilleures que celles données au théoreme 3.

Une toute autre méthode, pour obtenir une majoration de $\Sigma b_j (A)$, consiste à considérer l'ensemble réel A comme ensemble des points fixes de l'involution induite dans la variété complexifiée C par la transformation $(z_i) \rightarrow (\bar{z}_i)$ de l'espace projectif complexe $P_n(\mathbf{C})$; il résulte en effet de la théorie de Smith, comme l'a montré A. Borel dans [9], que, si l'on prend l'homologie à coefficients dans $\mathbf{Z}_2$, on a la majoration:

$$\Sigma b_j(A) \leq \Sigma b_j(C).$$

Or, si la variété (C) est une hypersurface (ou plus généralement une intersection régulière complète d'hypersurfaces), l'homologie de (C) est connue: elle est sans torsion, et nulle en dimensions (réelles) impaires, sauf peut-être pour la dimension moitié; de même, le $(2k)^{\text{ème}}$ nombre de Betti (pour tout corps de coefficient) vaut un, sauf éventuellement celui de dimension moitié.

Désignons par $H(p)$ l'hypersurface régulière de degré p dans $P_n(\mathbf{C})$; sa caractéristique d'Euler-Poincaré $E(H(p))$ peut-être calculée par exemple à l'aide du théorème de dualité des classes de Chern; elle vaut:

$$E(H(p)) = 1/p \cdot [(1 - p)^{n+1} - 1 + p(n + 1)].$$

On en déduit, que, pour n impair, H de dimension complexe paire:

$$\sum b_j(H(p)) = E(H(p));$$

pour n pair:

$$\sum_j b_j(H(p)) = 2n - E(H(p)).$$

D'où les majorations correspondantes pour les variétés réelles régulières A de degré p dans $P_n(\mathbf{R})$.

On peut adapter la méthode précédente au cas où l'ensemble A est affine compact; supposons A défini dans R^n par l'équation $F = 0$, où F est positif de degré p. Alors si U désigne comme précédemment le voisinage de A limité par $F^{-1}(a)$, alors on a:

$$b_i(K) = b_{n-i}(U, \partial U),$$

par la dualité des variétés à bord; mais la somme $\Sigma b_j(U, \partial U)$ est majorée par la somme $\Sigma b_j(P_n(\mathbf{R}), F^{-1}(a))$, en utilisant la compactification projective de $\mathbf{R}^n$. D'après le résultat cité ci-dessus, la somme $\Sigma b_j(P_n(\mathbf{R}), F^{-1}(a))$ est majorée par la somme analogue pour les complexifiés, soit:

$$\Sigma b_j(P_n(\mathbf{C}), H(p)).$$

Or cette somme vaut:

$E(H(p)) - n$ pour n impair, et $n - E(H(p))$ pour n pair. Finalement, on obtient le:

Théorème 4.   *Pour tout compact K de $\mathbf{R}^n$, défini par l'équation $F = 0$, où F est un polynôme positif de degré p, la somme des nombres de Betti mod 2 de K est majorée par:*

$$|(1/p) \cdot [(1 - p)^{n+1} - 1 + p(n + 1)] - n|.$$

On observera que cette majoration est asymptotique (pour p croîssant) aux majorations des théorèmes 1 et 2; elle est plus fine pour les petites valeurs de p.

On obtient donc finalement à peu près la même majoration pour un ensemble algébrique affine que pour une variété projective; par suite, si l'on considère les sections planes $A \cap P_k$ de dimensions décroissantes, on peut penser que l'homomorphisme d'injection

$$j : H_*(A \cap P_k) \to H_*(A \cap P_{k+1})$$

a la propriété approximative que voici : le rang total du noyau de j est voisin de la moitié du rang total de $H_*(A \cap P_k)$. C'est dans cette direction, semble-t-il, qu'on doit rechercher la généralisation en géométrie algébrique réelle du théorème classique de Lefschetz reliant l'homologie d'une variété algébrique complexe projective à celle de sa section hyperplane.

STRASBOURG

RÉFÉRENCES

[1] A. SEIDENBERG, A new decision method for elementary algebra, *Ann. of Math.*, (2), *60* (1954), p. 365–374.

[2] S. LOJASIEWICZ, Sur le problème de la division, *Studia Math.*, *18* (1959).

[3] ———, Une propriété topologique des sous-ensembles analytiques réels, *Colloque Internat. C.N.R.S.*, Paris, Juin 1962.

[4] M. MORSE and E. BAIADA, Homotopy and homology related to the Schoenflies problem, *Ann. of Math.*, *58* (1953), p. 142–165.

[5] S. CHERN and R. LASHOF, Total curvature of immersed manifolds, *Michigan Math. Journal*, *5* (1958), p. 5–12.

[6] R. THOM, La stabilité topologique des applications polynomiales, *L'Enseignement Math*, VIII fasc. 2, (1962).

[7] H. WHITNEY, Elementary structure of real algebraic varieties, *Ann. of Math.*, *66* (1957), p. 545–56.

[8] O. A. OLEINIK, Estimates of the Betti numbers of real algebraic hypersurfaces—Mat. Sbornik—N. S. 28 (70), 1951, p. 635–640.

[9] A. BOREL, ET AL., *Seminar on Transformation Groups.* Annals of Mathematics Studies, No. 46, Princeton University Press, 1960.

Added in proof: Un article de J. MILNOR: On the Betti numbers of real varieties, *Proc. Amer. Math. Soc.*, *15* (1964), p. 275–280, parut pendant l'impression de ce livre, traite du même sujet, avec des résultats souvent meilleurs.